MILLY

BY

M. C. Nash

For Duncan Holmes, who after reading this book whilst seriously ill, encouraged me when I was reluctant to publish.
He urged me to, "Go for it, whatever the outcome your book will be out there forever," I did Duncan. Thank you.
Forever in our hearts and memory.

This book is based on a true story, although the characters are composites of real people. Any references to historical events, real people, or real places are occasionally used fictitiously. Names, characters, and locations are plausibly products of the author's imagination. Any resemblance to actual persons, living or dead, events, or locales is conceivably coincidental.
M. C. Nash

Visit my Facebook page. @ MillyNash13
Twitter. @millynash8
Instagram. @millynash8
Email. millynash@mail.com

Cover designed by Steve Holmes

eBook ISBN 978-1-9162697-0-5
Paperback ISBN 978-1-9162697-2-9

First printing, 2019.

Publisher House of Holmes

The Early Years

Milly Nash, nestled snug within her mother's womb, was punched by her father.

Five minutes earlier, Horace Nash had been in a self-pitying mood, pondering over his misfortune whilst getting drunk to revive his flagging spirits, inevitably becoming more morose and angry. He reflected over the recent years, a period before his newly gained inheritance became depleted by a combined run of unlucky gambling and shoddy dealings, wondering why his carefully planned business deals went disastrously wrong despite all his deceit and cunning. He had been contemplating a catalogue of bad luck, with the last page written the following day when he would officially become bankrupt. The bank would ultimately repossess all his remaining inherited assets. They were going to leave him as penniless as the tramps he enjoyed chasing off his land.

In truth, his perceptible business acumen remained on a par with a 'penny for the guy' child. The notion he mostly devoted his life to womanising and heavy drinking during this period hardly registered. It was those, scheming, neatly trimmed and immaculately dressed swindling bankers and the hairy, four-legged creatures who remained responsible for his downfall. As always, the onus was on others.

He glanced resentfully towards his petite blonde wife, sitting on one of the twenty chairs that surrounded the baronial oak dining table his grandfather commissioned, a youthful girl blissfully unaware of the events unfolding before her. He reminisced over his long-gone friends, and the raucous parties held around that table in the expansive farmhouse. The grandest for miles around, they said.

When he married Jane, he confidently assumed it his life's new chapter. Horace had vigilantly selected her when he noticed her across the crowded dance hall. She was a pretty young girl with long golden hair and blue eyes, whose pale, dimpled rosy-cheeked face held an air of naivety. Immaturity hung over this young woman in expensive clothes like an informative cloud. He made a few surreptitious inquiries, becoming elated when he discovered Jane was an heiress and her mother, a wealthy widow. A glorious Eureka-like moment, he thought gleefully. She looked the type who could be easily fooled by the sincerity promised by his refined, extensive conversation. He was convinced that few ladies could resist his handsome face and sparkling blue eyes; eyes that gained further prominence and charisma when he put on his practised mischievous lopsided smile.

So over the next few months, he courted and wooed the young and vulnerable girl, who found it almost impossible to resist the persuasive charm he radiated. He did not, however, anticipate her mother would object to their planned nuptials. Gretchen, 'the old witch' as he called her, would remain steadfast to the end, even refusing to attend the wedding and maliciously stopping Jane's substantial allowance. His scheme disintegrated before reaching completion, for Jane's wages from Howells department store and her mother's generous subsidy were his main objectives. He considered Jane a short term investment, rather than a life partner.

Another setback for Horace occurred when Jane announced her pregnancy. To Horace's dismay, this became financially worse when only four months into the gestation she gave up her job. One year after they first met, Jane gave birth to their first daughter. They named her Greta, in an attempt to appease the old witch, though to no avail. To him, the baby was just another mouth to feed, someone else living off his dwindling finances.

His scowling stare caught Jane's eye. She interrupted his dire thoughts with an innocuous comment regarding his bad mood. He took her enquiring words as an insult that needed to be challenged and refuted, triggering the beginning of an argument that would push him into one of his uncontrollable violent rages, in which common sense, reason and logic vanished inside a red mist of alcohol-fuelled fury. His pregnant nineteen-year-old wife suffered many a mauling, though the depth of his foul mood ensured this assault the most ferocious of all his beatings.

When the initial frenzy, the surge of violence abated, he stood fists clenched, panting over the thin, prone body of the unconscious girl. He glared down, his rage gradually subsiding as his eyes refocused. Blood seeped from her mouth, dripping onto the plush cream carpet. Sobering up, he realised the consequences of his latest act of aggression.

He searched around as if seeking a way out of his predicament, seeing only his reflection in a window. A handsome, immaculately dressed, worried-looking twenty-three-year-old stared back at him. A man toned and tanned, with fashionable long strawberry blond hair. Hair he always neatly combed and kept in place by generous dollops of cream, surrounding a face dominated by his sparkling sky-blue eyes.

Pretending innocence was not an option; he realised any display wouldn't do him any good on this occasion. His marriage and aspirations lay in tatters, shredded by his uncontrollable temper.

Watching the reflection nod in agreement, ruefully thinking soon even his image, his ghostly apparition would be gone from this farmhouse forever.

On the floor, Jane regained consciousness. She moaned softly as she placed her palm to soothe her throbbing jaw, automatically licking the salty fluid she recognised as blood. She cautiously moved her other hand towards her stomach, as she remembered in terror that during the frenzied attack, a mighty blow had been directed at their baby.

In fear and anxiety, she recalled six months before when they had playfully christened her stomach, 'little one', the day she confirmed the pregnancy. Then he feigned elation. She reflected how things had changed since then, as the fog inside her head cleared, and she became more lucid. At the time she suspected it was all an act. The truth was he wasn't even a good parent to Greta who recently celebrated her first birthday, an event he had hardly recognised.

Jane told him that if he ever hit her again, she would leave him. He was so full of remorse when he vowed never to revert to violence; she believed him, even though he said the same before. She stared up at his gaunt face. The pallid, horrified look she witnessed gave her some solace. Despite his previous pleading, at that instant, they both acknowledged his actions had ended their marriage.

Without another word, Horace helped her up from the bloodied carpet, paying no attention to her grimaces and positioned her on the sumptuous leather settee. His brief attempt at repentance fulfilled; Horace made for the door. He paused as she reached for the telephone, briefly glancing back as she placed a bloodied finger in the nine and swung the dial around three times. He heard her say, ambulance please in a quiet hoarse voice as he left.

In the next fraught minute, Jane strained out her words, repeating her request and address until satisfied the operator understood. In a daze, she staggered to the cot to pick up the crying Greta before she sat to stare blankly at the wallpaper. Outside an engine purred. She glanced through the big bay windows of the five-bedroom farmhouse, thinking the ambulance had arrived until she realised it was Horace driving away. For a while she followed his vehicle's headlights dancing through the hedgerows as it traversed the winding lane towards the main road before she turned to stare at the wall, trying to keep calm. She waited, relieved he had gone and hopefully heading out of her life forever, anxious that she and her baby were not permanently disfigured.

Two miles down the road Horace heard a cacophonous ringing of bells, heralding the imminent arrival of a speeding ambulance. One that soon appeared around the next corner, passing his Land Rover seconds later. He glanced at it briefly as it sped past, instantly knowing its intended destination. Staring determinedly ahead, driving faster down the twisting road, his thoughts racing from his past to the possible future as rapidly as the scenery flashing by.

Horace wondered if Jane would be back in the house by the next morning. His lopsided grin appeared briefly when he callously thought, perhaps he should have mentioned it was the day the bailiffs were coming to repossess the re-mortgaged stables. The house was listed for two weeks later.

He thought of his father, who would have been horrified, for the stables, land and house had been in his family for generations. Horace remained the last of the Nash lineage, his father; the only surviving sibling of seven brothers died three years before, leaving him the sole heir to a crumbling business he was incapable of saving.

His grin faded when he realised horse riding was the part of his current life. He would miss most of all. The neighbours wouldn't see his immaculately dressed figure riding the gallops of the riding stables any more, clip-clopping across the countryside like the lord of the manor on his trusty steed.

His mode of transport hereafter would be less salubrious and rather pedestrian, for his new Land Rover was number two on the bailiff's register. They will have to pick it up from the brewery, he guessed, his face again morphing into his cheeky grin, until the reality of the situation made his jaw drop.

The brewery had been the principal source of revenue for the Nash family; who supplied all the Shire horses that pulled the brewery drays, each packed with barrels and kegs to deliver to the thriving clubs and pubs. His kith and kin used to breed and sell the gentle giant Percheron draft horses, and at one time they had over thirty horse and cart teams bustling around the streets of Cardiff, the capital city of Wales.

He could still envisage those magnificent beasts, dominating the traffic lanes as if part of a royal procession, pedantically clip, clop, clip, clopping along, with an occasional shake of the head and a demeanour suggesting they were bored with performing the same display for the onlookers who watched with open-mouthed admiration. The development of the diesel engine and the modernisation of the breweries, both ensured that Shire horses were all but redundant. His last four teams were number three on the bailiff's list

"Never mind it is Saturday night. There are sure to be some girls around," he said aloud in an endeavour to bolster his flagging morale. He considered his options, and the smile returned.

A flash of lightning lit up the dark evening sky as Horace continued to drive fast along the snaking route, chased by a thunderous roar from overhead announcing the arrival of the first drops of rain. Others soon joined the wobbling droplets until a shimmering mass of water covered the windscreen.

He stretched a leather-gloved hand towards the windscreen wiper control, his fumbling fingers not finding it at his first attempt. Peering down angrily to flick the switch, hearing the wiper blades swish, the first sweep merely rearranging the water. He could distinguish nothing until the blades became more effective, seeing in horror the vague shape of a tall telegraph pole materialising as his vehicle bounced across a grass verge.

Jane's ambulance was delayed by traffic congestion following an accident. Not that she knew or cared, securely strapped onto a warm bed, unable to see further than the internal walls, leaving the crew to worry and become concerned with the delay in the rush to get her to a hospital.

Two days later, on the eighteenth of April nineteen fifty-five, at ten-thirty in the morning, the traumatic events culminated when Jane gave birth. Milly Nash inhaled her first breath of air in a nursing home located on the eastern side of Cardiff, becoming the second daughter of Jane and Horace Nash.

Jane endured problematic birth-labour, and her baby arrived in a distressed state with a bluish skin colouration. Milly was placed in an oxygen tent as the doctors initially suspected she had 'blue baby' syndrome, a congenital cardiac or pulmonary defect. This proved a wrong diagnosis, for all her bodily bits and pieces were functioning normally. The discolouration was due to a parting present from the drunken father, a birth gift and a bruising obtained while still inside her mother's belly. Even so, she recovered quickly enough to become a healthy baby.

Soon after the birth, Jane came to understand the inevitable conclusion she could no longer avoid. She was now a destitute mother, lacking a husband, a job and facing imminent eviction. This mental bruising lasted longer than the brief outburst of fury that had marred her baby during the early days of her existence; she grudgingly accepted her own survival was also threatened.

How to clamber out of the status quo was her dilemma. She had no answers, no friends or family who might help. She knew her mother well enough to know she would not help. So the despondent young girl studied her options. The most obvious was that she first needed a steady source of income, this meant finding employment. A situation made more difficult with two dependants, burdensome young babies.

Jane concluded she could not cope with her two offspring in the present circumstances. In desperation, she placed them in the temporary care of the Poor Sisters of Nazareth; a home for orphaned children on the outskirts of Cardiff city centre, while she attempted to sort out the complications in her life.

Was this a bold, rational decision of motherly concern for her children's welfare? Or a diverse cold cowardly deduction, determined by her desperation. Only time would tell. It was irrelevant to Milly. She was handed over and abandoned, possessing just a Christian name and a family name. Her parents and the traditional society as such had initially failed her and so, began her early life of confinement.

Temporary Care

A five-year-old stick thin girl with sky-blue eyes stood before the massive wrought-iron gates of Cardiff's Nazareth House. That small, wide-eyed innocent youngster, a brown paper parcel containing all her possessions grasped tightly in one hand, was me, Milly Nash. I gazed in trepidation at the new home where my package and I had just been delivered.

Though my journey to this location was no longer than one hour, my own passage began soon after my birth, when I was transported from the Cardiff nursing home where I had been born to Nazareth House in Cardiff, then onto another institution in Swansea before being returned to Cardiff.

The Sisters of Nazareth managed both orphanages, they were but two of many places in Wales that looked after the newborn and infants until they were either reunited with their parents, adopted or sent into foster care.

In today's world, this would not have happened. Social workers would have intervened, they would have been on hand to help and give advice. Almost certainly a financial package would have been made available. Even so in the nineteen fifties, this practice was acceptable; I was just one of the many unjustly treated.

Nazareth House Swansea does not figure too much in my memory, for I was far too young to remember, but I am sure after my birth, I had the natural survival instincts of every healthy baby. I have no doubt that I smiled, chuckled and surely gurgled the responses to any emotions I perceived. My early years are a blur; an existence lost in the mists of my prehistory, a period before I gained the awareness to recall facts in my lonely reality. It was highly likely more frightening than loving in those days.

One legacy I have from those years is a flat head; well, the back of my skull has a distinctive flat spot. It is not noticeable or visible, but when I run my hand over my hair, I can feel the difference. I have always presumed my little flat spot is the consequence of lying for hours and hours on my back in a crib. One of but a few memories I have retained is of a poorly lit room filled with lines of huge wooden cribs, like a formation of ancient galleons disappearing into a mist, an image, that I expect emerged from a latter interpretation of the memory.

There are no incidents of neglect I can recall from those early years, well not in corporeal terms. On the psychological side, I am positive my development lacked the conditioning a pair of loving parents would have provided. Not having a mother must have affected my early development. I never had the chance to bond with any particular person. There was no time spent safely snuggling whilst listening to the comforting heartbeat that had kept me content throughout my time developing in the womb. I had never sat on her lap, wobbling like an agitated jelly trying to stay balanced, had at no time listened to her tender voice or being made a fuss of whilst being kissed and cuddled. Then I must have been gratified that every essential comfort, food and warmth, was assured.

After all, the nuns that cared for me were not my mother. They were barely capable enough to cope with the youngest of children;

they were more devoted to their God and Church, bringing up and nurturing children was not their speciality. However, this was standard procedure; any emotional mistreatments were more than likely due to their lack of intellection.

One young nun whom I remember with something approaching fondness did show she cared, although I can't recall her name. She never hugged or showed me too much affection, but was gentle and quiet and used to spend a long time plaiting my long blonde hair. I adored the attention and closeness of this act for it made me feel warm, calm and comfortable. I can still mentally picture her face, which radiated charm. She had predominant, kind, shiny eyes, surrounded by a white shroud, her white habit contrasting with black rosary beads and the large silver crucifix she wore around her neck. She was the nun who packed all my worldly possessions that morning, placing them on a square piece of brown paper which she wrapped and tied with string. The one now clasped in my hand, as I stood remembering her tearful final words,

"May God bless you, Milly."

The first inkling I had that something was different occurred early in the morning when I sat on the edge of my cot. I noticed an unusual amount of activity. The nuns were rushing around as if the end of the world was near; a beehive of activity as they performed their specified tasks for their queen bee. Even stranger, they were talking. They rarely spoke, unless they wanted me to obey some order or to administer a sharp admonishment.

Then, with no warning, came the fateful words.

"You are going now."

So on a sunny morning, a nun escorted another bigger older girl and I to the courtyard, our small parcels containing our possessions grasped in our hands. They bundled us into the back of a small minibus, accompanied by two strangers, nuns we had just met in the grounds.

I did not understand where we were going, so I was quite upset and confused by the abrupt change to the routine. Once the journey began, I soon became mesmerised by what the passing world revealed. I saw unfamiliar scenery pass, I was transfixed by the limitless expanse of open spaces, fields of green grass and enormous trees fighting for attention in the bright sunlight. It was a glimpse of the vast world outside the walls that had been the boundaries of my life; a view too infinite to absorb, to gape at in awe, a landscape far too substantial to comprehend.

The two nuns sitting next to us had friendly faces, they appeared kind. Any questions I asked regarding the animals, the moving white fluffy balls in the green foliage and the monstrous four-legged beasts I saw wandering in the fields went unanswered. They mumbled and fiddled with the beads hanging over their black habits, absorbed in their own world of which we were passing through.

As the journey progressed and we approached our unknown destination, the mountains and fields diminished while the number of houses increased. At first, these were enormous with breath-taking landscaped gardens, each with more space than our previous play area. These grew in number, cluttering up the view until we were passing through brick and concrete canyons filled with a jostling multitude of people, who travelled along traffic-filled roads.

The noise was incredible; the surrounding colourful activities astonished me. Before that momentous day, I lived in a near-silent monochrome world where everything seemed colourless.

Cardiff had gained city status the year I was born; we were transported there a year after the Empire Games. The remnants of this were the recently built Empire pool, and the transformed Arms Park rugby ground, venues, within a mile of our destination, yet it would be many years before I knew or saw them.

We were being conveyed into another world, another existence for which I wasn't prepared for after my time in confinement.

The forty miles travelled from Swansea to Cardiff, had passed as if in a dream, leaving me comparatively happy and excited by the change. It was a feeling enhanced by the hot sunlight, suggesting everything was bright, it was a time to overlook the dark, baffling and menacing shadows. I distinctly remember staring in awe at the towering mansion, my body trembling with agitation, wondering what would happen next. I glanced around, noticing the other girl, a larger version of me who had a similar sceptical look on her face, her long blonde plait waving from side to side as she examined the surroundings.

We were soon obediently walking either side of the silent nuns, taking our first steps through the oversize wrought-iron gates, being escorted to the Mother Superior's office. Once through the impressive building's large entrance door we found ourselves staring wildly around our new environment, walking down large, dimly lit, high ceiling whitewashed covered passageways, our faltering steps and the quiet swish of habits the only accompanying sound.

By now my brief, peaceful mood had faded, I was filled with trepidation, becoming more agitated by the second. The tension was building to almost unbearable levels, a disposition the relative silence and the nun's ceremonial demeanour did nothing to dispel. Such was my growing apprehension that by the time we reached the office, behind a dominant, monument of a door, my skinny knees were involuntarily crashing into each other.

We did not have to wait long before the first knock on the door finished reverberating down the long corridor. The door creaked open, and the girl and I were roughly steered into the office. Once inside, we were pushed forwards until we stopped in front of an imposing desk.

A tall nun dressed in black stood up slowly, with only the front of her plump face showing through the white shroud around her face. It was similar to seeing a bright, happy moon rising in a clear night sky as she stood to her full height and smiled radiantly down at us. I did not know it then, but she was the Reverend Mother Superior. My first impression was that she had a lovely smile and a kind face. I found my initial uncertainties begin to waver and found it easy to smile back.

"The Nash sisters," she said as if asking a question, looking us both over, scrutinising every detail. Her hazel cat-like eyes darted back and forth as though pondering some dilemma, before her strangely hairless eyebrows lifted in unison, indicating she had reached a decision.

"You must be Greta Nash," she said softly.

Greta gave a timid nod of confirmation.

"And you must be, Milly Nash."

I nodded in confusion, before that time I had purely been Milly, now I was a Nash.

"Welcome to Nazareth House… Milly, you will be staying in the nursery. Greta, you are to stay in dormitory two." She said in an almost singing voice while putting on a pair of spectacles to scan the paperwork one nun had handed her.

"I see your mother said, she'd return as soon as she can arrange to take the two of you back home."

At first, these words were bewildering but stuck in my mind. I did not understand what a mother was and nor did I have a clear understanding that Greta was my sister. I just thought of her as a bigger, older girl. It was all too perplexing. After all, I was cared for by sisters, who were not my mother, sisters who had never been mothers, a team run by a Mother Superior. It would take a few years before I abruptly grasped the enormity, the true meaning of that short sentence. When I finally understood, it caused an emotional flood gate to open in my already confused mind.

The Mother Superior started whispering to the two diminutive nuns who had accompanied us to Cardiff. When finished, they slowly moved apart to perform the practised traditional routine drilled into them. All three crossed themselves, firstly moving the tips of their fingers of their right hand to touch their foreheads, moving down to their stomachs, before tapping their left and right shoulders, the performance finishing with a mumbled Amen. Sacred ritual accomplished, the Mother Superior picked up a small bell from the office table and rang it.

Almost immediately a black-clad, sinister-looking nun came into the office; a woman who seemed to have the width and the bulk of one of the massive animals we had recently seen in the fields. One look at her hatchet face, a glance into her cold black sunken eyes, seeing her sallow cheeks either side of a large pointed nose instantaneously set my knees dancing again. The room felt colder as she blocked out the light; her swishing black robe appeared to absorb the heat in the place.

I vividly remember what happened after we vacated the office. Even today, I shudder at the memory and putting it into words is deeply emotional. We were about to discover the dubious delights of living in an orphanage.

The big black-clad nun dragged Greta and me back into the labyrinth of passages. We went through a side door into a stark-looking bathroom, containing a cast-iron bath and two tin baths hanging on the wall. Opposite them a big wooden table and in a corner, two white china Belfast sinks, with two separate taps above each of them at differing heights. A room with only the minimal amount of furniture, but adequate to perform its function.

Now she was motionless in the large room, without the sweeping animated robe, the silent ominous black-clad nun's palpable size came into perspective. With her hunchback, she was possibly two inches shorter than the mother superior and about the same stature, more chubby than fat. I gasped for breath, gulping, sensing we were there for a reason that would not be too enjoyable. Greta must have been feeling similar thoughts; for she was trying to hide behind me with little success.

As we stood shaking and waiting the nun looked us slowly up and down, her black eyes examining us until a satisfied look on her pale face stated she had arrived at a decision. In a swift movement, she stooped down even further and hustled me to one side, grabbing the terrified Greta firmly by the shoulders and hoisting her up onto the table. Belying her considerable size, she quickly transferred her attention, turning speedily, to lift me unceremoniously onto the table next to Greta. I glanced at her and acknowledged the fear in her sky-blue misty eyes that were undeniably reflected by mine.

The black-clad nun had in her hand what I first thought was a heavy metal cross, then I realised she held a sturdy pair of scissors that opened with a startling snap in her large hand. She put one hand behind Greta's neck, lifting her long blonde plait. At that instant, I believed she was going to kill her, but I dare not move, I was rooted to the table in shock.

Then a quick movement of her hand, and she chopped the plait off, followed by a cursory look of triumph as she nonchalantly tossed it in a bin. Greta sat there staring at her braid, grief-stricken, and began to wail. Before I could react, my own twist had joined it. I stared down in disbelief at my beautifully plaited hair, with a pretty pink bow still tied on its end, lying discarded like a piece of litter. An image that remains imprinted in my mind. I joined Greta, sobbing, gasping, and panting, each gulp for fresh air generating a peculiar noise.

Not content with this act, so ungracefully given, the ugly nun continued our humiliation. With a callous indifference to our feeble struggling, our vociferous wailing, she placed what looked like a pudding bowl over Greta's head, then using the massive pair of scissors, snipped away at what remained of her hair sticking out from beneath the basin. Then it was my turn, she placed another smaller bowl over my mop. It slipped without difficulty over my head, possibly because of my flat spot, but it seemed nothing would stop her frenzied assault. All I could do was gaze down at my lovely strawberry blonde hair sprinkling down onto my blue skirt, mingling with the tears that were now flowing freely. Like slabs of uncaring meat, she had hacked and trimmed us into a state deemed acceptable.

"Shut up and stop crying you stupid girls," the nun shouted at us in a shrill voice, the first words she had spoken.

An instant later, she grabbed our hands, hauled us off the table and manoeuvred us into the passageway where she pulled us into another large room and shouted, telling us to get undressed. When Greta hesitated, she slapped the back of her legs, and shockingly did the same to me, the stinging sensation stunned me.

"Hurry up," she screamed.

After complying, we were both shaking uncontrollably, barely able to hold the garments thrust into our hands. The black-clad monster gave me a cotton dress that was far too big for me and a pair of cumbersome black clod hopper boots. I looked at the back of the nun through my tear-blurred vision as she tied my boot laces, feeling a deep embryonic sense of hatred. A heightened state of emotion I had never experienced before or indeed since.

So we had been initially processed, she completed the first stage of crushing our independence. Forcefully demonstrating to us we had to be compliant children, with no chance to develop or display signs suggesting we were any different from other children. We should be uncomplaining, silent conformists, but at our age, we were uncomfortable and uncomprehending of such undeniable hostile behaviour. Our life as Nazareth House new recruits and becoming clone Catholic orphanage children had begun.

When we had finished changing to the nun's sanction, and she was satisfied our appearances fitted into the required standard, our hands were again grabbed. I shuddered; repulsed as her sweaty, clammy hand grasped mine, and we were partly hauled out of the room. We travelled along a dark corridor heading towards big double doors dominating the far wall. My feet were slipping inside footwear three sizes too big for me. Greta still sobbed loudly. I never saw my brown paper parcel again.

I held the belief, this day, which was initially the most exhilarating of my life, turned out to be the saddest in a little less than an hour. While the Mother Superior's smile had given me the promise of love and hope, the truth lay in the contained grimace of the black-clad nun who was a void of empathy or emotion.

Welcome to Nazareth House, Cardiff, home of the big bad, black-clad nun, I thought derisively, feeling a more profound sense of foreboding, growing with every strained, slipping footstep, dreading what the future might bring. If the last hour was a traditional mundane welcoming, all new children went through, what terrible events lay waiting for us through the doors we were approaching? It was the beginning of the impending colder reality.

The Nursery

I would soon find out as the next wooden obstacles to our progress opened into a sunlit lobby. As we entered this space, the doors, closed behind us with an ominous solid click. The brutal, black-clad nun continued onwards, stomping forward like an animated statue treading out a pre-programmed path, pushing open another set of doors, revealing a large dormitory, disturbing a white-clad nun who sat behind a table. I had a deep sense of foreboding and was dreading every future second.

"Sister Anna, this is Milly," the dark mountain intoned, without waiting for a reply she turned around and left, dragging the fearful looking Greta, shutting the door, abandoning me to the company of the latest stranger.

"Hello, Milly. Sit down, sit down," Sister Anna said in a high-pitched voice talking with an accent I could barely understand. Later. I would learn she originally came from Limerick, a town in Southern Ireland. She pointed towards a chair.

I complied by sitting, leaving us to stare at each other for a few moments. Sister Anna was wholly different looking to the previous monstrosity. She was waiflike; her young face was dotted with freckles, in which startling unblemished green eyes shone beneath eyebrows that were a curious, bright orange as if borrowed from a clown. Suddenly she smiled at me; I assumed to make me feel more comfortable. I sensed this was a rather tepid response. It was not a natural reaction expressing warmth, not even the type of smile a religious devotee could generate, a pursed-lip smirk more than cordiality.

More likely her traditional response to any awkward situation she perceived. She gazed at my face, which was still wet with tears.

"Would you be wanting something to eat? How about some nice bread and dripping?" she asked, breaking the strained silence.

I nodded, and we renewed my bewildering initial tour of the institution as she guided me further into the dormitory, through another side door into a room utilised as a small kitchen. As I stood silently taking in the new surroundings, she efficiently and swiftly spread bacon fat over two pieces of bread, which was accompanied by a plastic tumbler of watered-down milk. I must have been hungry for I devoured the tasteless offering without a pause. When I finished, she gestured for me to follow her, which I did. We traversed the kitchen, heading for the room I would be sleeping in.

A creaking swing door with a round glass porthole opened to reveal the nursery dormitory. Sister Anna informed me I would have to go to church early each day, and I would be helping her with the younger children. She talked a lot, telling me how I should behave in various situations. What to do, when to do it, what not to do. Her what's, when's and where's were numerous, and I tried hard to remember them.

She showed me where I would sleep, a skeletal metal framed single bed with a thin, uncomfortable-looking mattress. The dormitory resembled a train carriage, with about two-bed spaces down the middle. A small bedside cabinet and a rickety old wooden chair were positioned either side of the ten beds that occupied each half of the dormitory.

Its external walls mainly consisting of large windows, and under each one, a sturdy cast-iron radiator stood solidly between every bed. About five of the beds had a partial metal grill around them, most probably to stop children falling out. As we walked the clunk of our boots on the bare wooden floor echoed off the flaking Spartan whitewashed walls.

Sister Anna looked over her shoulder to make sure nobody was listening, even though she knew no one was there and whispered in a honeyed voice.

"Another important thing you must remember Milly. You must only speak when you're spoken to."

She next showed me the bathroom saying, "Now Milly, go and wash those tears away."

The bathroom was at the entrance of the dormitory on the opposite side of the porthole door, it had two baths, two cubicle toilets and a tin bath hanging on the wall, plus two big square Belfast sinks, one of which was set lower than the other. A room similar, but much smaller than the one I had left a short while before. I washed my hands and face with the soap provided, an orange slab that had a potent and pungent aroma. Even today, I still hate the olfactory sensation produced by a bar of carbolic soap; I find its distinctive smell always reminds me of Nazareth House.

Sister Anna poked her head around the door and said, "Okay, Milly, let's go, and you can meet the rest of the children."

I offered my hand to Sister Anna for her to hold. She glanced at my open palm and ignored it, saying in stony, emotionless tones, "Follow me, Milly, and keep quiet."

Bewildered, I tagged along, passing another closed-door before going back through the double swing doors into the central passageway. Sister Anna walked briskly. I had trouble keeping up as she turned right and then left into yet another long hallway with glass windows running down one side of its entire length. Here I could hear the barely audible sound of young voices close by. Unexpectedly, she stopped to open a glass side door and went out into the bright sunlight. I followed, noticing the conversation stopped the instant she went through the door.

"This is Milly," was all she said, in her broad Irish brogue, before turning rapidly on her heels to stride back the way we had come.

I recollect feeling frightened and uncomfortable standing in the bright sunlight as I scanned the scene before me. In the near background, daunting high stone walls formed a barrier before me as high as a double-decker trolley bus, and in the foreground was a playground containing the children. There were a couple of girls languishing on two swings swaying above a concrete courtyard, with two more standing nearby. A revolving roundabout turning at a snail's pace, held two more unsmiling kids, a boy and a young girl and three mischievous looking young boys were on a slide, the showpiece of the playground's attractions. And every single eye looked at me suspiciously.

I stood there for what seemed like an eternity in a dilemma of what to do. Then a young girl wearing spectacles appeared from the general direction of a large wooden shed in the playground's corner, a smile gradually growing on her freckled face until it ultimately revealed a full wide-mouthed grin containing a gap where her two front teeth had been.

I forced a smile back, feeling slightly more comfortable, but I was still in a state of shock and feeling extremely sorry for myself. She gestured with her head for me to follow her, I obeyed her silent command without question. Another nod and gesticulation from the girl and I sat on a small bench next to her. Our attention was side-tracked by two curious little toddlers who seemed to have materialised out of nowhere.

The two little infants who both looked malnourished began tugging at the young girl's blue dress for attention. She smiled a warm toothless smile at the two inquisitive faces. They called her Pat. I couldn't distinctly hear what they were saying as she bent over with the two little girls shyly whispering to her simultaneously, one in each ear, like she was wearing a giant pair of earrings.

"This is Milly. She's come to stay with us," she announced in a high-pitched, squeaky voice.

"Hiya, I'm Pat," she added as she stood and turned to me.

I suddenly realised they all looked the same, the same as me now. We all had similar pudding bowl haircuts and were wearing identical boots with matching clothes, although the boys were wearing short grey trousers.

"Hello," I replied solemnly, though not discourteously, I just didn't feel like speaking too much. I actually didn't want to be there at all. I yearned to curl up in a ball, close my eyes and lock the nightmare away.

Pat was unique in appearance. She was a short, sturdy girl with a chubby freckled face, had thick brown hair, snub-nose, with nostrils that perfectly matched the shape of her round metal framed National Health Service spectacles, lenses that were so thick they resembled the bottom of empty milk bottles. From the magnified blur, I could see her eyes were speckled brown. I wondered if she could see me clearly through them.

I watched as she fussed over the little ones like a miniature mother, the trio talking in cautious whispered tones. They were so quiet I could barely comprehend them, curiously they frequently stopped to cast furtive glances towards the door that opened into the corridor.

Pat and I sat in peaceful silence as we both watched over Janice and Heidi playing quietly close by on a grassy patch, names I had learnt from their muted monotone chatter. It wasn't long before the two little ones suddenly ran off towards the large wooden shed.

The hushed laughter and subdued cheerfulness of the play were only interrupted intermittently by a nun appearing in the corridor. I noticed even the little ones demonstrated the same level of anxiety as the older children. So I sat still, while some other children appeared now and then to say what seemed to be a friendly inquisitive hello. I meekly responded, but I definitely felt out of place, an intruder within their domain.

In the background, I could discern the noisy, curious clatter of crockery coming from the other side of a fence enclosing the playground, and wondered what it was. At one point, I saw Greta marching down the corridor heading towards the commotion, sandwiched between half a dozen morose looking children who were all following a nun.

The clamorous, ringing of a bell interrupted what was slowly becoming a slightly more pleasant day. Well, I hoped it wouldn't get any worse at the very least. The tears were dry, but the memories of earlier were still fresh and raw.

Sister Anna stood in the corridor's entrance adjacent to the playground, the source of the noisy interruption dangling heavily in her small hand. The response of the children was immediate; my fellow inmates formed into a single file in front of her, their actions synchronised and well-rehearsed. I took my place at the end of the line behind Pat. Sister Anna counted out loud until she reached twelve, satisfaction loomed on her pale face indicating we were all present and correct. Without further commands, she turned and marched down the corridor, holding the brass bell in both hands to stop it clanging, the silent train of children following closely behind her, heading to the nursery unit.

When we returned to the nursery, there was another surprise waiting for me. The Sister opened a big cupboard in the dormitory to reveal an assortment of mops, buckets, dusters, and rags, some scrubbing brushes, green soap and a lot more cleaning equipment in large quantities. The top five shelves held abundant white starched sheets, towels and pillowcases.

She barked out monosyllabic orders assigning our various tasks, inadvertently giving me the names of my fellow inmates. It appeared Pat the two little ones and I were allocated the bathroom. David and Gareth were to clean the windows. Lucy, who had a long thin face, was to polish the cupboards. Tall Paul, the kitchen. While a stocky little lad called Duncan was allocated the dining room. Two sullen-looking kids of about eight or nine, Kate and Ruth, along with the blond-haired Derek, had to sweep and mop the sleeping quarters. Little hands reached inside the cupboard, grabbing the required tools for the job.

I watched Pat get the necessary equipment for cleaning and place them in a bucket. She nudged me in the ribs and nodded toward the toilets, all the time Pat's little shadows remained gripped to her dress. Considering their ages, Heidi and Janice expertly started to clean the sinks, while we filled the bucket with warm water. With the bucket full, I began to scrub the tiled floor of the bathroom as indicated while Pat mopped up after me.

Much to Pat's amusement, I cleaned the toilet cubicles and proved the gap under the door was large by crawling under it on my hands and knees. We worked in silence, a pointing finger here, a shake of the head there, a grave-looking frown in my direction, then a final nod of approval from our foreman Pat meant our next job was over. It was a hard slog, my knees were sore, and my arms were aching. My three workmates were obviously used to the labour for they showed few signs of fatigue.

The sound of the bell produced the most dramatic effect on my fellow inmates. Promptly, all the equipment used for the cleaning was expertly and efficiently stowed back in the cupboard. After the doors slammed shut, we stood and waited, forming an organised line with our backs to the closet. Sister Anna emerged through the swing door, inspected the result of all the hard work, her white face impassive. An eerie silence and a tense atmosphere engulfed the dormitory until she finally said, "Hands."

The next stage of the routine began as the kids rushed to the bathroom to carry out her one-word instruction. There was a distinct pecking order as we queued in two lines to wash our hands. I was in the smaller sink's queue, was also the last one to dry my hands, or I should say try to wipe them, as the towel was almost wet, so was the floor we had just pointlessly cleaned.

Pat stood by the door, patiently waiting for me wearing a small smile. I glanced at her lovely, endearing freckled face. I realised in that fleeting moment I had a friend. Gently she took the wet towel from my hands, placing it in a full wicker laundry basket.

Once in the dormitory, we all queued in a line and marched through the swing door into the area set aside as the dining room where I had eaten bread and dripping earlier. I took my place at a small table opposite Janice and Heidi, with Pat sitting next to me. Three boys and a girl sat at the big table, none of whom looked older than seven or eight. The boys were Duncan the stocky kid, blond Derek and Paul who was the tallest inmate and was black and talked with a strange accent, the girl was the amber-eyed Lucy who was dark-complexioned with a prominent chin. David, who was as tall and thin as, Gareth, who sported a black bruised eye, sat opposite Kate and Ruth on the medium-sized table.

Sister Anna stood in the kitchen, her pale, freckled face framed by the serving hatch as she peered through it.

"Bless us O Lord," she started, instantaneously all the children including myself had our hands together, our heads bowed while we all chorused as one.

"Bless us, O Lord, and these, thy gifts, which we are about to receive from thy bounty. Through Christ, our Lord."

"Amen," we all sang together.

Lucy detached herself from the big table and went to the serving hatch, where she waited as the Sister served up the evening meal. I sat entranced by the prospect of food, intrigued what it would be, watching as she placed twelve plates, each containing four half slices of bread and a piece of cheese on the serving hatch shelf.

When these were delivered, she grabbed hold of a big gallon-sized tin can. With her arm embracing it, she prised open the lid using the handle of a spoon, before reversing it to stick into the tin. I was delighted to see her scoop out a heaping dollop of bright red strawberry jam and unceremoniously plop little blobs onto each of the plates. Four plates of food, four plastic beakers containing watered-down milk were soon competently transported to our table, placed between our knives, forks and spoons by a solemn-looking Lucy. I noticed that when she was engrossed in a task, her tongue was just visible between her compressed lips.

"Thank you," was politely echoed four times.

I made jam with cheese sandwiches out of mine, whereas Pat made a cheese sandwich and finished with a jam sandwich. There isn't a lot of variation possible with cheese, bread and jam.

A minute bowl of cold custard with a smaller globule of jam completed the measly snack; again, we expressed our gratitude with four more politely spoken thanks.

The inconsiderable meal consumed, they all chorused a prayer I would soon learn and chant.

"We give thee thanks for all our benefits almighty God who livest and reignest, world without end. Amen."

Our servers cleared up the empty plates and beakers, taking them into the kitchen next door to do the washing up. Sister Anna, who was now wearing a pristine white robe, wimple and shroud, stood watching them before she abruptly left and walked out of the room. When they finished the dishes, the children came back into the dining room and started chatting with each other.

"She's gone to evening prayer," Pat said as a way of explanation, meaning as there was no nun present it was all right to talk. I realised except for saying grace and an odd thank you, little or nothing had been spoken since leaving the playground.

A small wooden cupboard in one corner of the dining area provided a small selection of harmless toys, to be played with when the children were deemed to have been good, and locked otherwise. Little Heidi and Janice darted towards the unlocked cupboard as soon as the coast was clear.

Pat told me one of the nuns said she was in the home because she had been a naughty girl. She confided to me she didn't like most of the nuns, in particular, Sister Anna, who was prone to rages, but if I did as I was told she would leave me alone. I was amazed when she said there were about thirty nuns at the orphanage. I began to speculate in fear what the rest were like. The top of my imaginary list of most disliked nun up to then was definitely the evil black-clad nun. Besides those snippets of information little was said.

I spent most of the next hour listening to self-effacing conversations while watching the mite's lacklustre activities, as memories of the day's sorry events darted back and forth in my mind. My legs still tingled, but the raised red finger marks had faded. Suddenly, and in an instant, the children sat up straight, standing kids stood to attention, Janice and Heidi scuttled to their chairs. Sister Anna announced her return, by loudly bursting through the set of double doors into the now silent dining room, shouting "Bedtime," to no one in particular.

She tossed a damp cloth to Duncan, who immediately started to wipe down the tables as we filed out the door and through the porthole swing door towards our beds.

It was clear we could speak at this time of the evening while we prepared for bed, as nearly everyone was chatting away reasonably comfortably without looking warily around, although in quiet, hushed tones. Pat explained the reasoning behind the sudden silence before the nun's grand entrance. She said there was always the warning click of the outer door closing a few moments before her arrival. Thus they could avoid any castigation.

A grey nightshirt had mysteriously appeared on my rickety old chair, along with a plastic tumbler containing a used toothbrush in my cabinet. It was an enormous relief to see Pat had the bed next to me. On the other side was Janice, who I now noticed had a gap between her front teeth and spoke with a lisp, and whose blond hair was slightly lighter than my own. Little Heidi with the jet black hair and unusually red lips, had another caged cot next to Janice. Lucy's bed was on the same side of the room next to my bed.

I watched as Pat changed effortlessly into her nightshirt, taking care to fold up her dress and gently drape her blouse over the back of her chair, using it as a coat hanger. She finally popped her little white socks inside her boots and slid them under her chair, which was next to my cabinet. With her job done, she skipped past me smiling, going to help Janice, who was sitting patiently on her cut down chair waiting for help.

I caught Pat grinning at me from the corner of my eye, as I looked open-mouthed at the nightshirt I was holding. This would have been much too big for Greta, I thought. When I put it on, I saw the funny side of the situation, folding up the arms and bottom until they were a suitable length, before I padded around my bed to help the cheerful Pat who was now assisting Heidi.

With my recently acquired plastic beaker in one hand, my toothbrush in the other, barefooted I followed my three new pals to the end of the queue outside the bathroom. David, Lucy, Paul and Gareth who had already brushed their teeth were standing to attention at the side of their beds, quietly talking.

Kate and Ruth, who had been sitting at the medium-sized table, came past the dwindling queue, their faces expressionless, their lips toothpaste smudged. I had noticed these two girls kept themselves to themselves. Everyone I'd met did, I suppose, but this was different, it was more intense, it sounded like they had their own language; so different that I couldn't understand a word they were saying.

Pat reached the front of the queue where Sister Anna, a sullen look on her freckled face, was waiting with a huge tube of toothpaste in her hand. Pat held out her toothbrush, the nun put a tiny spot of toothpaste on the brushes. I received the same amount and dutifully went through the motions of cleaning my teeth and rinsing, returning to the dormitory bedroom to copy my fellow inmates, I was soon standing to attention besides my bed.

"Pray," the nun barked.

Everyone instantly dropped to their knees onto the bare wooden floors, our elbows resting on the beds, our hands held together. There followed a few minutes of praying, in which we thanked God, Jesus, Mary and the Holy Ghost for the past day. My thoughts did not agree with the spoken words.

"Bed and keep quiet," she growled as she headed to her cell, in her rush, leaving the door to wave noisily to a standstill.

That night I was lying in a strange bed, with my arms crossed over my chest like a cadaver lying in a coffin; a position Sister Anna told me to adopt, saying it would protect me and keep the devil away while I slept.

Those insensitive words gave me scant comfort with my tears dripping onto the pillow. I think I almost cried myself dry that night. Even though it was warm, I was shivering and shaking. I was still hungry after the inconsequential meals. Such was my depressed state of confusion I irrationally wondered what I had done wrong to deserve such treatment, why were the nuns so horrible to me? On top of which I was dreading the next day, my feverish mind imagining many terrible things I would have to endure until I eventually fell into a restless sleep.

Monotony of Bells

Early the next morning, the ear-piercing, persistent clanging of a bell jolted me awake. Unknowingly, it was the signal for me to learn the routine. A routine I would have to carry out each morning. The person yielding the bell with relish was Sister Anna, who had woken us to her satisfaction, barked out the monosyllabic commands I soon learned we had to obey at all times.

The first of these was; pray. I followed the others, kneeling at the side of my bed. When sufficient time had elapsed, it was time for the second order, bathroom. In single file we traipsed off to the bathroom to perform our ablutions, queuing silently in line waiting for a free cubicle, oblivious to the sounds emanating from within. Another wet towel later, and it was time for the third command; beds. At first, this confused me, as we had just woken up, following the others I found this meant we were to form into pairs and make our beds in complete silence.

The other children were proficient in this well-practised drill; for them, it was an everyday mindless commonplace chore, helping each other to make their beds. Pat aided me first, then I helped her to make her bed, duplicating her actions, keeping my mistakes to the minimum. I felt a surge of relief when she timidly smiled at me, informing me I had copied her activities correctly. The next part of the routine was more easily achieved when she took her clothes from her wooden chair and began to dress. I followed her movements until we were ready to roll up our discarded nightshirts and tuck them under our pillows.

Heidi, the little girl of about three years old, had wet her bed. Another side of Sister Anna's character emerged. There was no comforting of the girl, she exploded and went into a rage, her bright eyebrows boogying up and down her pale face while she shouted and screamed at the cowering child.

She slapped her across her naked shoulders and shouted, "Once more, and you're for the bath."

I felt so sorry for the tiny waif; it was pitiful watching her pleading with the bullying nun. Sister Anna joined my imaginary list of nuns to keep away from, straight in at number two.

We ate a breakfast of bread and milk, while Heidi, the little bed wetter, was forced to stand beside her cot with the soaked sheets shrouding her head. It transpired bedwetting was a recurring event. So a vacant chair at a table and the sight of a tearful child, standing with wet sheets on their heads, became a regular breakfast time occurrence. Further punishment for what the merciless nun considered being persistent bedwetting was; the bath.

After eating we were all ushered through the warren we were housed in, down long corridors and through several doors until arriving at the institute's church. I was astonished to discover the orphanage's actual size. It was absolutely enormous, so large it had its own church and parish priest. The entire space seemed to be filled with a multitude of nuns and sorrowful children.

When the service was over, I glimpsed an unhappy-looking Greta, then in an instant, we were going our separate ways again.

In those initial weeks, my understanding and knowledge of my fellow dormitory comrades increased as I became aware of the situation in which we had been placed. We were living in an establishment controlled by nuns who followed stringent routines, with no chance to express ourselves. We were basically the next batch of twelve children to be processed by the institution.

Over the next few weeks, the dreary routine remained the same; Sister Anna would make us undertake minor tasks such as clearing up after meals or laying the tables for the next meal. She made sure we kept the bathroom clean, swept the floors, polished anything that faintly gleamed; in fact, almost anything menial she could think of to keep us busy and to pass the time. Even if someone else had just completed their assignment, she still made us do it again. Before long it felt like I had scrubbed or polished every inch of our dormitory inside the big swing doors that served as the only entrance, doors that were locked on the dot at seven-thirty pm and then unlocked twelve hours later. Freed once a day into the ample free space of a playground to provide our own verbose and carefree entertainment; to have the chance to bond and relax, but more often than not we were confined to a room for the nuns' gratification. Then Sister Anna would interrogate us, asking us endless questions about the Holy Bible or the previous Sunday's sermon. She would also teach us the Mass in Latin, or try to, as her monotone drones and accent were disconcerting. Inevitably, one of us would make a mistake and be reprimanded, receiving a slap, punch, pinch or a swipe from her cane.

Paul, the black kid, was picked on more than anyone else. He was a kind, good-natured boy. The only boy who really conversed with us girls, as his bed was opposite the five of us at the bottom of the dormitory. Duncan, Gareth, Derek and David were friendly enough but kept us at arm's length, whilst Ruth and Kate remained more distant than their couple of empty beds away warranted.

To begin with, everything terrified me. I was predominantly miserable and tremendously sorry for myself. Almost every night, I would cry silently, consoled by an imaginary friend. A friend who kept the devil away, who gave me the reassurances I urgently needed. A friend who appeared after the priest told us about guardian angels during the obligatory weekly hour-long Sunday Mass.

They reinforced their essential spiritual Catholic messages daily. We said prayers before and after every meal, sandwiched between praying, awakening and before sleeping. I was rapidly becoming a devoted Catholic clone.

"Have faith my child, have faith the Lord knows what he's doing," was a mantra drummed into us daily until I unconsciously frequently repeated, "Have faith."

I used to think if I had not cried so much, I might have wet my bed, which thankfully never occurred. I wasn't the only one who cried, for sobs of anguish would echo quietly throughout the nights.

My partial insomnia brought to my attention some motivating observations. A distant rumbling, emanating from the general direction of the kitchen that overlooked the nursery playground, broadcast the start of another day. Immediately after was the barely audible sound of a light switch from Sister Anna's cell, followed instantly by a faint beam of light that shone through the porthole door onto my bed.

This and other observations shared by my fellow inmates, like the click of a door closing, or a shadow seen beneath, or the subtle change in air pressure when the soundproof main doors opened, were all distinctive early warning signs. Twenty minutes after the dim light appeared, a distant bell would sound, signalling others to peal. Then the last clangour, the delightful small nun would sweep through the door shouting more often than not our greeting for the new day.

"Get up, you lazy bed wetters."

I soon came to realise the waiflike Sister Anna was a monster in nun's clothing. The penalty she dished out for what she considered frequent bedwetting was abhorrent. 'The bath,' as she called it, was barbaric.

Little Heidi was the first victim I witnessed receiving the punishment after wetting her bed two days in succession. At first, she suffered the usual slap on the legs or across the shoulder. Then she had to stand with the wet sheets dangling over her head and back as she missed breakfast. For the rest of us, breakfast was always a rushed affair. We had to finish quickly in order to witness the punishment we would suffer if we soiled our sheets.

A use for the tin bath hanging on a nail was about to be demonstrated. Silence ensued as we all watched the callous nun remove the tub, place it in the middle of the bathroom where two buckets full of cold water in the Belfast sinks stood waiting. Heidi, who was trembling, knew what was imminent and took off the wet sheets still adorning her head, placing them in the wicker basket. She tentatively approached the bath with tears in her eyes, wearing only her white knickers she sat down with her legs crossed and her head drooped. The sickly smiling nun then poured the buckets of cold water slowly over Heidi's black hair, ensuring the cold water poured over her entire body.

Sister Anna's manic face appeared to age considerably as it distorted in delight, and synchronised with Heidi's whimpering, her wide glowering green eyes blinked rapidly like she was taking snapshots to enjoy later. Fulfilled, her sadistic pleasure had been consummated, she left the room. Two boys, Paul and Duncan, emptied the bath and replaced it. Paul walked away with glistening tears streaming down his ebony face, while Pat and I dried down an upset shivering three-year-old. We helped her get dressed and then we went to church to pray. I used to stare at the back of the nuns' heads thinking things that shouldn't be considered in the house of God. I imagined Sister Anna sitting in the bath and us pouring cold water over her.

It was not long after being admitted that I began to suffer some punishments automatically delivered for all minor offences and petty misdemeanours, such as talking, running and laughing, not that there was much to smile about. The nuns were always quick to enforce their rigid discipline. Their punishments varied from a slap to a whack, with a stout bamboo cane some carried tucked in their leather belts, to any exposed part of your body, their particular favourite being a pinch on the back of your arm just above the elbow. However, I must emphasise that not all the nuns were like this.

Still etched into my memory, like a fearsome nightmare, are the sounds that accompanied or were the precursor of our punishments. "Shut up girl… Shut up, you charity case… Shut up, or you'll get a smack…. Stop talking… Stand still face the wall and don't ask stupid questions… Stop crying you, big baby. Shut up; speak when you're spoken to…" Whack, pinch, slap. It was horrible.

While we had to say; "Sorry, Sister. Yes, Sister… Thank you, Sister… Please, Sister." We were considered impolite and punished if we didn't use the term, 'Sister' when replying. How could they have been so cruel?

I soon became accustomed to the mistreatment; there was no other way than to accept this as being normal. I believed that all other children's lives were like ours. It was likely instinctive on my part, I never showed my true feelings. I kept my emotions bottled up, only to be vented at night when I was alone in my bed.

Although I was not particularly happy. At least I had the stimulating company of other children now, something I'm sure I lacked before. I thought it took a long time for the other children to accept me, in reality, it was probably only a week or so.

After all, we were just the latest batch to be processed, until ready to be passed on to the next stage of this traditional programmed life; children to be gradually matured into the next generation of God-fearing, dutiful kids. I wondered how many of the nuns I had met so far were similarly treated when younger and thought this a normal childhood.

My budding friendship with Pat steadily developed. One of our primary tasks after going through the morning routine was to help the two little girls Heidi and Janice get dressed, periodically they still wet their beds, being only about three years old. Notwithstanding our own infancy, we both showed a natural protective instinct towards the two innocents. It's ironic to think most girls our age would have baby dolls to play with, yet we had the responsibility of real babies.

School

As the days progressed, and the routines became more accustomed. I realised the same cast of characters were running our lives.

There was the neurotic Sister Anna, who was in charge of our nursery, whose locked door and living quarters guarded the only entrance. Sister Mary, another nun who regularly assisted, was much kinder, but even she behaved differently towards us when she was with other nuns. She had a pale face that featured outsized flared nostrils and a prominent scar that ran from her ear to the side of her mouth; a possible explanation why her light brown hooded eyes held a deep-seated sadness. Then there was the helper who used to come to the dormitory periodically with clothes, provisions and fresh laundry.

The nuns cleverly used the good nun, bad nun, psychological technique, to achieve their goals. I am not sure if this was a deliberate or trained response. As it transpired, Sister Anna was a perfect bad nun, so passionate was her performance she was practically psychotic. Sister Mary was the nice nun; genuinely so as I would later learn.

The helper, Mrs Gittings, was a dumpy miserable looking woman who had a beehive hairstyle, a red bulbous nose and red pockmarked cheeks. She had been a homeless person but was now living and working at Nazareth house. She was cold and impassive; her unsmiling face was always an unwelcome sight. She lived in the women's dormitory in the old people's section of the home. Strangely, the helper wasn't allowed to hit us. However, she took great delight in stepping on your toes, bumping you into the cold iron radiators or slyly giving you the nuns' pinch.

After a while, I came to realise the nursery nuns wore white robes and shrouds, whereas the other nuns wore an assortment of blue or black gowns. To accompany these, was a blue, black or a white head covering worn over their wimples, the variable colours defining their precedence.

Some nuns looked at you with pity in their eyes, others with cold-blooded contempt, several simply ignored you completely, and the odd one would just hit you because you smiled at them. I quickly learned to keep my face expressionless.

I was in bed one evening, in my now accustomed position, like a corpse, when Sister Anna came up to my bedside and put some clothes on my wooden chair.

"You're going to school tomorrow," she stated, showing no emotion before leaving for her cell, leaving me wondering what that would imply.

Another big decision in my life had been arranged without me being aware it was about to happen. I later deduced that my transfer to Cardiff was organised to coincide with my first year of school. It must have been half-term when I arrived, as the home was full of kids all the time.

The next day, after following the usual routine of bed making, dressing the kiddies, eating a simple but not filling breakfast of bread and milk, we attended morning Mass before an hour of cleaning anything that stood still and did not object to another unnecessary dusting, buffering or polishing. Then we were all ready for school, except for the two little mites Janice and Heidi.

Smelling of carbolic soap and feeling very nervous, I stood in line with the other children. Sister Anna, Sister Mary and the helper inspected us to make sure our school uniforms were in order. Mine was second-hand and far too big for me, though five minutes of fastidious polishing ensured my oversized Doc Martens boots were gleaming. A succession of previous inmates had probably worn my loose-fitting dress countless times. The institution had years to learn how best to recycle all their clothing resources for the minimum cost. Not that that worried me then. I was more concerned the ample dress would flutter in the briefest wind, exposing my knobbly knees or a flash of baggy white knickers.

They checked our severe haircuts were tidy, that there were no errant strands that needed the bowl to be brought out again, then inspected our hands to ensure they were clean and polish free. Bizarrely, this happened every day from that day on, the nuns were obsessed by the ritual. After the inspection, Mrs Gittings, who Pat thought was a witch, ushered us through the imposing gates to wait for the school bus.

I sat next to a trembling Pat on our first ten-minute trip to St David's Junior School. We were both anxious and frightened but did our best to reassure each other. Like my journey to Nazareth House, I was soon engrossed, fascinated by the scenes before me, the crowds of people and magnificent monumental buildings we passed. It was all so strange, yet astonishing, travelling through the world outside, not being confined by double doors, or interned within high-ceilinged rooms or walking along corridors that never seemed to shrink in length. We were being transported through a world whose dimensions had no limit.

What struck me most was the vibrant mix of new visual sensations, the abundance of colours, carefree pedestrians walking down a succession of seemingly endless streets, people walking with a purpose that was not assigned to them by a nun. A crowd who could happily keep walking, and perchance stop to look in shop windows, or even join a bus queue to take them where they wished. While we were unhappily travelling to an unknown destination, dreading we would soon suffer the school's equivalent of the welcoming scalping I had undergone at the institution.

My misgivings proved to be somewhat misguided; my first day of school was surprisingly enjoyable. The classrooms seemed relatively small as we were used to the large dormitory. There was a supply of paper, strange pens with sharp pointy nibs and a choice of blue and red half-full or half-empty inkwells, depending on your outlook to life. I was most definitely a pessimistic half-empty person by then. The woman teacher was friendly and didn't shout or pinch us when we digressed from what they expected. I soon relaxed and began to enjoy comparable freedom.

In the morning break, someone gave me a little bottle of milk with a silver top, that was just for me. It was deliciously creamy and not watered-down. The midday dinner was mouth-watering, unlike anything I'd ever eaten before. These reassuring and nourishing sessions made a most favourable impression on me, the intellectual nourishment, the lessons we did, I barely remembered. I found the short time I'd spent in the home had already changed me. I couldn't really concentrate, I was worried about the little ones and remained afraid the nuns would harm them while we were at school. The daily routines at the institution were becoming more transparent, and though onerous, were expected. I had, without effort, become acclimatised to being there. After a short time in the orphanage, it had become my way of life. I didn't know any other existence.

During our first playtime, Natalie, Pat, Lucy, and I watched the other smartly dressed children from a distance, acutely aware of the differences between us. We may have been dressed like nineteen forties vagabonds, but our clothes were spotlessly clean, as were our shiny scrubbed faces.

"Cleanliness is next to Godliness," to quote Sister Mary, an overused saying that was not one of my favourites. I hold it entirely responsible for all the additional cleaning the nuns made us undertake.

What was curiously different at first was the toilets had mirrors. There were no looking-glasses in the dormitory, or anywhere else we could move around in Nazareth House. We were not allowed to gaze at our reflections at the institution, it was unacceptable to preen or attempt to look different. We were positively discouraged from trying to be individuals. Did this explain why the nuns and helpers were so fastidious when inspecting us? Where they looked for any signs of contamination, we may have picked up at school from the other children?

Pat O'Toole had been at Nazareth House for as long as she could remember, like me, she had no real recollection of any previous life, other than an orphanage. As kindred spirits, our bond was to become almost indestructible. In class, we thankfully sat next to each other behind Lucy and Natalie, at playtime we all steered clear of the outsider children, standing as far away from the others as we could in the playground's corner. For an unknown reason, Natalie, a clever, independent five-year-old girl from dorm one, took an instant dislike to me. Not that I was bothered.

From my first day in school, the other children and their different lives intrigued me. I used to listen shyly to their conversations, which seemed to me to be dominated with talk about their mothers and fathers. Mum this, dad that. I'm going swimming with my parents tonight. I'm going to Brownies this evening. I always felt perplexed when they talked of their parents and was no doubt jealous of their obvious affection for having a family life to talk about. Now I was being introduced to another cuisine, school dinners. At least they were more varied and somewhat educational.

I enjoyed school. Our form teacher, Miss Brown, was an excellent tutor who was kind and tolerant. I remember once, a long time later, she held me back from going to the playground to say she thought I had the potential to go far, as long as I didn't waste the opportunity. Unfortunately, playtime, dinnertime and home time were my primary concerns.

Now today I wonder how far my education would have progressed, what sort of life I could have had if my full potential had been realised at an earlier age.

Nazareth House

The Nazareth House kitchens were always a hive of activity on non-school days. It was efficiently managed by the unimaginative and even less creative Sister Maguire who was probably the hardest working nun in the orphanage. The daily menu rarely varied, to such an extent that porridge with golden syrup, bread and watered-down milk, cheese and strawberry jam could be served for any breakfast time. On the odd occasion, we had a hard-boiled egg, another unexciting one was bacon dripping on bread.

After our first day at school, there was a change to our dinner meal routine. Now once we had changed our school clothes and completed some scrubbing and cleaning, at about five-thirty, depending on Sister Anna's mood or if there were any impending punishments, Sister Mary would usher the entire nursery group the short distance to the great hall. There we were led to a big table to sample the delights of the day brought to us by the older children.

It didn't take me long to learn the rudimentary meals we were given throughout those years. Monday we usually had stew, which was lamb stew containing more fat than meat, the bulk consisting of big chunks of potatoes, carrots and parsnips. It was very greasy and gritty; I hated the smell. On reflection, it was probably very wholesome food. On other days we would eat boiled potatoes with cabbage, one sausage and no gravy, sometimes we had Macaroni cheese, then the most regular of all meals mashed potatoes and baked beans. Catholicism considered it a sin to eat meat on a Friday, so in general, we ate a dinner of fish and soggy chips. The fish contained a multitude of bones. Weekends we usually ate egg and chips, or baked beans and powdered mash which I liked, even though you would always find dry bits in the potato paste that stuck to the roof of your mouth.

There were always a pair of gallon-sized aluminium teapots, each filled with tea, sugar and milk, though invariably the mixture would curdle. Pudding was a different kettle of fish; there were only ever three types, sago with jam, semolina with jam, and everybody's favourite, jam roly-poly with custard.

The great hall was enormous, almost as big as the church, with curtained windows that looked out onto the corridor next to the playground. The dining area was dominated by a dozen, two-foot square pillars, stretching fourteen feet from floor to ceiling, supporting the dormitory and rooms above. The periphery of the walls was bordered by dark wooden backed benches, each one solidly secured to the brickwork.

There were about eighty or more children to feed, this did not always include the nursery inmates, as we mostly ate breakfast in the nursery kitchen. The nuns and the residential older people ate at differing times to the children. To facilitate an efficient serving procedure, there was a gap for a large serving hatch that opened inwards to the central kitchen. At mealtimes, systematic lines of well-disciplined children queued impatiently, expectantly for their mundane offerings. A meal served by helpers from covered steaming tureens. (The home employed five or six helpers who were all day workers except for Mrs Gittings.) Children with plates in hands sat on designated long backless wooden benches at one of the six long, dull wooden tables standing five feet apart. At the head of each table, was a high-backed chair with padded seats for the overseers, lofty positions from which to chastise and ultimately discipline the ten children on each bench.

One corner of the great hall was set aside as a lounge primarily for the old-age pensioners, on a shelf was one of those new-fangled contraptions, a television set. As time passed, I realised this room was the heart of all group activities. Occasionally we were allowed to watch films on the television. I remember one time, *The Sound of Music* was being shown and all the kids from the nursery were there, happily joining in with the old people as they sang along with the film's songs. It was immensely enjoyable.

The parquet floor was always shiny and clean because it was us who did the scrub and polish. The old people sometimes held dancing sessions, we loved to watch as they slid and tottered across the vast expanse of the polished floor.

The great hall also doubled up as a reception area for visiting outsiders to inspect their prospective new family member. The cavernous room was always spotlessly cleaned and polished before Saturday visits or special events like Christmas parties. We would use dusters on our feet and skate over the floor to relieve the boredom. The nuns didn't seem to mind the skating. It was as if they were preparing themselves, as they always behaved differently when confronting the outsiders. Most of the time, parties were staged, managed affairs, designed to impress the visiting outsiders. The fare dished out was far superior to the typical offerings. There was also a lot of friendly banter arising from a relaxed atmosphere. I wished it was like that forever.

Not everything in the home was a dire routine. I remember with great delight the Christmas time parties. They gave each child a stocking containing an apple, orange and banana, some nuts in shells and a couple of bars of chocolate. We were also given little presents like jigsaw puzzles, some of which strangely disappeared a few days later. Easter was another pleasurable time; the outsiders would provide us with chocolate.

During my first year, I experienced what was to be another ritual. One I liked and thought to be tremendously exciting. At bedtime on Christmas Eve, we found smart, clean clothes that were much nicer than usual. Later that night while we were all tucked up, snuggled under the heavy woollen winter blankets, looking forward to the next day with the promise of treats and presents. Sister Anna came bounding through the porthole door into the freezing dormitory, furiously ringing her bell. I didn't know what time it was, but I knew it wasn't morning.

I soon found out though, when Sister Anna, wearing a false smile on her freckled face, announced in her insincere sounding, sweet dulcet tones.

"Get dressed children... We're all going to midnight mass."

It was standing room only in the church as it contained every single occupant of Nazareth House, in addition to many outsiders in the congregation, including the helpers. Some of these had to stand at the back of the church, below Sister Norma, a very fastidious, agreeable nun of about sixty years, who was sitting high up on the balcony in front of the organ keyboard. In the galleries, either side of her sat two rows of smartly dressed, innocent-looking children waiting to sing. The altos to her right, the trebles to her left. The name treble was the immature equivalent of the tenor. Sitting under the galleries they occupied were the institution's old women. Opposite them and below the trebles, three more rows of pews held the institution's old men.

The Mass celebrating the birth of Jesus Christ was especially poignant with the sixteen dynamic Nazareth House Choir sounding like little angels. My own angels were feeling tired and emotional during the beautiful conducted hour-long ceremony. Before I knew it we were back to the dormitory and in bed, all of us looking forward to the rest of Christmas day, when we eventually woke up.

I also loved the trips to the seaside, the May Day parades, the summer fetes and the other disparate events scattered throughout each year, which sometimes included the visit of a major celebrity. There are photographs somewhere of a young Milly Nash sitting on the late Jimmy Savile's lap. I vividly recall the picture being taken, there were about three or four grownups in his entourage and a photographer with a blinding flashbulb. Sister Margarita, the other nuns and kids alike, laughed melodramatically as he bounced me up and down while I straddled his knee. He held my head with both hands and nuzzled my face with his Lucy-like chin. I recollect the sickly, pungent smell of cigar smoke on his breath. Even at that young age, I felt desecrated as he squeezed my body and pushed his leg between my own legs. Perhaps the photograph is now languishing in a police file in New Scotland Yard.

Home Sweet Home

At first, I knew nothing about the history of the imaginative tiered architecture that is Nazareth House, my knowledge of architecture was non existent, and a wedding cake was an imaginary slab anyway. It would be much later in my incarceration I would learn the famed architect John Prichard had designed Nazareth House. A building commissioned by the second Marquis of Bute, who unfortunately died a year after the building work began, so he never saw his magnificent gothic-style building in all its glory. Construction work on the unique structure commenced in eighteen forty-seven and was completed four years later, a monumental inheritance for John Patrick Crichton-Stuart, who became the third Marquis of Bute on his father's death when he was only six months old.

In due course, he became the wealthiest man in the world, and in later life, he became widely known as a philanthropist. At the age of twenty-one, he converted to Catholicism, seven years later he gave his manor house to the Poor Sisters of Nazareth, on condition it became an orphanage and an old people's home. Colum Road, the present address of Nazareth House, is named after the youngest son of the third Marquis who was Lord Colum Edmund Crichton-Stuart. He died in nineteen fifty-eight, three years after I was born.

The east and west wings became the orphanage dormitories, while the south wing became the old people's home. The configuration of the Nursery dormitory and its connecting chambers made it entirely self-contained, leaving the rest of the building to be converted for the essential practical everyday necessities required for the running of an efficient orphanage and old people's home.

The east side of the building had a new magnificent church, in which the religious folk can sit, gazing up in awe from their solid pews to the transparent and brightly opaque stained glass windows soaring up angelically thirty feet above them. Such is its size; it can contain all the Nazareth House inmates plus the nuns and still have room for more.

The gothic-style mansion had a multitude of grand windows, most of which overlooked the well-groomed and extensively manicured gardens. The centrepiece of these is a larger-than-life statue of our Lord Jesus Christ, whose open-armed gesture was intended to welcome all those who entered through the main wrought-iron gates. There are six dormitories, each more than capable of holding more than twenty children, two of which were on the first floor and two on the second floor. The nursery was on the ground floor next to dormitory one.

During the time I was in the orphanage, flowers were abundant and were everywhere all year round, except for the dormitories. A full-time gardener kept the lawns and flower beds immaculate, weeding, however, was done by a small army of gardeners, the children. The two nuns whose duty was to tend the garden were pleasant enough but not overly friendly. They would show us what weeds to pick out. When they were bending over we used to throw little stones at their backsides, sometimes they took that in good fun and sometimes they didn't. Anyway, there were too many innocent faces for them to pin the blame on any one individual.

Even though there was a football pitch expanse of a well-mowed lawn, kids could only engage in recreation in designated areas. The nursery kids had their own caged-in play space. Most of the time we were penned inside the playground which was v-shaped and had a small section for the tinies. It contained a roundabout, two swings and a slide enclosed within the high walls surrounding the home, making it almost impossible to kick or chuck a ball onto the road. Not that you wanted to, for the only visible object above the wall was the electric trolley bus wires, that made a strange humming noise on rainy days.

A game Pat and I liked to play as often as we could, the game we called catch. We would throw a tennis ball to each other, trying to make it harder and harder to grab. A purloined tennis ball from the school ensured we had many more hours of enjoyment back at the nursery playground. Frequently, a visit to the Nazareth House clinic was necessary to dress a grazed knee caused by our strenuous exertions.

The Dawn Crusade

I suspect that at some time the explanation as to our incarceration must have percolated through to Sister Mary. She was the lovely kind, scar-faced nun; who had sad brown intelligent-looking eyes that missed nothing. All the kids liked her, for she occasionally talked to us, her sermons and stories from the Holy Bible were sometimes mesmerising.

We were in the nursery one day, the usual storytelling time while Sister Anna was at prayer, when Sister Mary singled out Pat and me, her purpose, to detail what a mother and father were; what home life was like. She tried to tell us why we had both been taken to Nazareth House orphanages soon after we were born. Despite her intentions, we were unable to comprehend her verbose words. In the back of my mind, the Mother Superior's statement from my first day echoed back, when she said our mother would take Greta and I back home as soon as it could be arranged. My beseeching, nightly prayers were never answered.

Befuddled, I packed away all the unpleasant, confusing thoughts into my subconscious suitcase, which was becoming filled with things I did not fully comprehend. I had trouble understanding and putting them in context, even though my natural inquisitiveness and memory were flourishing. I had already developed a state of mind formed throughout my time in institutes.

Through our observations, we had established a multitude of opportunities that could be used to our advantage, like the faint sounds when Sister Anna was about to enter the nursery; the noise of the corridor door as it clicked shut a few seconds before her grand entrance through the big double doors.

From my bed, I could see a dim light appear through the portal door; a warning sign that Sister Anna had switched her cell light on. A slightly brighter light meant she had opened her cell door, giving us a two or three-second delay before the imminent arrival of the nasty nun as she burst through.

We held rehearsals where, on my signal, a quiet little bird sound, we would all adopt the dead body position and feign sleep. When these trials proved successful, we were confident enough to have long and pleasant whispered conversations during the evenings, something we were all too frightened to do before.

Pat, Lucy and I used to speak softly, discussing and plotting ways to make our lives easier. I was still suspicious of everyone, except for my fellow inmates. Pat, with whom I was bonding with comparatively quickly, was like a breath of fresh air blowing my anxieties away. Despite all the mistreatment and bullying, she said she had endured, her constant cheery disposition, impishness and happiness were infectious. Lucy, who attended the same school as us, always appeared to be concentrating on something important, with one eye half-closed and her tongue nearly always poking between her lips.

The monotony of each day created my own *Groundhog Day*, making it increasingly difficult to put in chronological order the earlier events of my life, as the tediousness was only sporadically interrupted by a special occasion. Even then, we nursery captives attended a few of these, as we were mostly incarcerated within the confines of our domain. So I'm not sure precisely how much time had elapsed when the hazardous plan formed between the three of us, one which could result in dire consequences if we were caught. It was during this time that Lucy first came up with the stratagem that was to change our lives. A plan was hatched, though it would take many months before I plucked up sufficient courage. The thought of being caught out by Sister Anna was terrifying.

I have no idea how long we contemplated the scheme before acting. It was probably not until I had downgraded it to a misdemeanour rather than a sin before I felt comfortable enough to proceed.

Pat and Lucy had nominated me as the best one for the job. Though I suspect it was for them to appear blameless. From my bed, I was in the best position to see the light through the porthole door, and I was the lightest sleeper. I decided not to disclose when I would carry out our plan, so as not to incriminate anyone. I had the thought some might unintentionally reveal culpability and give the game away.

One morning, soon after, I was lying awake in bed. The distant, quiet clatter from the central kitchen signalled preparations were underway for the morning's routine. The mornings were now starting to get a little darker, I could clearly see the dim light through the porthole door a few moments after the first clatter; a positive sign Sister Anna was awake and getting ready for the day ahead. I had about fifteen minutes to complete my mission.

My potentially perilous, planned operation had started the evening before while the wicked nun was at prayer. I had slipped away from the other kids in the dormitory and moved my rickety old chair up to the big cupboard. Standing on the chair, I selected the essential sheets for two-bed changes, pulled them out and rushed to hide them out of sight behind my iron radiator, replacing the chair to complete the camouflage.

Silently I crept out of bed and tiptoed to the two cots containing the toddlers, knowing it was not the thing to do. I slipped my hand under the sheets of bed one finding the bed was dry. I sighed heavily in relief. Bed two held no such luck, Heidi had wet her bed again. My little heart raced. A gentle nudge roused her from slumber, and a whispered order found her standing yawning by her cot, furtive glances around showed no signs of disturbance. I had to act fast. With a great deal of haste, I removed the sheets, using the dry sections to wipe down the rubber covering, then put the blankets aside. I feared the noise emanating from my skinny knees and ankles clashing together would wake the entire home. With shaking hands and knocking knees, I completed stage two. Heidi slipped quietly back between the dry sheets grinning like a Cheshire cat. I concluded my plan by creeping to the bathroom and hiding the wet linen deep down inside the wicker laundry basket under a pile of damp towels.

As I approached my bed, I noticed another cat was smiling, a now unfamiliar semi-toothless smile, as her new teeth were almost fully formed. I smiled guiltily back at her and with my heart thumping, breathless and shaking, I leapt into bed with only a minute to spare.

"Get up you lazy bed wetters," trilled the heartless nun when she barged through the door.

Only this time there wasn't any. The usual expectant smirk would soon turn into a disappointed scowl.

Pat and Lucy, who only then realised their plan had worked, were adamant they would help in future dangerous operations. So every morning after that day, we would leap into action at the first sound of distant noise, not waiting for the cell light to come on. We would swiftly change bedding when necessary; becoming more adept by the day, with the rest of the kids now aware of our escapades watching in admiration. On the odd occasion, they changed their own wet sheets from my supplies. Luckily, we never even came close to getting caught. However, the horror of the consequences was always present.

Over a short period, bedwetting gradually became less frequent until it almost stopped completely, proving perhaps, that the fear of the punishment dished out, was the most likely cause of bedwetting in the first place. On top of which, with the peaceful hushed chatter at night and the morning sheet changing, the nursery became a calm and serene place where the unanimity of its inhabitants, remained palpable. The night-time sobs, though still present, were not as often or as intense.

Saturday Auctions

The nuns could be sadistically cruel. I remember when we were in the great hall on a Saturday morning. All the kids from every dormitory were in attendance, shepherded into groups by attention-seeking nuns for an event that occasionally occurred. When we were ready, the Mother Superior would enter, leading men and women. Three or four pairs of the outsiders and sometimes more. They would then saunter up and down the great hall inspecting the children like a farmer might check the livestock at a cattle auction.

Nuns then herded off any lucky selections to spend a weekend with the saintly Roman Catholic folk who had chosen them. Sometimes you never saw the children again. Neither Pat nor I had ever been among the favoured few, or the sad-looking Greta. This day was no exception.

Sister Terry was a small stern-faced vicious nun with a sadistic temperament, she had a hooked pointed nose, sallow cheeks and wore big rimmed black spectacles which made her witchy nose look even more protrusive. She would talk down at us as though we a bit of dirt. A nun we always tried to avoid. A strategy made harder by the fact she was small and sneaky; attributes she applied to intimidate the children. We considered her as the institute's main predator; with us the youngest, most vulnerable. She was the lioness and us her prey, skittish gazelles whose only objective was to eat and survive, a herd forever looking around for danger, wary of any unknown strange sounds.

She was the nun who had told me with relish about how I was hit by my father before I was born. An incident I assumed Sister Mary must have indiscreetly told her about.

She glided over to where we were sitting, gaped at us and said with venom, “Nobody will ever want you two because you’re so ugly. That’s why your mothers dumped you here, you repulsive animals.”

Pat looked up at Sister Terry’s supercilious unattractive face. Slowly Pat’s freckled face distorted as she scrunched up her nose. The effort caused her cheeks to rise; lifting up her round thick, opaque spectacles as her quivering bottom lip gradually covered her philtrum. When it almost touched her nose, she let out the most heart-rending pitiful yelp of anguish, before beginning to snivel and sniffle quietly. I gulped a sob and buried my head in my hands, heaving my shoulders up and down as if in distress. After waiting a few seconds, I peeped through my fingers to see Sister Terry slithering away around the corner with satisfied squinting eyes and a self-righteous smile on her face. I turned toward Pat to find her beaming.

“How did I do?”

“Brilliant,” I replied, mirroring her smile.

“Good. That should keep the old cow happy for a while.”

Pat rarely spoke like that, but I understood why. It was because she hated Sister Terry. Every time she encountered Pat, she would pinch, whack, slap or goad her. We all received pretty much the same, though not as frequently as Pat.

We had practised that look of grief for hours on end in playtime until we were satisfied. It was almost the same look on Greta’s face the day our plaits were chopped off by the big black-clad nun. Such minor victories over our persecutors helped to keep our spirits up and were worth practising and waiting for.

On another Saturday, about four or five pairs of outsiders, each escorted by a nun, were milling around the hall. Greta, Pat and I were on one of the long benches, sitting together on the edge of the seat, swinging our legs in unison at least six inches above the highly polished parquet floor we had helped to buff hours earlier.

I recognised one husband and wife who had been to Nazareth House on several Saturdays. The first time I had seen them was on a rainy Saturday morning when I was with Sister Mary. We were huddled in the doorway of the big entrance lobby, watching the rain splashing down in pools of water on the large tarmac drive. As we stood there, the man and woman had approached the entrance gate, their heads down to keep the rain from their faces. Most of us would never dream of being comfortable in the presence of a nun, let alone converse with one. Sister Mary was different, she revealed in a whispered tone through partly closed lips, that they were unable to have children of their own and wanted to adopt or foster a child. She told me to be on my best behaviour and shooed me away.

We had been through these weekend routines more than twenty times and had never been picked. This particular Saturday looked to be different. The same man and woman were with Sister Mary, who pointed in our direction. They walked purposely towards us, the trio advancing in slow rhythmical strides. We gazed at them fixedly as they approached, my heart skipped a few beats, wishing, hoping, and straightaway wanting them to take us to a beautiful new home.

I heard the woman say, “Oh, look at those three little girls. Aren’t they lovely?”

I recollect blushing furiously as I gave them a small smile. The couple listened intently to something Sister Mary was murmuring through her partially closed lips, an idiosyncrasy she must have refined over the years as though she had been a professional ventriloquist in a previous life. The couple listened to her muted words for a few short moments when I heard the man say, “Oh, really?”

I couldn’t hide my disappointment as they turned and walked away. The nice woman turned around at that moment, her lovely eyes meeting mine before she turned away and carried on walking.

I wondered why the man had said, “oh, really?” I was upset, but I didn’t cry, I hadn’t cried for a long time. We sat on the bench disappointed, dejected and in silence, staring at the floor.

Unexpectedly I was staring at two pairs of shoes; a pair of man’s shoes and a smart pair of woman’s shoes. I looked up, it was the handsome couple, and they had come back. My mood immediately changed as they sat down next to us, the wife next to me and the husband next to Greta. Pat was in the middle beaming broadly.

The wife introduced herself as Mary, told us her husband was called Peter, both names sounded exceedingly saintly to me, Auntie Mary and Uncle Peter as they asked us to call them, wanted to know how long had we been in the home? Had we ever been on holiday? What did we like to eat?

Uncle Peter and Aunt Mary talked with us for quite a while. Although I was a wary little girl by this time, I relaxed, beginning to like them more and more by the minute. He was a tall and slim good-looking man with short brown curly hair, even teeth and a warm smile. Auntie Mary was of medium height with tied back shoulder-length golden-brown hair. She had a round face with dark blue eyes, rosy dimpled cheeks that made her appear particularly congenial. Her clothes seemed extremely expensive, elegance came to mind. I immediately thought she would make a great mother.

"We will come and see you soon," they said as they left.

Their parting words left us feeling highly delighted, Aunt Mary's farewell words were my last thoughts before I went to sleep that night.

After every time we were overlooked, we would sit at the large table in the dining room, discussing our favourite subjects in quiet tones. The conversations were inevitably prospective variations on a common theme, our possible adoption and foster parents. Pat would say if her mother didn't come back for her, she would like to be adopted by a King and Queen. She would ensure I went with her so I could become her lady-in-waiting. I'd say when my mother or father comes for Greta and me, I'd make them take Pat as a housekeeper. Or I would make believe my stepfather was a famous actor who had a beautiful wife, adding I would make sure they took Pat so she could be my maid. Whoever the unlikely step-parents were to be, we always included each other.

We never set eyes on the pair again. When it finally became apparent that they were never coming back, we discussed the subject as pragmatically as young abandoned children could and dismissed it, with Pat concluding, "They wouldn't have taken all three of us, anyway".

While we were mostly disregarded, the turnover in the nursery was recurrent. Faces appeared and disappeared, giving me the impression that the nursery was the first point of call for newcomers, a dormitory in which they were assessed before being relocated.

Time passed slowly as for any prisoner, for anyone contained within a monotonous environment, like the tide, it was predictable but changed slightly every day. As was my progress and education. I assimilated knowledge without realising as it occurred at such a slow speed I never noticed.

Two years went by, and my daily routine remained the same. At regular points in time, there were about twelve kids in our spacious dormitory; the boys had beds on the right, the girls on the left. Pat and I, by age and experience, by a version of natural progression, had become the self-appointed nursery matriarchs. We had three tiny tots to care for, as well as pointing the newer kids in the right direction. Weighty responsibilities for our fledgling ages perhaps, but at least we were performing useful duties we liked.

Sister Anna and Mrs Gittings were more than happy to allow us to help with the little ones, which gave us the scant pleasure of being able to relax with the tiny mites. This sometimes gave us the opportunity of being able to do other things, like change soiled clothing or sheets and hide them in the big laundry basket without them noticing.

During the early years, I was forever cold and hungry, there wasn't an extra bit of fat on me. Pat used to jokingly tell me, I was as skinny as a rake. I became used to the cold and didn't mind. Hunger, though, was another thing. Sister Mary, who by then played a more responsible role in running the nursery, put me on extra rations. Regrettably, nutty Sister Anna still had overhaul control. Except for the two extra slices of bread, my diet included an evening glass of Horlicks; a malted milk drink containing wheat, barley and vitamins in a powder form which she mixed with warm watered-down milk and a raw egg.

“This will build you up, just the job to bulk up a young belly,” she said in a gentle voice each time she gave it to me before bedtime.

I couldn’t even share it as no one liked it. At least I slept much better at night, though I was still a light sleeper. I wasn’t as restless, if this was due to the Horlicks or Sister Mary’s explanation of sleeping with our arms crossed across our chests was undeterminable.

“It’s not to keep the devil away,” contradicting Sister Anna, “It’s for God to protect you,”

Either way, it worked for I piled on at least the extra weight of a feather during the next six months before she eventually surrendered. My elation was such I conveyed my gratitude to God.

During one of Sister Mary’s sermons, she enlightened me as to my future. She surprised me by informing me that my baptism name was Catherine, so my name was Milly Catherine Nash. It took me five years to discover my surname and the fact I had a sister, then another two years to find out my baptism name. The pace of enlightenment was alarming.

At the time, I thought my mother must have had the decency to arrange my baptism, which was my first sacrament. Thinking she had to have me baptised before she could get rid of me to a Catholic orphanage. This wasn’t the case, though.

Now it was the time for me to receive the Eucharist, my First Communion. During the Catholic ceremony, you accept the body of Jesus Christ in the form of a small circular white unleavened edible disc. The priest places the small circular wafer on the extended tongue of the kneeling recipient, where it is allowed to dissolve while the receiver mentally recites the Lord’s Prayer.

“This is my body… This my blood.” The priest recites while blessing the wafer and wine. Once consecrated, the wafer becomes the body of Jesus Christ and the wine his blood through transubstantiation, consequently creating a miracle on each instance.

Sister Mary explained the procedure for this special occasion in a proud, excited voice that was louder than usual,

“No less than the man, himself, is conducting the ceremony.”

She studied my puzzled expression and burst out laughing; it was a soft, gentle laugh that made her appear radiant, even with that awful scar, she looked beautiful. She had guessed my assumption.

“No, No. Milly not him! The Bishop.”

Accompanied by Pat, Lucy and Natalie, I attended my first confession the Friday before our first Communion day. Natalie was a dark-haired girl the same age as us who now lived in dormitory one. She had left the nursery the same day I arrived and initially resented me for taking her place.

My original thought on entering the confessional box, on the side of the church aisle, was that it was more like a cupboard. The entrance door opened outward as there was not enough room for it to open inward. The only item in the cubbyhole was a padded leather cushion on the floor, inviting the confessor to kneel. I stood facing a grilled window, behind the grill was a black curtain about the size of an adult face, the sinner was expected to plead guilty facing the cloth barrier. I used to scrutinise the curtain looking for signs as to the identity of the person behind it, in fact, each time I went to confession, I wondered who was in the other room. I pondered whether a nun or nuns were in there as well listening as we unveiled our inner thoughts.

This incidentally wasn’t that often, for I was demonstrable, by then, a saintly Catholic girl. The sinner confesses their various sins and asks for absolution. Behind the shimmering curtain, the priest then absolves you of your sins, in the name of the Father, the Son and the Holy Spirit, specifying the repentance. The amount of penitent time, depending on the intensity of the sins committed. Repentant time is served by kneeling at a pew in church, silently thinking or mouthing the words of either, 'The Hail Mary' or 'Our Father,' followed by 'I confess to almighty God'. In Latin, it's called 'Confiteor Deo Omnipotenti'. I can still recite it in Latin, as well as the entire Mass.

My first Communion day was unforgettable. I was one of eight pure of soul children kneeling at the altar waiting for the man himself, the Bishop, to place the unleavened bread on our protruding tongues.

The Bishop was a tall, especially so with his white and gold mitre, a dignified slim man with a saintly smug smile, who cut a dashing figure dressed in his black robes and a purple sash. Previously he had spoken for half an hour, given us an attention-grabbing sermon. I still remember his sonorous tones.

There are seven sacraments: baptism, Eucharist, confirmation, reconciliation or confession, anointing the sick, marriage and Holy Orders. Then, I had two. I had been baptised and gone to confession. The next would be my first Holy Communion or Eucharist. My confirmation was four years in the waiting. Looking at the seven sacraments, I noticed that no one person can have all seven, to take Holy Orders you can't be married and vice versa.

The local paper sent a reporter and photographer to cover this important event in Catholicism. Although I cannot recall the photograph being taken, I know it appeared on page three in the following day's edition of Cardiff's Echo, because I acquired the original newspaper and the unique black and white negative many years later. I call it my Caravaggio. The picture is of a pretty girl kneeling on a table, me, looking relatively healthy and particularly happy, with a nun beside me adjusting my white veil. I am wearing a white dress and black shoes, shoes I only wore once, while in the background admiring children look on. Among those were Pat, Lucy and Natalie, each of us sporting the same hairstyle, the straight-line coiffeur of the establishment.

The paragraph underneath the obviously posed photograph states; *'Sister Margarita is seen fitting a headdress on Milly Nash, a pupil at St David's Junior School. Milly and thirty-nine other girls from Nazareth House will take part in Whitsunday's procession.'* The parade, on the tenth of June nineteen sixty-two, was an exciting, unforgettable day.

Two things stand out for me in the photograph; first, the nun in the picture is Sister Margarita, the most compassionate of all human beings I have ever met. So much so, I chose Margarita as my confirmation name. I remember laughing many years later when I realised I had named myself after a favourite cocktail and similar to the famous Margherita pizza. Second, and less happily, the table I was kneeling on is the same one used when my long hair was hacked off by the big black-clad-nun.

Donkeys, Chips and Sea

My first annual beach trip to the seaside would prove to be an incredible experience; it was the summer of my second anniversary in captivity.

Charitable donations were a significant source of revenue for Nazareth House. Luckily, there were some extraordinarily kind and generous people around in those days, as indeed there are today. One of the very many benevolent donors was Currans, a large Cardiff based company. Not only did they give financially to the orphanage, but they also ensured the kids had a good time too. During the summer school holidays, they would dispatch their works coach and a driver to Nazareth House, with the intention that its destination would be Barry Island beach and the fairground complex about ten miles away. Each day, for five consecutive days, the bus would convey an assortment of older and younger children from various dormitories, with the older children being expected to look after the younger brood. These were accompanied and supervised by three or four nuns, with a couple of the old people thrown in for good measure, to make up the numbers and fill the coach.

Looking back on these trips, I realise the logistical skills required to arrange the outings needed to be extremely consummate. The delightful Sister Margarita who organised all the social events on the Nazareth House calendar achieved this. She was like the public relations guru of the institution and a shrewd choice, for she never failed to demonstrate she had the capabilities, nuance and knowledge to accomplish such tasks.

Typically we knew nothing about any forthcoming events, but the Barry Island trip was one exception. About two weeks before the departure date, we were told which group we would be in and what day we would travel. Of all the nursery inmates, only Pat had ever been on the trip before. She had made the journey the summer before our first meeting. In recalling her previous jaunt, all she talked about was riding the donkeys, eating chips and playing in the sand and sea. I'd seen pictures of horses before, and I'd seen some during my journey to Cardiff but donkeys, the sea and sand were a complete mystery to me.

All the nursery inmates had missed the Barry excursion for the previous two years. The excuse for the first year, about a week after I first arrived, was a suspected outbreak of measles, one identified by Sister Anna that eventually proved a misdiagnosis. She had unnecessarily confined a dozen unhappy kids to the dormitory for a week.

The following year Sister Anna had banned our attendance for disruptive and heathen behaviour. Gareth and David became mortal enemies for reasons only they knew, so the nursery captives were anxiously waiting for the next explosion of temper tantrums, hoping it wouldn't occur so near to the outing. Unfortunately, we all missed the early warning systems so diligently adhered to over the previous years. It happened while Sister Anna was at evening Mass. When she returned, she had crept in silently to witness what she perceived to be a mass brawl. It wasn't, we were trying in desperation to separate David and Gareth to avoid missing out on the seaside visit again, but in vain. Their appalling behaviour had cost us dearly, we were excluded once more.

As it occurred, the day we were scheduled to go, we had to stay in our dormitory for the entire day, because of a summer thunderstorm and torrential rain that continued throughout the day and night. The same weather the soaking wet visitors to Barry Island had to endure. I confess I was quietly relieved. However, some laughed and sniggered for days.

I prayed that nothing would prevent me from going on the third opportunity. And this year the build-up to the event was going smoothly. During the fortnight before the first bus was due to leave, the nursery and orphanage became a calm stronghold of compliant composure.

Luckily by then, Gareth and David had left the nursery. David had happily been fostered, and Gareth was cheerfully staying in one of the boy's only dormitories. David didn't completely vanish. The following Monday he came strolling through the gates of Saint David's school, looking happy yet self-conscious in his new uniform. We had a brief chat before the school bell; bells really controlled my life then; when he revealed he was amazingly happy with his foster parents who had two daughters. We were pleased for him and couldn't wait for our own dreams to come true.

All nursery internees remained on tenterhooks, mindful of keeping on their best behaviour, all careful not to be added to the nuns', 'You're not going' list. Everyone survived those two weeks, fulfilling their duties without displeasing the nun, and we were all going on the first bus of the week.

The night before the trip, a near feverish excitement gripped the nursery, for once everyone was looking forward to the morning wake-up bell. When we awoke, we were pleased to see bright sunshine peeping through the gaps of the heavy curtains, like searchlights stabbing through the room, a sight we took as a good omen, an auspicious bright start to the day. Though before we could depart, we had to complete the early morning work.

When we returned to the nursery, after the morning session in church, we found the clothes we were to wear in neat bundles laid out on our respective chairs. There were also a pair of elastic-sided white canvas plimsolls; I had meticulously whitened the previous day, to complete my attire for the day. Had it been three years later, they would have fitted me perfectly.

Sister Anna, Sister Mary, the helper and Lorna, one of the older girls from dormitory two, marched with us down the long corridors to the waiting coach where Sister Margarita and another nun Sister Toms, alias the black-clad nun, were waiting apparently good-naturedly by the doors. Already on the bus were about ten of the older kids. Through the dazzling sunshine, I noticed that Greta was one of the girls. I didn't have too many chances to speak to Greta unless we both attended an event. Most of the time, I would only see her in church. I didn't think much about her, so conversations were never missed.

There were also five women and a man from the old people's section, sitting ensconced in their high seats squinting down at us. I noticed it was the man who never smiled. Each day when I returned to Nazareth House from school, I would skip through the big iron gates, and the first sight to greet me was the sad face of this old man who stared at me through the window of the pensioner section. I smiled at him every day, but he never responded. One day he would, I thought.

The doors of the coach opened, and there was an orderly yet frantic rush to get to the rear seats. I ended up sitting opposite Pat, about two rows down from the back. Janice was next to me, while Heidi sat next to Pat, a vice-like grip on her cotton dress. Both the little ones looked very nervous. They were two years older than when I had first seen them, even so, they were still almost totally reliant on Pat and me. Natalie and Lucy also played a big part in looking after the mites, inevitably all of them developing an emotional attachment. So it was quite a wrench for the girls when Natalie was abruptly moved to dormitory one, the day I first arrived in the nursery.

Sister Margarita was the last one to board the coach, carrying a mysterious tattered big tan leather suitcase. Then we were off.

The journey to the seaside was fantastic, with me, as usual, staring out of the window fascinated by the landscape flashing by as the bus wheeled towards our mysterious destination. Everybody was smiling and became animated when the old-age pensioners began to sing. We all accompanied the singers except for the miserable old man,

"Ten green bottles hanging on the wall, and if one green bottle should accidentally fall, there'll be nine green bottles hanging on the wall. Nine green bottles hanging on the wall."

It has to be the most natural nursery rhyme in the world to learn, yet there were a few of our party who hadn't quite mastered how to count in reverse.

Sister Margarita handed out five pink cardboard tickets to everyone. They were by courtesy of the generous Currans organisation, each one promising the recipient a free ride at the funfair.

The coach became quieter when our destination neared, as nearly everybody strained to see the first sight of our journey's end. Finally, the coach crested the brow of a hill where we could initially distinguish the scenic railway, the main attraction of the park looming in the distance, and behind it a vast glittering expanse of water that seemed to have flooded the world. With three exceptions, everyone else, including the bus driver, cheered.

By the time the coach pulled up on the promenade of Barry Island, even the two little ones were happy and beaming broadly. Sister Margarita then stood in the aisle with a clipboard in her hand and began reading out instructions as to the day's agenda. When she had finished talking, we all said a prayer in thanks to St Christopher for our safe journey, and with the traditional response to our safe passage over, were eager to leave the coach.

Sister Margarita said, before opening the coach door. "Now everybody, best behaviour please, for the good name of Nazareth House."

Within minutes she was leading a regimented, orderly line down to the sandy beach, then along the sand until finding a suitable spot near the promenade wall. Here, following the tradition of previous visits, deckchairs were acquired and strategically placed to create a large stockade on the soft yellow sand. We had established our base camp.

Outsiders peered curiously over the promenade wall at the unusual sight before them. There were four nuns, two wearing black habits, one in blue and Sister Anna in white, six adult pensioners, fifteen young girls and eight boys, all floundering around in the sand of our base camp; the youngsters all sporting the same hairstyle and wearing similar clothing.

I remember being mesmerised by the view as we all gazed across the horseshoe-shaped sandy beach stretching from the Bristol Channel towards the Atlantic Ocean. We stared in awe at the vast ocean shimmering towards the distant horizon with America's New York three thousand three hundred open sea miles away. The keen-eyed Sister Margarita must have noticed our thrilled expressions because she hastily organised a small scouting party. I joined Greta, Janice and a reluctant Mrs Gittings, accompanied by Sister Margarita, Lorna and a beaming Pat who still had an equally beaming Heidi firmly attached to her dress.

The wet sandy shoreline was some distance away. As we neared the frothy water's edge, the grumble of the crashing waves increased in intensity. My initial fear and apprehension quickly faded like the popping bubbles, and soon we were having a great time splashing about in ankle-deep water; running away from the flowing tide as it came rolling up the sandy beach, pulling at our feet as it receded as though tempting us to join it more permanently. Greta and I played together for the first time as the lovely Lorna took her turn to watch over us.

After a while, Sister Margarita, who was standing patiently next to an extremely impatient-looking Mrs Gittings, called us back. We obediently, yet reluctantly, began our return journey to our base camp. It amazed me to see how quickly the beach had become so crowded during the brief time we had spent frolicking in the sea. It was as if our exploits had encouraged everyone in the vicinity to congregate on the beach.

By now the sea had travelled quite a distance up the beach towards the soft sand where our rows of deckchairs were aligned. The ebb and flow sea movements of Cardiff and Barry are some of the largest in the world, regularly experiencing tidal ranges of up to fifteen metres. A fact the former owner of Nazareth House, John Crichton-Stuart the 2nd Marquess of Bute, used to his advantage when he built docks and the transport system necessary to export millions of tons of coal all over the globe while amassing millions of pounds of money in the process.

On our return towards our soft sandy fortress we encountered a large, round-bellied man, who had a happy, jolly red face and a roguish smile, though at first, all I noticed were the four donkeys he was leading. When he saw us, he pulled up his pack of docile donkeys.

"Hello, Sister, how many children have you today?" he bellowed.

Except for Sister Margarita and Pat, we took two paces back away from the sad-looking creatures, as though blown away by the gale of his breath, the sudden explosion of words, a startling exclamation that even made little Heidi loosen her iron grip on Pat's dress.

"Hello, Mr Haggerty. How are you this fine day? We have twenty-three today, thank you," Sister Margarita returned, utterly unconcerned by our reactions.

I held my breath as Pat walked courageously towards the donkeys and stroked their big noses. The man smiled and turned the handle of a machine hanging on a leather strap around his neck, in a short time handing the smiling nun a small bundle of green tickets, before turning around to tenderly lift a surprised Pat onto the back of a grey donkey whose nose she had just been stroking. She sat comfortably on top of the gentle-looking creature; her, smiling, freckled face was a picture of pure happiness.

"I'm just starting work, so I'll give the girls a ride back with you," he boomed.

In a minute our misgivings gave way to cordial compliance, soon each of the girls sat, their legs either side of an itchy hairy back, though no amount of coaxing could entice Heidi onto a donkey, not even the sight of a smiling Janice who was sitting in front of Lorna. We trotted triumphantly back to camp led by the kind Mr Haggerty, we returned to whoops of delight from Lucy, Natalie and all the kids.

As soon as we returned to base camp preparations for the picnic urgently commenced, as according to the panicking Sister Mary; we were fifteen minutes behind schedule. Sister Margarita explained the presence of the leather suitcase when she opened it, to reveal it was full to the brim with an assortment of egg, cheese and fish paste sandwiches.

Sister Mary then handed out paper plates full of sandwiches to everybody. Even the typically grumpy, Mrs Gittings smiled while pouring fresh milk into our beakers. Sister Toms, who thankfully was in charge of the old people, had to wake a few of them who were already snoozing in their comfy looking deck chairs. The morose-faced old man, the one I smiled at every day after school, sat uncomfortably on the edge of a deckchair looking like he didn't want to be there. Strangely, Sister Anna was on another deckchair blending into the background; she was unusually quiet, her pale face looking pasty and dejected. It transpired she had travel sickness, according to Sister Mary. I wondered if it was divine retribution by Saint Christopher.

Pat whispered to Heidi, just loud enough for me to hear, "See… I told you God would punish her."

Heidi looked skywards a slight smile on her pretty face. I could see her red lips moving, you didn't have to be a lip reader to know what she was saying. It was a definitive, thank you.

We must have looked a strange sight to the holidaymakers passing by, as we recited the words daily drummed into us, with our heads bowed and hands together, thanking God for thy gifts we are about to receive, and from thy bounty. Amen.

After the fabulous picnic, plastic buckets and spades appeared out of nowhere. A little later, I was surprised when some of us were given summer clothes to wear that fitted. I had a lovely red patterned sleeveless dress with shoulder straps. We played and cavorted in the sand, building sandcastles and burying each other up to the neck. I noticed Greta was thoroughly enjoying herself. I felt elated, relaxed and gratified. Those few hours in time were, without doubt, the happiest I'd ever been during my short life.

One hiccup to the glorious day was some of us getting red and sunburned. The nuns didn't seem to notice, well they wouldn't would they the only exposed part of their bodies were their hands and face, their faces shaded by a wimple. That was until Pat bravely and politely pointed it out. Sister Margarita hastily produced a bottle of pink calamine lotion and applied the liquid to sensitive skin.

The trip had regenerated our dormant natural good humour. Smiling faces within the home were not commonly shared with the nuns. For the simple reason, they seldom displayed emotion. Here everyone appeared in a different light, as though the sea had washed away our inhibitions, wave by wave dissolving our institutionalised barriers.

The now recovered nutty Sister Anna, and grumpy Gittings were not the same people at all, showing signs of humanity they usually kept hidden. I didn't know the black-clad nun well then, I steered firmly out of her way that day. I thought about Sister Anna and her sickness and wondered if that might be the reason for the nursery missing the two previous jaunts to Barry. There wasn't a shout, pinch or a whack during the entire day. I had never seen any of my fellow inmates looking so happy and relaxed. I suppose it was as close as it was likely to be to a family day out. If only our lives could have been like that all the time.

There was a steady stream of visitors to our sandy area. One man, who owned the café on the promenade, came down with a big box full of ice cream cornets and ice lollies. Delicious is the only word to describe my first ever ice cream. Sister Margarita had even arranged for a photographer to be present, which probably explained the half-decent clothing that fitted us, a man looking out of place, yet seemingly significant in his brown woollen suit. His lapel badge informed all who could read, he was from the South Wales Echo, Cardiff's daily evening newspaper.

I have in my possession three unique, professional photographs I acquired from their archives over forty years later. I have tears in my eyes at the moment, tears of joy that is. My memory is full of great pleasure and happiness from that remarkable day. One photograph portrays a beaming Milly Nash, a grinning Pat, a serene Greta, two cute, coy little angels Heidi and Janice; a snapshot of an instant that amazingly depicts the most important people in my life. Incredibly, in the picture's corner is the tatty tan leather suitcase. The image is priceless, it's my *Mona Lisa.*

Another portrait that wasn't published shows a beautiful girl called Jeannette, a Down syndrome child who unfortunately was precluded by her parents.

There were quite a few children in the home who were disfigured, mentally challenged, or abandoned to the institution by families who didn't want them.

The day became better and better as we played with balls and built sandcastles, before using our green tickets to ride on the donkeys. After some persuasion, Heidi plucked up the courage to ride on one, albeit with Pat, and on the same donkey. Much to the hilarity of everybody, the sad-looking little donkey refused to follow his fellow-creatures until he had finished his poop.

Mr Haggerty shovelled the mess into a sack and said good-naturedly, "It's good for the garden."

He really was a lovely man, the jolly and generous Mr Haggerty.

A little later on in the afternoon, we visited the incredible, noisy, busy and terrifying fairground, in groups of about eight. As it transpired, I found myself in the same octet that had first gone down to the sea.

It was so strange to be surrounded and jostled by what appeared to be an army of amiable giants wearing an assortment of multi-coloured clothing, and in some cases, hardly any, beachwear which barely covered more than my dress would have if draped over a grossly larger form. Suntanned legs supporting torsos that brushed past enclosed us, they carried heads that sometimes looked down to mutter an apology or nod a smiled greeting, though most remained fixed on the latest attraction to gain their attention. We were objects to bypass and ignore as we danced between the never-ending streams of long limbs happily trying to ignore them.

Sister Margarita took it in her big booted stride, oblivious of how different she appeared to the mass of holidaymakers; a crowd amusingly disturbed by a nun, leading a bunch of children, some wearing clothes that were obviously borrowed for the day from a class three years older. There again, perhaps we did fit in well, we were just another attraction, a further distraction in the hustle and bustle.

All the time we were battered by blaring music, the noise from the various stalls as each loudly proclaimed their relative merits, propositioning the crowd with false claims of how easy it would be to win at their particular attraction. Our nostrils were assaulted by continually changing smells; of hot meals left too long in an oven, then fried onions, petrol fumes, the sweet smell of candyfloss, discarded toffee apple cores decaying and roasting in the sun.

Each stall was a visual interruption, each an oasis within the park. A concrete block where we would strain to peer through the mass of sweaty bodies, tempted by every stallholder's spiel, confounded by the ribald jokes and banter of the colourful adults who took on the various challenges.

As the experience was so new and entirely different for me, so exciting and fun-filled, I preserve many memories of our encounters in the fairground. The look on Sister Margarita's face was amusing as she climbed clumsily into the middle carriage of the exciting scenic railway ride. She looked very apprehensive, sitting between a grinning Lorna and Greta as the train slowly click-clicked up the gradient towards the first seventy-two feet drop from the ground.

The man on the entrance gate had said, "I am really sorry, Sister, but these four children are too small for the ride."

Pat, Janice and Heidi were genuinely disappointed. I gratefully pretended I was.

Mrs Gittings stayed with us as we watched the carriage slowly making its way up, when it dramatically dropped, briefly before disappearing around a bend twisting its way up and down and around the mile-long big dipper ride. From where we watched we could see and hear almost everything, of all the thirty people in the three carriages we could quickly pick out the silhouette of Sister Margarita.

The ride had been designed with that intention in mind; it went around the entire periphery of the impressive fairground. I had the thought people could hear the screams for miles around.

Three minutes later, when they clambered out of the carriage, Greta and Lorna were doubled up with laughter, while Sister Margarita's face was as white as her wimple.

I used up one of my priceless pink tickets on the goldfish stall. To my utter delight, and much to Mrs Gittings disgust, I tossed one of my five allocated ping-pong balls into the middle of one of the scores of goldfish bowls standing on the huge round table in the centre of the stall. The jovial man behind the barrier gave me a theatrical wink, then presented me the prize, a glass bowl containing an energetic goldfish in a couple of pints of water, with a small pepper-like pot containing fish food taped to its side. Years later I realised just how kind he was, ordinarily the prize for getting a ball in the glass bowl was a goldfish in a plastic bag full of water.

For the rest of our time there, I was bitterly disappointed to learn we were restricted as to what rides we could go on, like the big dipper. I was constrained more than anybody else, what with Janice to look after and my new friend's home sloshing all over my red dress. Though that did not prevent us from going on the dodgems, which was totally brilliant. Sister Margarita drove Heidi and me first, and then the other kids had their turn while we watched, her skill and enthusiasm were impressive.

After our nun-driven vehicle had successfully negotiated the heavy traffic and had suffered the appropriate number of bumps and bangs, we proceeded to the next attraction. It's funny, but whenever I think about the dodgems, I remember the smell, the distinctive whiff of graphite and ozone, mingled with the aroma of fried onions. Within five minutes, seven happy souls went on the merry-go-round, while Mrs Gittings stood by the candy floss stall waiting for us, resentfully holding a goldfish bowl. By this time any inhibition we'd had for displaying our enjoyment had entirely deserted us, the screams of all the other kids were infectious. I remember it was a pleasure witnessing so much entertainment.

The candy floss man gave us all sticks topped by a fluffy looking pink cloud that stuck to our faces. Then Mrs Gittings, as though not to be left out of our enjoyment, gave us her five pink tickets. Would wonder never cease on this day? We used them to go on the Helter Skelter. The last treat we had before we had to leave was a visit to the House of Mirrors, it was hilarious. The distorting mirrors made Goldie, as I'd inventively named my goldfish, look like a giant golden shark.

On the way back to our base, Sister Margarita explained to me it wouldn't be fair on Goldie to be on her own all day in the dormitory, cleverly insinuating it would not be in the goldfish's best interest to be cooped up. Yet kids can be I thought, but kept quiet. It was her way of reminding me that pets were only allowed in the old people's section, ironically they could only have captive pets, and that no child should take preference over another.

I understood immediately what she was trying to say; as I was no stranger to sadness and loneliness myself. That left me with the problem of what to do with Goldie. On our return to our sandy base, a solution soon became apparent. Mrs Thomas, one of the old people, was sitting in a deckchair clicking away with her knitting needles, looking as gloomy and forlorn as she habitually did. I went straight over to her and without a word held out Goldie as an offering. She took the bowl containing Goldie with tears in her eyes; the most vibrant I'd ever seen her.

"Thank you, blue eyes. Thank you blue eyes, God bless you,"

I noticed the cantankerous dejected old man, who I had recently heard being called Mr Noland, was smiling serenely in the background, that is until he saw me smiling at him. He directly turned away to gaze down at the sand, the smile evaporated from his face.

The day was almost at an end. Janice and Heidi were cuddled up sleeping happily on Mrs Thomas's deck chair, while she was sitting on the sand having a one-sided in-depth conversation with Goldie, who looked as though she understood every word.

Then the final surprise of the day was delivered by the all-conquering Sister Margarita, who returned to camp carrying the box which had earlier contained the ice-creams. This time it had newspaper-wrapped bundles that enclosed light brown crispy chips. The chips were undeniably gorgeous, there were a few sandwiches left in the suitcase, though by that time some of them were more sand than sandwiches, this didn't stop us stuffing them with chips. It was a meal to remember and enjoy.

Our day trip was nearly over, so we all went for a short stroll on the promenade while we waited for the bus. Sister Margarita continued where she'd left off from our last conversation, trying to tell me about my mother and father. I was too tired to care. I was only aware of the staring faces of the outsiders.

As my time in the home evolved, I began to know Sister Margarita better, I realised she never ever laid a finger on any of the inmates. But even she behaved differently as if it was a display put on for the benefit of the outsiders.

When we returned to the orphanage, we were all shattered. Sister Anna was quiet and looked as white as a starched sheet.

The entire nursery had been awake since before dawn. We had finally used up all our emotional and physical energy. Before I knew what was happening, we were back at the home, in bed and smiling contentedly, our arms across our chests.

Sister Nash

I was talking with Sister Mary about the Barry trip. We were both laughing over some minor incident, and I felt comfortable in her company. It was at that point I allowed my mouth to act before my brain.

"I want to be a nun when I'm old enough," I blurted out.

The pride she displayed embarrassed me when I fully realised what I had implied. In reality, I had decided a long time before that I couldn't wait to get out of the place. I hoped and prayed I'd soon be reunited with the parents I'd never met.

Our conversation that day proved to be the foundation of an unexpected period of my incarceration. Mother Superior summoned me to her office the next day, and I was allowed to go unaccompanied, a milestone in itself. I walked through the quiet corridors in trepidation, not missing the swish of an accompanying nun's habit.

I needn't have worried for the Mother Superior had been informed by Sister Mary of my intention of becoming a nun. The pleasure she exuded made me feel deeply ashamed.

I confirmed my statement of intention, thinking I would not mention this blatant lie to the priest during my Friday evening confession. A friendly conversation followed as I mentally squirmed.

She dismissed me by saying, "May God bless you, child. You will learn the ways of the Sisters of Nazareth, and Sister Mary will be your mentor. The moment I saw you, I knew that you would become a nun." Mistaking my self-conscious look for pride, she continued, "Now go Milly. And may Christ be with you."

After that day, a remarkable change to my regimental routine transpired. I was given a metaphorical key to practically the entire home, which did nothing to alleviate my shame. On top of which, Pat and I were allowed a significant amount of freedom. I thought maybe the Mother Superior supposed Pat would follow me in my chosen path. And as another privilege, if we wanted, we could have our meals in the big dining hall with the seventy-something other kids. It was in this period of my stay I began to understand, appreciate and marvel at the true extent of Nazareth House as The Mother Superior intended.

However, there was one person who wasn't pleased, Sister Anna was mortified. During the previous few years, she had become noticeably even more malicious and unpredictable, her temper was uncontrollable. She hated everything and everybody.

The atmosphere within the confines of Nazareth House appeared to have changed for the better after the Barry trip. It was as if a new regime had toppled the preceding dictators. There was still a multitude of rooms and areas considered out-of-bounds, strict rules had to be obeyed at all times. We continued to scrub and polish. The nasty nuns were unchanged, we unremittingly felt their pinch and wrath. While our own routine remained, the same, subtle changes occurred.

A communal playroom that lay undiscovered behind a locked door was suddenly made available; it was to prove especially useful on rainy days. Except for the tinies, all the kids could congregate in the large high room that was as big as a dormitory. The tinies, as the nuns called them, were kids up to junior school age. I had the impression the doors that had previously been locked were opened and the keys thrown away.

Now, nearly all the religious occasions, Christmas and Easter parties were held with outsiders in attendance. Plus, more and more families visited the home on auction days. Subsequently, more kids had weeks or weekends away.

The downside to this occurred when Lucy disappeared one weekend, leaving an empty bed and eleven sad kids behind her. I was distraught; for she was one of my best friends. There was a void in my life. Strangely, any change to the monotonous routine unsettled me; I had come to believe boredom was homespun.

Lucy had taught me a lot. She didn't say much, but she was one of the best at observing the little traits and idiosyncrasies of our adversaries. We would miss the thoughtful girl and her quiet, shy ways. I was used to her unique features, her close together brown amber eyes, and a long thin face that had a chin jutting out at an angle, the girl whose protruding tongue was forever peeping from between her lips. But even though her features were unusual, she was attractive, they displayed her strength of character. We weren't as close as I was to Pat, Janice or Heidi, but we were still close confidants, more to the point, she was one of us.

"Lucy was fostered by a family from Cardiff," Sister Anna said, no more no less.

We were supplied with an unsurprising lack of information spitefully designed to keep us guessing what actually happened to her. So that's what we did, we speculatively considered what her new house was like while Sister Anna was at prayer that evening.

"I bet she's living in a big house and has her own bedroom crammed full of toys and chocolate," offered Duncan in his broad valley's accent.

Pat thought she might be living in a big castle with a moat and massive wall surrounding it. Kate and Ruth, who had both left the orphanage, always presented the same opinion regarding the destiny of our fellow inmates. They thought the other nuns had killed them.

From then onwards children came and went more regularly. It was like the January sales, adopt one child and get one free. Why the sudden departure of children now? During the previous years, only a handful appeared and disappeared. The cynic in me suggests the transformation was all down to finances, which were lucrative for the nuns, the potential fosterers or both. Nevertheless, it gave me enormous pleasure to see happy kids returning to the home after a weekend away with the promise of being in a new life, once the fostering process was completed.

Though, the dire consequences of the coordinated sales drive resulted in the disappearance of Lucy. Then a little later, both Heidi and Janice vanished. We didn't know where they went, like on other occasions they were just not there anymore; all traces of their existence hastily erased.

During my time in the orphanage, several tragedies left an indelible mark on me, no doubt on my friends too. One stands out more than the others, because of the importance of the people involved and the events surrounding it.

Paul, the tall black kid with big white teeth and a big red-lipped smile like Heidi's; was a streetwise nine-year-old boy. His afro Caribbean tight-knit hair was the biggest ever challenge for the harridan hair cutter, whose attempts at restyling it, always failed miserably. He initially lived with us in the nursery for about a year, after which he was moved to dorm three, a boy's dormitory on the first floor of the east wing. Paul was a good friend of ours. He was a sensitive young lad, who nearly always sat with us girls in the playground. Both Heidi and Janice trusted and loved him. He would regale us with stories about his life in the outside world, most of which was punctuated with, "do you know what I mean?"

Although he appeared happy enough, there was a profound sadness deep within him. He told us about the mother he adored and the father he despised. A man who disappeared one day, who had abandoned him and his pregnant mother six months before she died of blood poisoning soon after giving birth to their stillborn daughter. The girl would have been Paul's only sibling. With no other known relatives, he was placed in an orphanage he loathed. His mother's best friend, whom he called auntie, had offered to look after Paul but the unimpeachable authoritarians of the time had rejected the obviously mutual joyful solution.

One bright sunny afternoon, Paul went missing. He was last seen getting off the school bus. A search party was organised by angry nuns. We could hear Sister Terry shouting for him, opening doors and cupboards before slamming them shut as she frantically searched the scores of potential hideouts. I had the idea he might be happily hiding in the corner of a dark cupboard refusing to smile just in case his brilliant white teeth exposed him. Sister Terry could be heard threatening to beat him until he was black and blue unless he revealed himself. I tried unsuccessfully to envision the image of a black and blue-black boy.

The hunt for Paul continued both inside the orphanage and outside and ultimately far and wide until well after dark. Reluctantly and eventually, the Reverend Mother was compelled to inform the police.

He was found the next day. His body was discovered in the River Taff. The tragic news was splashed over the front pages of both local and national newspapers. Mystery surrounded his death. Sanctioned conclusions were, Paul had run away, gone swimming in the River Taff, had got into difficulties and drowned.

I, for one, knew Paul couldn't swim. Most of the kids held the notion Sister Terry had found Paul first, confronted him and in a rage thrown him in the river. Even some wiser kids thought there may have been a smidgen of truth mingled with the supposition. Who knows? The nun's foremost concern over the tragic event was the defamation Nazareth House was receiving. They regarded death as natural as living.

Paul's open sarcophagus, a small white coffin that had shiny satin fabric adorning the sides; lay in state at the Nazareth House church for four days until his requiem mass. I vividly remember looking at his peaceful motionless dark face resting on a contrasting white silk pillow. He had rosary beads threaded between his entwined fingers on his unmoving chest. Unerringly the sleeping position I'd been forced to adopt for years.

Half an hour a day, for four days, we stared at Paul until the hour-long requiem mass was conducted by the man himself.

I remembered our conversations, the laughter, his big bright smile, his dry chuckle. Thankfully his wooden tomb was sealed just before the requiem mass, for by then his appearance had changed, his head had shifted, and his chin had drooped revealing a slightly open mouth, now he looked dead before he appeared to be sleeping peacefully.

For children, some as young as four or five, compelled to witness the sight of a dead child, a deceased friend, a young boy once full of vitality lying motionless in a wooden box, would be outlandish to think of today. Though then, it was a scene our fearful young faces were compelled to witness. My innocent little charges were too frightened to sleep; the enforced darkness did nothing to ease the nightmares that inevitably followed.

For weeks afterwards, sometimes in the twilight between dusk and dawn, as my eyes began to focus, the big cupboard would frighteningly merge into the shape of Paul's coffin. The trauma and side effects for young kids from those few days was both insensitive and brainless. I have no doubt that many of us were left mentally scarred for life.

Vanishing Kids

Four years after I'd first stepped with trepidation through the big gates into my new home, wondering what would happen to me, Pat and I were the only ones left out of all the original inmates in the nursery.

The replacements were a varied mix of confused and frightened children who we educated to the ways of the home. About every couple of months or so, a close friend would vanish, resulting in a great sense of sadness, even though we were happy for them.

The numbers rarely went below ten or above twelve. Though there was a period once when there were only two empty beds. I had a multitude of friends who were my surrogate family, that have left my life, leaving me feeling helpless and melancholic. Not knowing when or where some of them went was the most unpleasant part of the scenario.

There was one new young girl who was about nine years old called Linda Evans. She was taller than us, a noisy boastful girl, with an attractive heart-shaped, pleasant-looking face that belied her personality. I found her to be exceedingly disagreeable; various hostile reactions met all my attempts of proffered friendship. Pat and I tried our best to help ease her into the ways of the home, but she was a freethinking spirit who thought she knew better than everyone. For no reason, I can recall she took an immediate, intense dislike towards us both. Unusually for us, the feeling was mutual. Most of the other kids tried to avoid the unpleasant girl with a superior attitude, a situation almost impossible in the nursery and playground.

Linda had only been with us for about a month when the accident took place. She was swinging on the metal roof gutter in the playground one morning, showing off by jumping from the bench to a rain gutter on the ground floor lean-to, when without warning, the weighty trough became detached. She crashed back to the ground, the channel still grasped in her fingertips, tumbling onto her neck. The piercing screams from her and her previously admiring audience reverberated around the playground.

We rushed over to help, and with another boy, we lifted the heavy object from the crying girl's neck. The gash on her neck stretched almost from ear to ear. The amount of blood pumping from the wound looked terrible enough, but the spectacle of a flap of skin hanging from her chin like a half-peeled potato was worse. By then, most of the kids were backing away, screaming and covering their eyes with their hands.

Pat's face went a greenish colour. She heaved twice before she threw up against the wall of the lean-to. The blood and gore didn't affect me so much. It was the sight of Pat's hunched back and the flowing sick that made me retch. Alerted by the sound of my heaving, Pat turned towards me. I could suppress it no longer and suddenly vomited my breakfast all over her front. I can still see her face now, the look of horror and utter disbelief on her open-mouthed face as she wiped the mess from her dress, dangling her dripping hands outwards in front of her like two wriggling spiders.

The girl's agony was directly forgotten. I smiled sheepishly and shrugged my shoulders. Pat gave me a look of wild-eyed extreme displeasure. A look I found so comical I started giggling. Then Pat started sniggering, which set me off laughing. Within a few short moments, we were in uncontrollable fits of laughter, despite the awful scene we had just witnessed. It was, without doubt, an adverse reaction brought on by traumatic shock, for we were neither malicious nor vindictive kids. Both of us suffered extreme embarrassment for quite a while after, even so, the image I have of the incredulous look on Pats face never fails to make me snigger.

Linda had fifteen stitches and an overnight stay in the hospital. She never came back to the nursery. On her discharge from the hospital, she was placed in dormitory one.

During the previous four years, the original inmates had either become old enough or big enough to go to other dormitories. Some were either fostered or adopted, we just didn't know for sure. It wasn't worth a slap or a pinch for probing, a lesson we had learned when Heidi and Janice disappeared, for on both occasions I had received a slap on the back of my legs for enquiring where they were.

When Lucy first left, we were dreadfully downcast. Then Heidi went missing a few months later, Pat, little Janice and I were distraught, grief-stricken and broken-hearted. Guessing what had happened to them; we presumed they may have been fostered or adopted, perhaps were even back with their mums and dads. Janice vanished only a few short weeks after Heidi. Then I was distressed and inconsolable. The culmination of my three best friends not being with me anymore was almost too much for my young mind to grasp.

The sagacious words of Pat did nothing to alleviate the pain and suffering deep inside me. Although I was distressed, I prayed they would be happier wherever they were. I thought of Paul, now in heaven, with his mother and baby sister looking down on us, a tear in his eye.

I recalled the words, have faith my child, trust in God, and repeated them aloud several times.

The pain and anguish slowly dissipated as the weeks progressed. I frequently wondered what happened to my two little angels. I always found it extremely unsettling when someone suddenly wasn't there anymore. It made me feel particularly insecure and vulnerable. Made me think I was trapped within the walls enclosing me, increasing my sense of isolation from the world outside where there was a possibility of another life, where I could be someone different from a prisoner. But by then, I had become more hardened to all phases of experiences within the home.

Sniffles, Nits and Bones

Throughout my early years, I remained in general good health, suffering only the usual amount of colds and flu, the sniffles any infant would catch from their peers but nothing serious. Perhaps this was because I had been case hardened by the conditions, toughened by the cold winters and continual labour.

I was thankful that verrucas and warts were more prevalent in the other dormitories, although we had the odd outbreak of nits, which, on average, occurred during school holidays. To combat the infestation, the nursery went into isolation like a Leper-colony, with Sister Toms administering the severest of scalping. Fine-toothed nit combs were distributed, then we would spend hours preening each other like chimpanzees. Each tiny black egg discovered was dispatched into oblivion by stamping on it. Only when the spate was contained were we allowed out of quarantine and back to the fold.

Though, I recall a few incidents. There was one occasion; I was probably about nine when a fishbone became lodged in my throat during a meal. I was choking and couldn't dislodge the spiky bone. It was so painful and frightening, I thought I would die. I was panicking and was on the verge of passing out. I remember being picked up by the overseer and slung over her knee; she whacked me on my back quite a few times until the bone suddenly shot out of my mouth onto the floor. I was heaving and catching my breath for what seemed a long time after, my throat and back where the nun had hit me was sore for two days. The nuns decided I didn't need any medical attention. I had one day off school, and a few days later, I had nearly forgotten all about the incident.

All the children disliked fish, more so after my perceptible close encounter with death. Friday evening meal times became considerably longer following my misfortune as they surreptitiously, carefully made a close examination of the fish. The girls on my table used to have a competition to see who could find the most bones. Natalie Ward had forty-two once, but I think she took some off Pat's plate. Surprisingly we all liked the chips even though they were soft and soggy.

On another occasion, in the same year, I had to have a day off school because of an earache which had kept me awake throughout the night. Sister Mary insisted that I give the school a miss and stay in bed. I had the dormitory to myself as I recovered. But by midday, I was sitting on my mattress feeling a lot better, other than hugely hungry as I had missed breakfast. So in desperation, I decided to transgress from the mentally implanted normality and sneak into the small kitchen to pilfer some bread from one of the cupboards.

Sister Anna was in church meditating. I knew she hid the bread out of reach from the children. So I fetched my rickety old chair, which also served as my wardrobe, and took it into the kitchen to stand on. As I stretched for the bread in the wall-cupboard, the chair collapsed, and my flailing hands dislodged some plates. These crashed to the floor with a reverberating racket, smashing into hundreds of pieces, with me sprawled amongst them, not suffering a scratch. But the chair had sustained a broken leg.

Not surprisingly, one of the nuns who must have heard the clatter of broken crockery, came into the kitchen as I was clearing up the broken plates. To my dismay, it was the harridan haircutter. I was expecting a beating and a severe telling off, or at least a clip around the ear; I was surprised as she appeared sympathetic and even helped me clear up the mess.

"Don't worry Milly. I'll fix the chair," she shrilled in her thick brogue.

We both went outside towards the big old shed wedged between the nursery playground and the main playground walls as if left there by workmen uncertain where to place it. She carried the chair, and me the broken leg. We reached the shed, she stretched a hand to the top of the door frame, after a quick rummage, found a key. The door ominously creaked open as she pulled the handle. Inside the shed, among a mist of cobwebs, was a clutter of miscellaneous furniture and broken chairs, with inconsistent tools scattered on wooden benches. She expertly cleared a space and quickly found a hammer and a nail.

The dark silhouette of the black-clad nun looked sinister in the dim light as she stood, a hammer in her right hand, moving with intent towards the chair. With her hunchback and pointy nose, she looked similar to the witch in Walt Disney's, *Snow White and the Seven Dwarfs,* I had seen on a billboard on the way to school.

After a few sharp clouts with the hammer, the chair's function was seemingly restored. Sister Toms handed me the quickly repaired chair with the same countenance of triumph she had when she chopped off my hair, the first day I arrived at Nazareth House. A facial expression that was almost similar to her look of revulsion.

"I enjoyed that Milly. It's reminded me of my home in Ireland helping my dad around the farm," I think that was the one and only time a nun ever said anything about life before becoming a nun.

Sister Toms had cut my hair many times over the years. I had forgiven her a long time before. As far as I was concerned, one of her jobs was to cut hair, and that is what she did.

I am almost positive the disgust on children's faces humiliated her while she unprofessionally scythed away. Even though she was exceptionally strict, she wasn't as cruel as some other nuns could be. I can only recall her admonishing me once with a slap to the back of my legs, though she gave me a mild form of the pinch on other occasions.

The chair only lasted two days before the leg dropped off again. I was sitting on it doing the laces up on my Doc Marten bovver boots when the limb gave way, and I tumbled to the floor. This time I bruised my wrist as I hit the floor. Six big books from the cupboard masquerading as a library proved a more permanent repair.

We were the old hands in the nursery, we had learned how to stage-manage Sister Mary, who was now in charge. Our prayers had been answered a few months previously when Sister Anna disappeared like Heidi, Janice, Lucy and the rest of our pals. She hadn't been moved to a different role, all traces of her were eliminated, we were too elated to ponder over the malevolent nun further, we took the view Kate, and Ruth expressed, that the other nuns had killed her, smiling even more.

Sister Mary took on the responsibilities of the nursery with relish. My conclusion as to the departure of Sister Anna consisting of two parts. First, her neurotic behaviour and excessive cruelty must have been brought to the Reverend Mother Superior's attention. I presume Sister Mary, who had to intervene on many occasions when the crazy nun lost her temper, accomplished this. At some point, we all displayed cuts and bruises inflicted by Sister Anna's buckled belt.

It occurred to me, at some time someone must have taught the novice nuns how to inflict pain on children without leaving a lasting mark and that pinching above the elbows and whacking knees didn't bruise. Also, perhaps someone insisted they should apply this method to keep the children under rigid control. Sister Anna had failed to do this. She had gone too far, I imagined she was subsequently banished to a convent in the Outer Hebrides. Second, the most likely and best explanation, she was taken away wearing a straitjacket by two burly men in white coats. Her accomplice to the atrocities, Mrs Gittings, was only given other duties as her punishment.

Now I was the oldest girl in the nursery, fifteen days older than Pat. The position of my bed, at the top of the dormitory next to the bathroom, confirmed my status. My bed, cabinet and the rickety chair had moved with me, with Pat's help.

"But child... The beds and chairs are all the same," Sister Mary had insisted.

I was adamant if I was to move, my bed and chair came with me.

The dull existence within the limitations of Nazareth house continued, the chores seemed endless and mostly pointless. Home from school at four-thirty to clean the dormitory, scrub and polish the floors; have something to eat, wash the dishes, attempt the homework, then get the kiddies ready for bed. I was asleep well before nine o'clock for most evenings.

Then before I knew it was early morning, the distant rumbling from the kitchen would rouse me from my slumber and Sister Mary would be ringing the bell. My restless nights, with little sleep, remained past tense; even so, I hated that bell. Sometimes I just wanted to stay in bed, but there were the kids to look after and a load of work to be done before school.

The weekends were much better; although we were still awake very early and had the usual weekend responsibilities. If no outsiders were coming to view the latest stock of children, we could go into the playground after we had finished, where we used to play with the little ones. We always thoroughly enjoyed ourselves.

There were three kiddies, two boys and a girl, I had become very attached to, even though I had tried hard not to grow emotionally involved, for it was always heart-wrenching when they vanished. At least the heartache, especially after the departure of Heidi, Janice and Lucy, was now a little more bearable.

We would still get up at the first noise emanating from the kitchens, giving us time to deal with any bedwetting by the new kiddies. Pat was brilliant with the new youngsters, her good-humoured mischievous face was contagious, their devotion to her envious. I would help them get dressed, while singing quietly for them, in my own way, making sure there were always reassuring hugs all around. Pat had recently had a dramatic metamorphic change, she was developing into a young woman, her curves and bumps were becoming evident.

With Sister Mary now in charge smiling became tolerated, but only in our little domain, plus the breakfast fare she provided had more variety and was much better. Even though Pat and I could eat in the dining room, we preferred the nursery. We now had porridge with jam or golden syrup, soggy toast, boiled eggs with bread and a strange one, bread with bacon fat, my first ever meal in the home, called dripping. We all agreed that the nuns took the best pieces of meat for themselves and ate all the bacon.

We still had to be careful to hide all forms of happiness when the other nuns became active. They didn't like laughter or talking, and it seemed a million other things, the crime of singing was almost punishable by death. With luck, we would all be ready for church and breakfast before the nuns emerged from their cells. It's incongruous to think the nuns lived in cells, yet we were the ones who were in prison.

On the plus side, there was a new helper now they had moved Mrs Gittings to another dormitory, although she still popped in occasionally with supplies. Fortuitously, I nearly always successfully managed to avoid the evil old crone. The new helper was called Lena, an Italian lady who was decent and friendly. Sometimes she would arrive in the dormitory pushing a dull metal food cart, its shelves stacked with plates of breakfast food like beans on squelchy wilting toast. In general, we had to prepare the breakfasts, so it was always a nice change from the mundane.

By this time, I had a much better knowledge of the organisation of Nazareth House outside the confines of the nursery. As Pat once said, there were about twenty-five to thirty nuns, with about ten running the home, and in the background a few others. The other nuns worked in schools and hospitals. Each of the orphanage nuns had a specific job to do, like Sister Margarita, who was the logistics expert and our public relations, Guru. She organised trips, the social events and was also in charge of clothes and the laundry. Throughout the week we had to wear the same clothes for school, if they became dirty before the assigned washing day, we were in big trouble from the other nuns.

The enormous black-clad nun, Sister Toms, whom we first encountered on our arrival, was the hairdresser. She was also second in command to the Mother Superior and flitted about the home carrying out her orders. About every four weeks, she cut all the inmates' hair, in alternation, by appointment only, fastidiously selecting the next scheduled victim from her ledger, cutting and hacking about four heads a day. As my flat head grew, I had progressed to the middle bowl out of the six pudding bowls on the top shelf in the bathroom.

Sister Maguire was in charge of the kitchens. She was one of only a handful of nuns who didn't have two or more roles to play.

Sister Terry was in charge of dormitory two and was also the keeper of keys; dorm two was at the top of the stairs above the main entrance. Her job was to answer the door and make sure it was securely locked at night; she had all the keys for the dormitories and rooms hanging on a ring attached to her leather belt.

Sister Norma played the church organ and doubled as the physical education specialist.

There were about forty-five girls in the institution, doubtless the same number of boys. The old people's section held about ten men and most likely the same amount of women. So altogether there were over one hundred plus people for the nuns to care for at one time. It must have been no mean feat to provide for ninety children, who would have been fifteen years old and under, as well as twenty adults over sixty-five, plus thirty of 'them', for twenty-four hours a day, seven days a week. The nuns at least need to be congratulated for that, even though some lacked the requisite sagacity and industrious social skills required.

The nuns had their meals together in the great hall in two sittings, clues to what they had were the dripping bacon fat we had on butterless bread. More evidence was the fatty lamb stew with the brown froth and the gritty taste of unwashed vegetables. A final indicator was a multitude of overweight nuns waddling around the corridors, pinching or slapping a skinny child.

I'm not sure what the old people section's cuisine consisted of, though I presume it was unlikely to be the same as ours.

Of the twenty-five out of thirty nuns, five were compassionate, two or three of them were almost saintly. A few of the others showed a total disregard towards us, some more so than others, a few indifferent, so closeted in their own world they would look at you through unseeing eyes. The Mother Superior was eminently pleasant; unfortunately, we encountered her infrequently.

We had school homework about three times each week, which we applied ourselves to after the obligatory scrub and polish of whatever the nuns decided deserved a rigorous cleaning. Sometimes the homework could be incredibly frustrating and challenging, mostly we didn't finish. Though we were hard-bitten and astute, we weren't the brightest bulbs in the academic chandelier, but some nuns were dimmer. There wasn't any point in asking them to help with the homework because they wouldn't. My conclusion for their reluctance to assist is quite straightforward. They couldn't.

All in all, it wasn't too bad for us in the nursery, as long as you acted subserviently obeying their rules. The other nuns were very strict, we had to be polite and docile at all times, or they would discipline us. A few kids were punished far more than others for being disobedient. Inevitably the most disruptive children were generally the newest inmates who had the most to learn; the nun's harsh treatment ensuring they quickly came to understand their place in the orphanage hierarchy. Be compliant, observe the rules, there was only one winner for any perceived dispute between the children and a nun. That was the nun.

As long as you played by their set of laws and kept out of the way of the nasty nuns, in particular, the sadistic Sister Terry, you would be relatively safe. The big black-clad nun, Sister Toms, the harridan hairdresser, was a saint in comparison. The rules were ridiculous, for some strange reason, they treated talking, laughing, and singing as the most significant crimes, as though we were deliberately disrespectful to their unquestioning religious fervour.

A nun's life was all about self-discipline and surrender following the tenets of chastity, poverty and sacrifice; it was methodical to the extreme. They expected all the inmates to approach their lifestyle in the same way. So they kept us under a strict regime of disciplined acceptance to all their arcane rules and routines. Our lives were restricted and totally monitored in the home, so inevitably time seemed to proceed at a snail's pace. Any changes that occurred were subtle and gradual, but the sadness and disappointments were unrelenting.

However, now Sister Mary was running the nursery, there were some reasonably pleasant times in our dormitory, and the beatings were scarce and mainly carried out by Sister Terry or a substitute nun. I was used to the laborious existence, I knew no difference.

Flag Day

I used to enjoy going to St David's school during the week because it was a welcome escape from the home, nevertheless I always looked forward to returning to see the tinies.

On a Saturday morning about every six months, St David's school would hold a bazaar for charity. On this particular Saturday, all the proceeds would go to Nazareth House. The nuns, Sister Margarita, in particular, were never ones to miss an opportunity to make more money, so they decided to synchronise this with their week-long Flag Day and brought it forward by two weeks. Nazareth House Flag Day was an annual event that lasted for a week in November. As custom dictated, we weren't allowed to go to the school bazaar. Sister Mary said some of us could go, on the condition we sold all of our allotted Flag Day flags.

Pat and I were only ten years old; even so, we were expected to sell our flags in the big city. Sister Mary placed a shallow usherette tray in my arms and slipped the wide red ribbon attached to it around my neck. Free from my clutches it dangled just above my knees, she tied a knot in the band to make it hang more comfortably about my middle. Then she gave Pat a collecting tin with a looped string handle.

We were joined in the great hall by five other teams of children and two nuns. I noticed with some worry that Greta was teamed up with the big bully Gloria. One nun proceeded to fill the trays with little blue and white cardboard flags. The flags were about five by two centimetres, attached to a small wooden stick, with the words, '*Support Nazareth House Flag Day*' on either side, as if we needed further advertising.

Loaded with our wares, we set off into the big city with the two nuns and the other teams of girls. We walked the half-mile to the city centre where we were allocated a position near the Cardiff train and bus station. On the opposite side of the road were Greta and Gloria, the other teams were in different locations. The nuns, one of whom was Sister Mary, flitted back and forth, making sure all was well. Though all was not well, because I could see Gloria taunting and pushing Greta around when the nuns were absent, as a consequence, they were not as successful at flag selling as we were.

The selling started off better than I had expected, we met many extraordinarily empathetic and generous people who stopped to chat. We became more relaxed with the outsiders as the day progressed. Looking back, I'd say half of the people who conversed bought a flag; Pat's collecting tin getting more cumbersome, while my tray became lighter until we ultimately sold all the flags.

Instead of keeping their word, another bundle of flags appeared along with an empty tin. We were both quite upset at missing the bazaar, victims of our own success. With the excessive weight, the knot felt uncomfortable on the back of my neck, while Pat complained of rattlers wrist fatigue. After a short time, we were back to having an ebullient time thanks to Pat's demeanour, selling about half the flags quite quickly as she proved to be a competent and confident salesperson shaking the tin noisily to attract the passers-by.

A woman walked purposely in our direction, holding the hand of a small child who looked like Heidi. My God, she looked like Heidi because it was Heidi!

I screamed, Heidi screamed. Pat cried as she flung her arms around her, the coins rattling in the tin still in her hand. I liberated myself of the flags and joined in, her mum was blubbing away too, it was sometime before any semblance of self-control resumed.

"So you're the two angels who looked after my little girl while I was in the hospital. We had no choice as my husband had to work, and there was no one to look after her."

"Dad said you were in prison, Mummy," little Heidi innocently remarked.

Mummy's face went bright pink. She laughed nervously but said nothing to explain, only adding that they had tried to visit us in the orphanage. The Mother Superior's response to the request. Apparently, it was out of the question.

We were ecstatic and talked for ages, laughing with joy until our stomachs hurt. Heidi was visibly contented and relaxed, there were no furtive glances or darting eyes, her gaze was steady, and her red lips exhibited a relaxed smile. We were all overjoyed, it was both unforgettable and comprehensively congenial. The only blip to the mutual hilarity occurred when Heidi asked after Janice.

In harmony, as one voice, as if mind readers. We both lied, "She's gone back to her mother and father."

Little Heidi had grown significantly during her few years of freedom. She seemed at ease and looked terrific. Her jet black hair was now long and lustrous, her pretty face glowed, and her unusually red lips were still as conspicuous as I remembered. I reflected back as to how much I loved her.

She lived with her mum and dad in a little village called Peterstone, some six miles away from Nazareth House. We exchanged invitations and addresses, though we all knew it was meaningless before they had to leave for their bus.

Was I sad? No, I wasn't. We were both overjoyed. Seeing Heidi happily returned to her parents made us think there was hope for us yet. Ironically, if the nuns had kept to the promised deal, we would have missed seeing them.

I said to Pat, mimicking Sister Mary. "The Lord moves in mysterious ways my child, have faith."

We both howled with laughter until our jaws ached.

Pat and I used to have hours of whispered conversations at night. We were exceptionally close and thought ourselves almost telepathic, particularly after our synchronised false explanation regarding Janice's whereabouts, during our encounter with Heidi and the ex-convict.

New Friends

With our new found freedom, Sister Mary allowed us to mingle with kids from the other dormitories, sometimes we even ate lunch in the great hall. By then, it was evident to the nuns that Pat and I were capable of looking after the kids, to such an extent, Lena the latest helper, only came once or twice a week. A situation we found gratifying yet perturbing, for we always had to be on guard and have our wits about us for the occasions when we had an unexpected visit from another nun.

My days of continual toil, sweat and inner tears became even more bearable when I was promoted to the home's equivalent of a gopher. I still had to scrub, clean and polish, though the tedious intensity of the chores seemed to diminish when I had other jobs to perform and distract me. Almost every day after that, I was given a variety of tasks to do, which took me to virtually every part of the building: in effect, I had the freedom of the home. One of my posts was distributing the haircut appointment slips to the various dormitories and the pensioners. On another occasion, I had to deliver a newspaper to Mr Noland, the miserable old man who never smiled, except the gentle smile on Barry beach. I heard Sister Mary talking about him once, saying he had lost the will to live since his wife died. It seemed he hadn't worked as a carpenter from that day, had given up his job, left his council house and came to stay in the home. I felt awfully sorry for him.

The empty goldfish bowl sitting on a shelf reminded me of Goldie and Mrs Thomas, both of them no longer on this mortal coil.

Expressionless, he took his newspaper off me and gave me a silver coin.

"For you."

Breathlessly I beamed at him, "Thank you."

As I went out through the door, he mumbled, his lips holding the tiniest hint of a smile,

"You have a beautiful smile, you know."

Although I hadn't reached the age, I knew senior school inmates had a weekly pocket money allowance. It wasn't much, but it was enough to pay for bus fares and buy some sweets from their school shop. Sister Margarita handed out the money on a Saturday morning; if any kids on her list had misbehaved, they only had bus money.

What Mr Noland had given me that day amounted to about a month's pocket money. I helped to increase the junior's school shop takings significantly the next day. The same night the dormitory had a silent banquet, as a thought of how to make Mr Noland happy again began to form in my mind.

Because of the monotony and the resulting boredom, I can never be explicit of dates, but this time it was about a year before my eleven plus exams so we must have been a few months older than ten. There was now another little girl who captivated my heart. A delightful olive-skinned, almond-eyed little girl called Lerina. She was the newest but not the youngest in the nursery and so, by order, by tradition, her cot was at the end of the dormitory near to the window. It was the cot Janice had once occupied, the one furthest away from mine.

She was remarkably knowledgeable for a youngster of about six years old, she had been with us for less than a week before she captivated my heart. She had shiny black hair cut in the same style as the rest of us, though incredibly I thought the fashion suited her. It seemed to frame her cute angelic face, as to enhance her little dimples. Her sparkling, almond eyes conveyed a mood of contentment. I didn't know anything about her, her history, or why she was in the home. All I knew was that she was a delightful little girl, despite the circumstances. By the end of her first week, Pat and I were her ardent fans.

Lerina and I were in the playground. I was pushing the swing she was clinging on to. She was urging me to shove her higher and higher. Laughing and spurring me on, on each return. Then without any warning, Sister Terry lunged through the doors into the play area. Previously, we had tried to explain to Lerina what might happen if she exhibited any show of exuberance while in the institution, without success. Sister Terry made our words more explicit in the only way she knew how, as the swing pitched towards her, she whacked Lerina on her shin bone with the stout cane she carried.

Sister Terry must have been waiting, hiding behind the door, listening for any sounds of enjoyment, ready in an instant to react to the sound of laughter. Finding Lerina was the perpetrator who was guilty of the joyous interjections was more likely a bonus for her sadistic desires, for she always liked to be the first to introduce a new inmate to her belt or cane. She gave me two whacks across my back and slithered away, undoubtedly satisfied with the conclusion.

Lerina was dreadfully upset; nevertheless, she proved her resilience and character by not crying and soon heeded all our advice.

Pat and I were both flabbergasted when Lerina later told us it was the first time in her life anyone had ever hit her.

"Milly, when is my mammy coming back for me?" she abruptly asked me in a pitiable pleading voice the same evening. I didn't have an answer. I had wondered, had thought the same question countless times before, and had prayed more times than I could remember. Even when enjoying ourselves, deep inside, we were all basically longing to be with others somewhere else.

About a week later, we arrived back to the nursery dormitory after school to find it was empty. We expected the little ones to be there waiting for us. At first, I was horrified, thinking Lerina had gone, upset I hadn't been given a chance to say goodbye. The other school kids were just as confused as there was no nun in attendance to provide us with any work.

Susan Clark, one of the newer kids in the nursery, a strange, moody bully of a girl with an unpredictable character, entered to tell us they were in the playground with a new nun. Like everything else that went on in the home, the only time we knew there was something different happening was when it happened.

We all traipsed out to the playground and there, sitting on the grass with her back to us was a nun. We could all see clearly the attentive faces of two kiddies, Asher and Sian, but my heart sank when I realised Lerina did not appear to be there. I was utterly distraught and on the verge of tears, tears I had learned to control a long time before until I unexpectedly heard little Lerina's delightful giggle. Moving to one side, I could see she was sitting between the nun's crossed legs, held in position by the arm affectionately around her waist. There wasn't one child watching the scene, or any of the other kids we later related our account of the story, that didn't have their mouth's wide open in complete and utter astonishment. Situations like that never happened.

The young nun turned around and slowly stood up, brushing grass from her white habit, her warm, welcoming smile captivating all before her in an instant. Underneath her audacious red-framed spectacles, her brown eyes sparkled.

"Hello children, my name is Sister Sandra," she said as she tucked away a wisp of brown hair that was just showing from beneath her wimple.

It was though there was an aura around her, she exuded warmth and serenity attracting us to her like iron filings to a magnet.

"You are my children now. Come on, let's go inside and get to know each other."

From the first day, Sister Sandra transformed the nursery dormitory and the lives of everyone in it. If Sister Mary had been a breath of fresh air after the stale breathed terror reign of Sister Anna, Sister Sandra was like an open window in summer. She was strict but ruled with tenderness and compassion, not with a rod of iron. The respect she had from everyone was astonishing; not any of the other nuns abused us when she was present.

According to the grapevine, Sister Mary, one of my favourite nuns, was transferred. Mother Superior decided her expertise and responsibilities were better served elsewhere. She was now running the old peoples section after the death of Sister Alphonso, whose demise was met with jubilation by the older girls. The cruel nun had been in dormitory two until one year before, then she was transferred to the old people's sector. Sad as it was to hear of the death of anyone, be it good or evil, another open casket and funeral followed to give young minds more nightmares.

Within two months, Sister Sandra had almost stopped the systematic bullying the younger and vulnerable kids had to endure daily from the other children; the atmosphere was now even more calm and restful. During this period, Pat and I became notably more emotionally involved with the lovable Lerina, who displayed exceptional warmth and intelligence that belied her age.

Before her arrival, Sister Mary would mildly chastise us at bedtime if we didn't have our arms folded. And before her, Sister Anna would tiptoe down the dormitory checking us, and if you didn't have your arms crossed over your chest, she would wake you up, by shouting and banging her fists on the thin rubber covered mattress or slapping you across the face. In contrast, Sister Sandra would wake us up in the morning with gentle singing and quiet words, waiting until we were all awake, before ringing the wake-up bell for the benefit of other ears. The younger kids, especially little Lerina, adored the lovable young nun.

I too felt unusually relaxed and gratified with the new regime. Even the routine, when we helped Sister Sandra with all the morning preparations for breakfast, church and school, seemed to be more acceptable.

Not long after, Lerina disappeared. She wasn't in the nursery when we returned after school. She had only been with us for a few short months, yet my heartache was similar to when the first two little ones left. We never did get to say goodbye.

My distress left me with a lump in my throat and a sensation of numbness. When would I learn? I asked myself. Pat, who was no stranger to disappearing kids and somewhat more pragmatic than me was also particularly perturbed. I even questioned Sister Sandra as to where and what happened to Lerina. Something I wouldn't have dreamt of doing under the old regimes. She shook her head and held out her hands with the palms up, indicating she didn't know. Her consoling sad expression was a refreshing change from the emotionless indifference or the slap on bare legs for any inquiries.

The Chocolate Lady

When I was about eleven years old, Mother Superior informed Pat and me this was to be our last year in the nursery. We were going to live in dormitory one, the better of the two girl-only dorms, thank God. Ordinarily, we would have known nothing about this until it happened. I think the transfer was to coincide with us leaving junior school as our eleven plus exam was a few months away.

We should have left the nursery at least three years previously, though I suspect we were kept there because we were too useful. We both had mixed feelings but were still looking forward to going to a girl-only dormitory. It was time to grow up, to be one step nearer to getting out of the institution, to progress from nursery duties into a new schedule.

So far, our routines had hardly varied during all the years in the nursery. When we finished school, we would go straight to the dormitory, or if the weather was clement to the playground, after which we were given menial tasks to do until supper time. Our day ended after we went to the bathroom, before returning to say our prayers just before it was lights out at seven-thirty on the dot. Even on summer nights, when it was still bright, and the sounds of outdoor activities seeped invitingly through the curtained windows.

Sister Sandra encouraged us to fold our arms across our chests, but we were never punished. She locked the dormitory doors until the helper, or one of the other nuns arrived the next morning. Any change was something to look forward too; though there was one drawback, we both thought leaving the little ones alone was a problem to be considered. However, there were two or three girls who were good kids, so we both hoped they could effectively take over from us.

Pat had lived in the nursery for all of her eleven years. I had spent about half of my life at Swansea and the other half at Nazareth House Cardiff. Except for a few trips to the seaside, several children's parties and school, we had had no real contact with the outside world; although I did have a few visits from a person, I called the chocolate lady.

The first time she came to the home was just after my first Holy Communion day when I was seven years old. Although she never mentioned it, my guess is the chocolate lady must have seen the news article and photographs from that day. I don't have a clue when I first realised the mysterious old lady, who came to visit my sister and me on the occasional Saturday, was actually my grandmother.

I always knew when she was coming to visit because I would find much better clothes on my wooden chair in the morning after church, put there earlier by the well-organised nuns. After dressing, I would be led by a nun to join Greta then both of us would be escorted to a large room in an out-of-bounds area. This was the visitor's room, a sort of halfway house between the spartan, functional and dour spaces inside the home, and the more frivolous, bright cosmopolitan civilisation beyond dormitory walls; a showroom containing furnishings far grander than any other part, except for the office of The Reverend Mother.

The first time my grandmother came to visit, she brought us sweets, which one of the nuns took off us after she left. At the time, grandmother was just another word I didn't fully comprehend, though a word I then associated with sweets. That's why I called her the chocolate lady. However, I had learned my lesson, whenever she came again, I would conceal the given sweets in the band just inside my dark blue visitor knickers and hide them later in my secret hiding place.

To the side of my radiator was a small section of wood at floor level that concealed the radiator pipes. I discovered it by accident when a coloured glass marble I found in the schoolyard rolled through the tiny gap. If I put a finger in this hole and twisted the piece of wood, it would easily slide away. To replace it was a simplicity in itself, tilt the wood and click. I was confident it was secure and undetectable. The only problem was that during wintertime, when the radiators were active, the chocolates would melt and take on different shapes.

I was surprised when this first happened as the dormitory always felt cold. Only the radiators in the kitchen and dining area were operational. I'm guessing Sister Anna, Sister Mary, and now Sister Sandra were all as warm as soggy toast in their cosy cell, which was a room I only saw once. I courageously stopped and peeped in one time when the door was slightly ajar. Sister Anna had left the tiniest slit of an open door. Through the gap, I could see her changing. She was almost naked and was wearing a pair of black knickers, black knee-length socks and black Doc Marten boots. Behind her, except for a small mirror hanging on the wall, the only object I could really see was a metal bed of the sort we used. I watched, terrified of being caught, she slipped the habit over her pale skinny body, reciting a prayer as the heavy woollen fabric slowly unfolded to the ground to hide her boots. Her slim, shapeless physique reminded me of my own tiny frame. Still praying, she placed the starched pristine white wimple over her short spiny orange hair, it was then I decided to get out of the nursery as quickly as possible. As I scuttled out, I reflected back to the sight I had just witnessed. It wasn't her near-naked body or her short, scraggly orange hair that shocked me; it was the fact she had a mirror.

My grandmother never came to visit alone; a man would always accompany her and not ever the same one. I remember being told to call them Uncle Bill, Uncle Albert or Uncle Tom. She was a big-boned, strong-looking woman of about fifty years old, with immaculately set grey hair, a woman who was always elegantly dressed in the obviously expensive clothing. As it transpired, she was a very wealthy woman, who lived a short distance away from Nazareth House in a grand three-story house, with her daughter; my mother's sister. She never really said much on her infrequent visits, though when she did speak her accent sounded particularly posh, reminiscent of the newsreader on the television.

I began to know Greta a little better throughout my grandmother's visits. My sister was a tormented spirit who was obviously more affected by being confined than I was. She had the misfortune of being incarcerated with children older than herself, in dormitory two, which was managed by two of the cruellest nuns in the home. Beatings in Greta's girl's dorm were frequent, with girls punished more than once a day.

She was also bullied by one of the biggest persecutors in the home called Gloria, who had bullied Greta on Flag Day, she was a dark-skinned mountain of a girl. I had seen Gloria brawl once, it was not even a fight. She squared up to another girl who I didn't know well, they began shouting at each other. To me, Gloria's intent was obvious, her right fist was clenched tight, her elbow bent away from her body, ready to swing into action. Sure enough, and with lightning speed, her clenched fist hit the girl directly on the side of her face, the girl fell to the ground like a stone, defeated by the self-satisfied bully her nickname was one punch, Gloria. I don't know where she was on my list of people to keep away from, but Gloria was definitely in the top ten.

Greta had left St David's and was attending another Catholic school. I rarely talked to her, for she used to spend her leisure time with other, older girls. At this time, there were seven children from Nazareth House in my class; three boys and four girls. Although we were all the same age, they were not in my dormitory. However, what we all shared was an unwritten rule; we never talked about life in the home to anybody. The standard that existed between Pat and me was used by all the other inmates.

There were us, them, and the outsiders and that included the woman called my grandmother, alias the chocolate lady.

We were about three months into our last term at St David's when I learnt I had failed the eleven plus exam, which was hardly a surprise considering the circumstances. Selfishly, I was pleased Pat had failed as well. If we had passed this entrance exam, we would have been eligible for a place at a grammar school, it would have been a unique achievement in the history of Nazareth House.

Mrs Brown was disappointed; she had thought I could pass. A belief I now share wholeheartedly. I guess it was testimonial evidence of the inadequacies of our institutionalised life, prejudiced by ineffectual nuns who devotedly thought the only book to pay particular attention to was the Holy Bible. Was this because of the influence the institution's restrictions and all the routines we had to follow? A regime no doubt designed by a hierarchy of pious old males with no experience of rearing children.

The nuns never encouraged us to study or to do homework at the orphanage. Instead, we suffered a tedious parallel existence imposed on us by seemingly uncaring nuns.

Cleaning and religious studies were far more paramount. However, there was a big cupboard in the hallway on the ground floor that the nuns called the library. The top half contained copies of the Holy Bible; more shelves contained an assortment of somewhat dusty unread books. The only time books on the lower shelves were useful was when they propped up wonky chairs, for use as substitute chair legs or to stand on, enabling you to reach the Holy Bible for use during Sunday morning Mass.

Nursery blues

The day before we were due to start our new school, Pat, and I moved to our new dormitory on the ground floor wing next to the nursery. My first impression was that it was horrible. It didn't feel right, it looked tired and characterless, the chairs and cupboards were even more rickety than in the nursery.

The girls who lived in the twenty-bed residence were all known to us, with ages ranging from about eight to fifteen years old. Two of the girls were in our class at St David's school, so Pat and I were friendly with them. One was Stacy, a ginger-haired spotty girl who had been in the home for about three years. The other was our friend Natalie, a quiet girl with glossy black hair, like us, Stacy and Natalie were inseparable. When we started junior school, they kept themselves to themselves at first. However, after a while, they slowly became much friendlier, especially during the school run and playtime when we would watch out for each other and band together if threatened by persecutors.

A plastic beaker standing on a chair with a familiar toothbrush and a comb identified my new bed. The chair also held my new clothes, a faded, ancient-looking dark blue school uniform with a white blouse and a blue tie already formed into a knot. I hadn't felt as anxious since my first day in the orphanage almost seven years before. I was terribly nervous and tried hard not to show it. Thank God Pat, my rock, had the bed next to me.

One of the older girls Nancy, who I guess was trying to confirm her status as the dormitory's head girl, immediately confronted us. I used to think she was a decent, thoughtful girl. I can't remember what she said, except her motivation was predictable, she intended to bully Pat and me into a subservient position.

Unfortunately for Nancy, she picked on the wrong girls. We were all tough little kids, after years in the home we had to be. Small, I may have been, but I was feisty and afraid of no one. I was in no mood for her. I stood up to her and aggressively told her we would not be bullied by her or anybody else. The words had an immediate effect; she backed down and skulked sheepishly away. I didn't think she was a bully, what she did was more bravado and showing off than anything else.

Almost like magic, the other girls in the dormitory changed, their demeanour transformed, and instantly relaxed. Soon they crowded around our new old beds, making us feel especially welcome until Sister Pointer, a short dumpy nun who must have been pensioner age, cut short the celebration to my elevated status.

"Bathroom girls. You have school tomorrow," she proclaimed in a no-nonsense manner.

As we said our evening prayers, Pat was still looking at me beaming proudly.

During that first night, I felt especially vulnerable as I lay in my uncomfortable new bed. I had spent many long years in the nursery and found I was surprisingly missing my old mattress, even my former chair, the dormitory and especially little Lerina.

My new enemy, five beds away from me, gave me some cause for concern, but I knew my guardian angel was by my side. She was always with me. I felt her protection whenever I was troubled, hurt or upset, unlike the other children, my guardian angel was a girl, and she had a name. It was a long time before I fell asleep, the abrupt changes to my environment, combined with the thought of a new school the next day, were not conducive for a good night's sleep. That night I had my worst ever nightmare, dreaming that all my teeth had fallen out. I woke up gasping for breath and bathed in sweat when the jingle of a bell released me.

I felt tremendously gloomy as I glanced around at my dreary unfamiliar surroundings, hearing the clang of a bell in the distance, one I instantly recognised as the tone made by the nursery bell. The irony of the situation was that I must have been homesick.

After church, we went back to the dormitory to find brand new pairs of black Doc Marten clod hopper boots on our chairs. This cheered me up slightly, for my old boots were so worn out on the side of the heels it made me walk as if I had a permanent limp. I was sure I was on the verge of going bandy.

The dormitory was a buzz of excitement as we changed for school; as usual, my new school uniform was far too big for me as well as being old and threadbare. I was still as skinny as a rake and less than five feet tall. Sister Pointer watched the proceedings through her thin-framed spectacles smiling serenely, while Pat had her usual grin on her cheeky face. Her uniform equally threadbare fitted her comfortably. She had transformed almost overnight it seemed from the dumpy duckling into an elegant swan. Shame about the glasses, I thought.

Then without warning, a face I'd luckily mostly avoided for the last two years came through the dormitory doors, Mrs Gittings moving with a purpose.

"Oh no," I whispered to Pat.

We all stood in line as Fat Git or Grumpy Gittings, as she was nicknamed, inspected our uniforms, hands, shoes and hair, stopping at me to say with a sneer. "So you've left the nursery, at last, have you?"

I looked up at her pockmarked face, my eyes going to the mound on top of her head, her fashionable beehive hairstyle, and inquired innocently, "Have you got any bees in there?"

Why I said it, I don't know. It was as if the change of the dormitory, the argument with the girl the evening before, the loss of Lerina had triggered a difference to my characteristic acquiescent demeanour. Was I turning into an anarchist? Her doleful face went crimson as she clenched her teeth, trying to contain her fury. The giggles of the girls did nothing to help control her anger, while Sister Pointer chose that moment to become deaf, though I'm sure she had a smile on her chubby face as she turned away.

As we were getting on the bus, Nancy patted me on my back, while saying, "Well done Milly. That was so funny. What's got into you?"

I simply smiled as mystified as she was. Her friendliness also astonished me, maybe she wasn't my enemy after all. I deliberated.

The School on the Hill

The double-decker bus, with thirty-odd noisy schoolchildren, eventually stopped at the bottom of a steep hill. About a quarter of a mile away on top of the crest was my new school, Mostyn, named after an admired Bishop, a sizeable secondary modern Catholic school on the outskirts of Cardiff, three miles from Nazareth House. As usual, I stared in fascination at a world that was getting larger and better.

We formed orderly lines and began the climb up the steep hill in pairs, following the Nazareth House head girl, lovely Lorna, who was marching briskly ahead. My new boots felt so comfortable. At long last, I had a pair of sturdy footwear that fitted me. They were one of my three worldly possessions; two and three were my comb and toothbrush.

As we stomped up the gradient, I had my first view of the new environment, the striking panorama surrounding the school. In the distance was the city of Cardiff spread out like a monster patchwork quilt. The nearside had open green fields and hills surrounded by forests, more wonders to behold and stare at, in what was becoming an infinite world.

From the first day, I liked my new school, it was huge. Around four hundred and fifty to five hundred bodies occupied that big white building on the hilltop. Morning assembly was incredible; I had never seen so many people in one room before.

The pupils of each year were split into three groups, A, B, or C, depending on their proven intelligence. Pat, Natalie, Stacy and I were all assigned to form 1C. Though we were not deemed the most stupid. There was another class for all ages, and that was 3R, the R standing for remedial. The remedial group of pupils was a mixed cluster of thirty-five kids. It's most likely that some of them had unidentified problems such as dyslexia. Eight of the class were from Nazareth house. In her first year, Greta was in 3R, probably by her own doing because her three best friends were there, for I thought she was quite intelligent. Although, in later life, it was confirmed she was dyslexic. Though now she was no longer a pupil here and had now left to attend another Catholic school. I couldn't work out why Greta and I always seemed to be kept apart.

Mercifully, Pat sat next to me in class, while Natalie and Stacy occupied the desks behind us. All the teachers were polite and friendly, and I began to enjoy the lessons.

Morning playtime was an eye-opener. The other new kids weren't overly friendly towards us at break time. It was recognisable we were from Nazareth House our clothes were shabby, and our haircuts looked the same. They called us the Nazis, the nickname they gave to everyone from Nazareth House. Nazis was the one thing we didn't enjoy being called, not because of the German connection, but it was a shortening of Nazareth. I don't think all the kids who made the comments and jibes were malicious, but their words were hurtful.

They didn't understand we never had parents to help us, to say reassuring words, words, like ignore the taunting. There was no one, no nun to give us advice, so we tended to stay in our own groups and probably became the outcasts they saw.

"My God," whispered Pat, suddenly poking her fingers in my bony ribs.

"That looks like Lucy Smith."

Our former fellow inmate, our friend, the comrade who shared our life, who shared our dormitory and used to be in the same form as us in St David's, looked a different person. Her hair was trimmed and chic. She was wearing a tailored and expensive-looking school uniform, her eyes sparkled, and her skin glowed, especially the prominent chin. She was even wearing smart shoes.

Duncan, who had a soft spot for her, would have been delighted to see her. I don't think he would have minded living in a castle and sharing chocolates with her. I was envious of her transformation, albeit thrilled for her, until she glanced towards us as if embarrassed, and quickly turned away.

"She's one of them now, isn't she Milly?" Pat said gloomily.

"Looks like it," I said, I remembered how we had missed Lucy, how the time had passed slowly after her sudden disappearance. How we had mourned over her. And now she didn't want to know us, didn't even seem to want to recognise our existence. Yes, she was definitely one of them now.

She was with the egotistical, sporty, talented and pretty, immaculately dressed Wendy Street. She and her little group of insular friends mocked and taunted us continually back in St David's. Not that any of us give an iota, we all had much worse to contend with back at our prison. Lucy confirmed her recognition by looking again, sadly, her eyes darted away to examine something on the floor.

When the afternoon playtime break came we were feeling more confident in our new surroundings, and so were the other newcomers, in particular, the tall, pretty girl with beautiful long blonde hair, Wendy Street. She was speaking with a noticeable loud voice, exhibiting the demeanour of a natural leader, a centre of attraction in a group of five other new girls who were all listening attentively, Lucy being one of them.

I was talking to Stacy, whose nickname was Ginger or Spotty by some when out of the corner of my eye I noticed Wendy draw back her arm as if to throw something towards Pat, who had her back to her. The tall blonde girl smirked as she hurled the missile in the direction of Pat's head. I covered the short distance in two leaps and caught the projectile on the run about two inches from her head. I pirouetted like a graceful ballerina and aimed, what turned out to be a tennis ball, in the direction it had come from.

The speed of my reactions surprised me, though foremost it shocked the tall girl who stood like an open-mouthed statue, stunned into stillness. The ball hurtled through the air and struck her directly on her attractive nose with a dull thud. My years of playing catch with Pat proved purposely useful.

For the second time that morning, I'd caused someone to turn blood red with rage. Again the situation wasn't helped by the pretty blonde girl's friends sniggering openly. I was pleased to see Lucy laughing the loudest.

Pat didn't help the state of affairs by roaring, "Another two inches down and it would have been a gobstopper!"

Peals of laughter echoed around the playground. The tall blonde girl and two of her followers strode menacingly towards us, their intent obvious. They were almost upon us when they abruptly stopped. Looking around, I noticed Natalie and Stacy had joined us, appearing out of nowhere. The four of us stood rigid, shoulder to shoulder, defiantly staring back at them. The potential persecutors decided on another form of action and walked away, mumbling something that sounded like Nazi gits.

I sensed rather than distinguished someone run towards us, Pat and I turned as one to defend ourselves and protect each other from the perceived onslaught. We stopped in our tracks as Lucy jumped between us, one arm around each of our heads nuzzling each of us with her protuberant chin.

"I'm sorry, I'm so sorry," she sobbed the tears streaming down her euphoric face.

We stood in a small circle, each of us with a hand on the others shoulder jumping up and down and revolving in harmony, all the time laughing. Oblivious that everyone in the girl- only playground was looking at us. When, after quite a while we separated, I noticed with some confusion the faces of practically every girl, wore a sympathetic, warm smile while looking in our direction. Perhaps they were human after all?

My first day at school had been memorable, to say the least, I hoped my luck would hold out in the future.

I found it very difficult to settle down in dormitory one. Pat knew how depressed I was, and like the good friend she was, tried everything she could think of to snap me out of the pit of misery. She must have been feeling whimsical as well; I knew she was missing the nursery and little Lerina herself, I came to the conclusion she had more resolve than me. The disruption to the only way of life I'd ever really known, left me feeling melancholic, more homesick, I suppose.

About a week after we started secondary school, I presumed Sister Pointer or Sister McCarthy, who managed dormitory one between them, must have noticed I was wistful. I was scrubbing the corridor floor early one evening when Sister McCarthy, who looked uncannily similar to Sister Pointer and even wore the same style of glasses, entered. I wondered amused if the Sisters were sisters? She asked me to go to Sister Maguire for a tin of jam and take it to the nursery.

I took the weighty gallon tin of strawberry jam to the nursery where Sister Sandra greeted me like a long-lost friend. We talked for a while, I could see all my old mates were looking reasonably happy and comfortable; everyone was contented. I was thrilled and relieved, nothing drastic had occurred, any qualms I had begun to waver as I saw life in the nursery was continuing without me.

The next Saturday, I found clean, fresh clothes on my chair, signalling the imminent arrival of my grandmother, the first time in many months. Greta and I arrived in the visitor's room to find Uncle whoever was with her, unusually so, the Mother Superior as well.

"Your grandmother is taking you to the city, to buy you some clothes," she casually announced.

Greta and I grinned at each other. There was the prospect of actually owning our own clothes and seeing more of the world. I hadn't really noticed Greta's white even teeth before, but they shone then.

The uncle languidly drove, while Greta and I sat jiggling with excitement in the back. We had never been in a car before, let alone one travelling through the big city. It was only a few minutes away.

As was typical, I was dumbstruck by a world beyond my understanding.

After parking the car, we set off on foot. Feeling vulnerable and diminutive, I walked hand in hand with my grandmother through the throng of people. The last time an adult had held my hand was when Sister Toms dragged us down the corridor, the day she scalped us, about seven years before.

It wasn't long before we were walking through the large glass doors of the Howells department store. My grandmother walked confidently past rows and rows of shop goods vying for attention; clothes, shoes, furniture, crockery, lipsticks, perfume and cosmetics, past each as she strode purposefully through the store until we finally reached our destination on the first floor in the children's clothing department. There she selected a duffle coat from a long rail of different overcoats, an item made from thick wool with strange fastenings using wooden toggles and rope. "You'll grow into this nicely," she said, holding it against my neck.

Meanwhile, Greta had found the most remarkable coat I'd ever seen, a garrulous garment that was primarily red, with green and blue tartan. She looked sophisticated, her cheery smile told me she loved it. Except for the funfair day trips, I'd never seen her smile so much, she looked happier than I'd ever seen her. I asked my grandmother if I could have the same style coat as Greta.

On the short car journey back to the home my wish hadn't been granted, and Greta didn't look very glamorous or happy in her new duffle coat either. She had her head down and didn't say a word.

I arrived back at dormitory one just before the evening meal, hung my new duffle coat on the back of my chair-wardrobe and made sure my sweets were safely hidden. When I returned to the dormitory after eating the evening meal, my brand new duffle coat had disappeared.

At least I found out my grandmother's name that day, when Uncle Chauffeur complained, "Them coats look expensive Gretchen."

Choirs of Angels

Sister Norma was looking for volunteers to audition for the Nazareth House Choir, as we were now in dormitory one and attending senior school, we were considered eligible. My passion for music and singing was fast developing. I was keen to take the plunge. Pat and Natalie, who had no interest in music were just as enthusiastic for other reasons, auditions and practice sessions were immediately after supper on a Friday, thus avoiding the big scrub and polish evening. That and practice was sometimes held, a cappella, outside on warm evenings sitting on the lawn. The other bonus was the fresh oranges she supplied.

"To lubricate the tonsils," she would say.

Of the four spaces available, I was enormously elated to be one of the girls selected as an alto. She nominated Natalie as a tenor, along with a boy from dormitory three who was chosen as a countertenor. When Natalie was elected, I wasn't surprised, but I was astounded that Pat was also selected as an alto. I supposed her squeaky voice was more in the soprano range.

We all looked forward to the hour-long practising sessions; they commonly held the rehearsals at the same locations unless it was cold or raining. Then it alternated between the church with its organ air pipes that stretched towards the roof like giant penny whistles, or the great hall where an ancient upright piano was next to the television set. We soon became proficient, learning hymns and arias, with tenors, trebles and altos on either side of the nun who was in the middle shouting orders. I was too self-conscious to sing solo though, but I revelled in singing Christmas carols.

Sister Norma's enthusiasm was contagious. She had a brilliant voice; her vocal range was exceptional, extending from mezzo-soprano down to contralto. She was also a perfectionist. We sometimes sang the same carol over and over again for the whole hour-long session. She used to swivel on her stool and intently study the eight faces of the choir sitting either side of her. Deciding who was out of tune, turning to the gallery on the right of her, saying something like:

"Milly, please don't sing the second verse," or she'd turn to the left, "Pat, please try to keep up," before pushing back her spectacles.

The empty church produced an exceptional sound, the notes escaping from the organ pipes resonated tunefully under the arched roof. Every so often, Sister Norma would just play a selection of sombre and some joyous music just to entertain us.

If anyone talked or generally didn't pay attention, she would stop playing and chastise the culprits. Although it seemed to me, she always picked on the children on my side of the church and never the kids on the opposite who were just as equally disruptive. The telling offs were unusually mild, so it didn't really matter. Nevertheless, it was still particularly confusing.

We had to learn three very delightful Catholic wedding songs, '*Come Thou Fount*', '*Ode to Joy*' and '*Make Me a Channel of Your Peace*', for a forthcoming wedding. On the day of the wedding, Pat and I changed into our wedding choir clothing. Each of us wore a stunning pure white frilly dress with equally white cotton socks and black patent leather shoes. Sister Toms cut our hair the day before the wedding, but with the stupid haircuts Pat, Natalie and I still looked like Mo, from The Three Stooges in drag. We were very nervous, I had to stand with my legs slightly apart to stop my knees banging together. It was a tense first for us, first wedding and the first time singing in public.

Nevertheless, the wedding ceremony and melodic singing was a great success. The bride looked radiant as she walked down the aisle towards her handsome husband to be, waiting for her at the altar in front of the grinning priest dressed in his finest regalia. I imagined it was me walking down the aisle to a waiting prince. After the ceremony, the handsome husband gave each member of the choir a crisp one pound note. We waved them a cheery goodbye as their wedding car drove off. When we went back to the church, the nuns made us place the money in a collection box. Natalie was almost crying. Neither Pat nor I were particularly bothered as we had my money, the money Mr Noland now gave me regularly.

We were now old enough to qualify for pocket money. Each Saturday in the great hall, we formed a circle around Sister Margarita who would then revolve gracefully, her arm moving like the metronomic hand of a ticking clock, pointing at each child in turn before saying their name. The kid selected, stepped eagerly forward to accept a handful of coins from a cloth bag. They distributed the same amount to each of us, that is, if you were believed to have been a well-behaved child, otherwise you only had bus fare.

One Saturday, as I elbowed my way into the circle, I was dismayed to see Sister Terry's sneering face inside. She started counting, turned through the ring until she was back to the starting point. Before she had a chance to yell one kid was missing, a squinting Pat nudged her way in next to me. Even though Pat wasn't wearing her spectacles, she could see who was dishing out the money. Sister Terry whacked Pat on her collar bone, tucked the cane back in her belt and threw a few pennies from the bag on the floor.

"That's all you're getting for being late," the sickening nun sneered. "Pick them up,"

Pat explained that she was late because she couldn't find her glasses.

Pat, who could barely see, frantically searched for the copper pennies on the brown parquet floor. She scrambled around the inner circle on her hands and knees, tapping her palms on the flooring feeling for the money. Sister Terry's face contorted into a grotesque sneer revelling in Pat's pathetic attempt to locate the pennies. She stared around the circle, grinning gleefully as though daring someone to utter a sound.

Seeing she was momentarily distracted. I took the opportunity to act. Without the nun noticing, I slowly moved the toe of my black boot in the general direction of one of the coins. Pat received the subtle message loud and clear, with the help of my pointing toecap soon trapped the last of the bus money under her hand.

Sister Terry looked down, yelled and stamped on Pat's hand, "Who told you where the money was? Who helped you?"

Pat screamed in pain as the nun twisted her boot on Pat's knuckles.

"No one did Sister," Pat yelped with tears in her eyes.

We had practised long enough for me to know she wasn't really crying.

Later in the afternoon, when Pat eventually found the spectacles we speculated on who was responsible, for it was evident that someone had deliberately hidden them. It could have been one of the bullies, but we concluded it was more likely to have been Sister Terry.

Trips and Pitfalls

One morning, as we four Nazis were walking to class; we could hear an unusual amount of noise emanating from the direction of form 1C. In the classroom, there was a lot of gossip and excitement. From what I could gather from the snippets of information gleaned from the animated conversation; there was to be a school trip to a West Wales resort.

Mr Jones, the teacher, who I liked, was a softly spoken man with a strong Welsh accent, a thin, intelligent-looking man with pale skin that looked like it never saw the light of day. When he arrived in class, he swept back his Brylcreem-smothered hair using both hands, tucked both thumbs inside his waistcoat and stood in front of thirty-five very attentive, and extraordinarily silent, twelve-year-old boys and girls. With his back ramrod straight and his chest puffed out, he announced in an unusually loud voice, he and another teacher, Mrs Evans, would be taking children from form 1A, 1B, and children from form 1C, camping by the seaside. The trip was to be for one week in five weeks, two weeks into our summer break.

"When your name is called out, come to my desk for a consent form and take it home for your parents to sign," then looked up embarrassed when his grey eyes fixed on my own eyes "Or-or-or g-g-guardian t-t-to sign," he stammered, before continuing more confidently.

"There are only thirty-two places, and the fee is."

He mentioned the price, but it didn't matter how much it cost. There was no way any of the Nazis would be allowed to go on an excursion. Though, to be entirely fair to Mr Jones, everybody in form 1C had a consent form to take back to their parent's or-or-or g-g-guardian t-t-to sign. That evening, Sister Pointer and Sister McCarthy had similar puzzled expressions on their leathery faces as they examined the four sheets of paper.

Two weeks after Mr Jones had announced the school trip, I was with Sister McCarthy one evening after school, changing sheets and making the beds, when she calmly said with a twinkle in her eye, "Milly. The Reverend Mother said I'm to tell you, you're going on the school trip."

The years I had spent in the institution had hardened me, taught me how to control my feelings. I had learnt the most prudent action was not to show any outward signs of sentiment. Brain first; mouth after consideration was the general rule. But after that important revelation, I couldn't.

"Pat... Pat, we're going on the school trip," I screeched. Pat jumped up from the floor she had been so vigorously and diligently polishing, whooping with delight.

"Milly. Milly you stupid girl... Only you're going." Sister McCarthy shouted.

I viewed Pat's tortured face and said petulantly, "I'm not going without Pat, and that's that."

As a punishment for my disobedience, I was made to go without the evening meal.

My best friend was almost inconsolable she wouldn't be coming with me, but not in the slightest bit resentful I was going. I so wanted Pat to be with me and selfishly didn't give Stacy or Natalie a second thought until afterwards. It transpired that I was the only one from Nazareth House being allowed to go. In reality, as far as I know, I was the only one who ever went on a school trip.

Although disappointed none of my pals were coming with me, I couldn't believe I had this impossible dream come true. It was worth suffering a bit of stick from the other girls, though in general, everyone was pleased for me. When it finally dawned on me, I would be alone, I started to get second thoughts about the trip. In a near panic, my mood changed from elated to terrified. I even begged Sister McCarthy and Sister Pointer to let Stacy or Natalie go instead of me.

The night before I was to leave on my big adventure, I was very nervous. I remember Sister McCarthy trying to calm me down; while I watched as she and Sister Pointer packed a small holdall. I reminded them I had to take pens and note pads before joining them packing all my toiletries. I'd never had my own flannel, towel or soap before and it wasn't even the smelly orange type. I felt so grown-up, but deep down I was frightened of the thought of being away from Pat and all my friends in Nazareth House for a week. I don't think I slept at all the night before I was to leave. The only consolation for me was one of our previous inmates, Lucy, was going on the trip as well.

The following day the weather was brilliant, but my mood was gloomy. I was in a coach going on holiday, and I should have been feeling happy, but here I was one hour into my journey, feeling insecure. Though, the excitement of the voyage, the ceaseless changing scenery to see, soon calmed my nerves. I wish today I knew exactly where it was so I could revisit the area. I think it was somewhere in the Gower which is in west Wales about forty to fifty miles from Nazareth House.

The campsite was only five minutes from the sea, near a long golden sandy beach. I will always remember struggling through those sand dunes. The site itself was unusual as there were no tents, only brick buildings scattered haphazardly around a large grassy field surrounded by a wildly growing hedgerow, the entrance to which was gained through two steel swing gates on opposite corners.

The building we were staying in was one of the biggest. The hall of residence could have housed our entire class. It was large enough to contain the seventeen girls and fifteen boys on the trip. There were separate dormitories and shower rooms for the boys and girls. The girl's shower room contained rows of cubicles, though none of them had a door. I remember my first ever shower, showering with my red woollen swimming costume on, delighting in the smell of the soap, standing under an unending waterfall of beautiful hot water, enjoying the freedom from not having a strict, disciplinarian nun telling me to hurry. It was absolute bliss; I was beginning to feel a lot happier.

We went down to the beach that first evening, to wallow and flounder in the depths of the foot-sucking, shifting sand dunes, where Mr Jones and Mrs Evans organised games to keep us further amused. I played baseball for the first time, discovering I could hit the ball with accuracy and timing, not once but often the ball went soaring off into the distance. It's amusing how something simple like that changes the attitude of people; after the game, I was one of the first chosen by the various captains whenever we played again.

The girls seemed much friendlier towards me, except for Wendy Street, who looked like she wanted to kill me. The loathing in her striking blue eyes was particularly perturbing. Lucy was a joy to be with, it was pretty much like old times with her. Pat and I were still great friends with her; however, sorry to say she now had more in common with the other girls in her class 4A. We jokingly called her Miss Clever Clogs.

The next day we all went swimming in the sea. Well the others did, I remember splashing in the shallows with the other non-swimmers. I wondered why they had not learned to swim. I knew why I hadn't. On reflection, I don't suppose there were too many real swimmers; they were just splashing about in slightly deeper water. My embarrassment compounded when my wet woollen swimming costume started to sag away from my bottom.

Throughout the trip, the food was outstanding, there were no soggy chips for every dinner, and the picnic table held fresh bread rolls with soft drinks, not water. The summer camp trip was both memorable and thoroughly enjoyable, that and the Barry outings were the best times of my life up to that point. I never wanted it to end as it was such fun. I didn't want to go back to Nazareth House.

The one thing that stands out about that jaunt is the memories. I recall with great pride being accepted as one of the girls, making friends with outsiders and not being treated like a leper which was how other children and I from Nazareth House were treated. The freedom was exhilarating.

Another memory from that holiday, which I keep to this day, something most people would take for granted, was when I washed and had a shower using imperial leather soap. It had such a lovely smell and seemed so fresh, not like the awful carbolic soap we used in Nazareth House. After a shower, I felt so clean and relaxed. I actually liked the smell of myself. Memories of the home can be so fantastic at times, sometimes not so pleasant.

When I returned from the camping trip, the bus dropped me at the front gates of a very unwelcoming looking Nazareth House. After the previous, marvellous seven days, the place looked bleaker than ever; I had such a peaceful time. I never wanted my camping holiday to finish. However, I missed all my pals.

I entered the big cast-iron gates feeling downcast, carrying my small light travel bag the short distance up the driveway towards the front door. A minute later, my knuckles were beginning to throb from my continuous knocking on the door, for as typical, the doors were locked. Abruptly, Sister Terry opened the door and without a greeting or a smile informed me the Mother Superior wanted to see me on my return.

I reached the girl's dormitory on the ground floor, welcomed by three high-pitched squeals of delight inviting me back, seconds later three wide-eyed, smiling faces joined me, waiting for a step-by-step account of my big adventure. I dropped my bag on my wooden chair as I explained the Mother Superior wanted to see me immediately. Their joyous expressions dissolved into looks of disappointment. I quickly told them I had had a fantastic time and I would inform them about the trip later.

Without a care in the world, I skipped down the corridors heading for the Mother Superior's office, which was adjacent to the church. I passed a nun who gave me a whack to my head for running, inflicting a short, sharp reminder, informing me I was back to this dark, dismal place, I had returned to the orphanage.

I rapped on the door, the pain of my earlier encounter with solid wood still throbbing in my knuckles reminding me not to knock on doors so hard in the future. Reverend Mother answered the door, allowing herself a glimmer of a smile as she waved her hand in a sweeping motion to beckon me in. I complied, entering the substantial immaculate windowless office. She pointed to a big cosy-looking armchair and told me to sit down.

The Reverend Mother Superior, to give her full title, was born in Ireland and became a nun on leaving school. She was about as old as my grandmother, very tall, by far the tallest nun out of those who lived in the home she had a warm, serene look about her. I suppose saintly would be an appropriate description. The one and only thing defining her status as Mother Superior was the gold cross and chain hanging around her neck; although all the nuns wore a crucifix, her simple symbol of authority was much grander.

She sat down behind the expanse of her tidy desk as I climbed up and into the big armchair and wriggled myself into a comfortable position. I looked up at her, she was smiling, her feline-like eyes twinkling through the glasses she was wearing. The white shroud covered her head, the only visible areas being her hairless eyebrows, cheeks and chin; it was comparable to seeing the face of a barn owl.

She asked me if I had enjoyed my holiday and, without showing too much emotion, I told her briefly about my time with Lucy and the girls from the school. I am uncertain why I erected the invisible barrier between us as she was a benevolent, caring person.

Experiences had taught me they rarely gave such gifts without expecting more in return. The Mother Superior stood up as I finished my summarising account of my holiday, her tall, stout frame began pacing the small area behind her chair. Suddenly she stopped, not looking into my eyes stared at the well-ordered table in front of her. I could see her chunky cheeks were gradually getting redder by the second. Then she hurriedly informed me I was to assist Sister Sandra in the day to day running of the nursery and Pat, my friend, my life, my soulmate, my rock would remain in dormitory one. My new bed would be my old bed nearest the corridor. The move would coincide with the end of half-term.

Her rapid proclamation left me stunned. I began trembling, my head was spinning as I tried to comprehend her words. I jumped off the armchair and stood defiantly in front of her, feeling my own cheeks burning bright red.

At the top of my voice, I yelled, "No. Not without Pat."

Without a doubt, I would have been reasonably happy in the nursery if Pat was with me, as I was missing it terribly. Defiantly I remained in my standing position for quite a long while.

"I am sorry Milly, but you will have to," the Mother Superior said in a sad voice.

I examined her face and instantly knew she wasn't going to change her decision, so without saying another word, I walked away. As I opened the door, I turned to face her, she was gazing down at the desk, her plump bottom lip trembling.

I sauntered back to the girl's dormitory on the ground floor, her words reverberating in my numb mind. I was right I thought, the holiday had cost me dearly.

The girls in the dormitory noticed something was wrong as soon as I entered, they flocked around my small bed waiting for me speak. Pat looked at me through her milk bottles, looking knowingly and wryly pensive towards me. Natalie Ward, fellow chorister and another good friend of mine, though we had a rocky start to our friendship, put her arm around my shoulder with a grimace on her pretty face.

"What have they done now?" she asked in her usual gruff voice.

I informed the assembled girls I was moving out and going back to the nursery in the east wing. At the ripe old-age of twelve, I was going to live with eleven other children aged between three and eight. Pat's face went ashen white a bewildered look accompanied the tears trickling from under her spectacles. Except for the pretend ones, I had never seen her cry before.

I often pondered during my holiday why I alone was allowed on the trip. Was it to see how I interacted with a group of strangers if I was capable of forming new friendships? Was it designed to reward me for running errands and looking after the children or simply to soften the blow of having to return to the nursery? Whatever, from now on, it was back to the toil and graft. It mattered little where I stayed. Drudgery, sweat and tedium were always in attendance and abundance.

My move to the nursery was completed the Monday after our summer holiday, our first day back at school. I had managed to get a few more days with Pat who tried to assure me, with little conviction, that with the freedom we now had the situation wouldn't be too bad.

Sister Sandra orchestrated plenty of diversions for me to coincide with Pat's movements and so a routine developed whereas we had a lot of time together but didn't share a dormitory. My old and some new group of charges were an affable lot under the guidance of Saint Sandra, a general atmosphere of ambience developed. We still had to complete our tasks, cleaning and polishing but only if necessary. So I busied myself in the nursery, trying to keep cheerful and trying unsuccessfully not to get attached or emotional towards the kiddies.

That winter was one when I missed the warm duffle coat my grandmother had once bought me. The weather was freezing, cold enough to give us a few days of wonder, when we had that occasional visitor, snow, instead of the more standard, dismal grey precipitation we were accustomed to in Cardiff.

One day a cute little collie sheepdog puppy came bounding over the snow-covered gardens towards the back of nursery playground. A few of us were having fun by throwing snowballs at each other. The dog snuck through a small gap in the fence and joined in the fun. I had a two-finger chocolate Kit Kat biscuit in my pocket that the hungry dog sniffed out. My big mistake was giving him a piece. I couldn't resist his pleading; he was sitting on his hind legs with his two front legs elevated, his paws extended in front of him like a boxer wearing boxing gloves. Even after I gave him all the chocolate, he wouldn't leave me alone. When the call to dinner bell sounded, he darted in through my legs as we all went through the door and into the corridor.

Sister Sandra was not pleased when a steaming collie followed us into the nursery, though this left the kind nun in a quandary as what to do; not wanting to turn the puppy out into the cold winter evening. She told me quietly to take the dog back through the playground and go to the police station. Once there, I was to say, the dog was a stray, then hurry back, adding she would keep me something to eat.

There were two things wrong with her plan. First, she knew there was a police station one turning right at the bottom of Colum Road; a ten-minute round trip even with the snow-covered pavements. Secondly and more importantly, I didn't. The only police station I knew of was the one, two miles away. The Canton Police Station I saw twice a day on my school journeys.

It was getting dark when I walked with my new pal through the doors of the police station. I was freezing cold, and the dog was sweltering like a sauna. We settled him in a warm cage, the kindly police sergeant towelled down the dog, after asking and discovering where I came from, he drove me back to the orphanage in a Morris

Minor panda car. I felt like a criminal as he escorted me to the double entrance doors, he even held my hand. Unfortunately, when he rapped on the door, it was Sister Terry who opened it. She thanked him graciously while placing one arm tenderly around my shoulder. For a split second, she almost had me fooled, the deceit wholly hoodwinked the sergeant. If he could have seen what happened the moment she closed the door, he would have arrested her.

The click of the door was like a boxing referee's bell to her. Sister Terry punched me on the side of my head and again to my face cutting my lip, hit my stomach, slapping my arms and legs until they were numb. Wanting me to cry and beg, but I didn't. I managed to run away from her, she chased me down the corridor towards the nursery. Sister Sandra was by the entrance waiting for me wearing a worried frown on her face. She smiled serenely when she saw me scuttle around the corner, her smile turning to quizzical when Sister Terry slithered into view. The two nuns stood facing each other until Sister Terry abruptly turned and went.

My stomach ached and throbbed though, I pretended I wasn't really hurt. The only outward sign of the beating was the split lip that Sister Sandra dabbed with saltwater. The warm, compassionate nun must have apologised to me twenty times by the time I finished the meal she had kept for me. After a short time, I was feeling relatively happy, more so with the knowledge, my puppy was safe and warm, as I was later in my creaky metal bed.

A New Best Friend

My new school and my latest routine soon became part of my life, I liked it despite missing Pat enormously during the evenings. Sister Sandra made sure Pat helped in the nursery on weekends, we had a lot of time together. I was unusually relaxed and confident, knowing the little ones were happy. Pat, Natalie, Stacy and I, along with two other girls from the institution, were a well-organised bunch of intruders. All of us successful in looking out for each other. We still had our constant persecutors who had followed us from Saint David's. Their group had, by now, recruited a few more followers who tried in vain to disrupt our lives and make us more miserable than we were. If only they knew what we had to put up with at our home, it made their misguided attention almost pathetic.

The morning ice on the inside of the big windows was, as in the previous years, a precursor to our winter ensemble; the double layers of clothes laid out for us each morning. I didn't mind the freezing conditions, and I still don't. Pat was a cold fish, who would run up the hill to school to get into the warm classroom as quickly as she could.

She'd shout to me, "Come on, Milly. I'll race you to the top," always something to encourage me to run with her.

I would typically saunter along, taking in the magnificent views of the world around me. Learning the sounds of most bird songs as I listened and mentally documented them, although, then, I didn't know their names. One morning I lagged behind happy, blithely lost in my own little world, Pat after shouting my name, urging me to join her, decided to catch up with the other girls. I stopped to tie my boot laces, pulling up my knee-length socks, humming contentedly, before trying to mimic the sound of a bird. I was kneeling by the side of a garden wall which was about head height when my sight became obscured by a shadow slowly covering my face.

Acutely aware of a presence, the hairs on my neck stood to attention; my habitual sharp defences had been caught off guard. I lifted my head slowly knowing that something or somebody was there, for by now I could see the plume of hot breath in the cold air close to my face. My instinct was to move slowly. Cautiously I moved my head enabling me to notice a black curly-headed scruffy dog looking curiously at what I was doing. I stared back, seeing her bottom teeth were completely covering her top lip. I unhurriedly stood up. Her uneven saucer-like brown eyes followed my every move, her untidy black tail remained defiantly and unfriendly static.

There was something about this dog, she had a confidence that flowed from her, yet she was not much taller than my boots. At first sight, her small paws, her skinny legs, comical teeth and her black shiny curly coat made her appear unattractive. But she wasn't though. She was unique, reminding me of Pat the first time I met her. The little black dog was beautiful, I fell in love with her in an instant. I had noticed the little dog on quite a few occasions before though never this close, she always seemed to show up when Pat shouted to me.

"Hello, little girl, how are you?" The tail gave a slight twitch. I went to smooth her head, but she quickly jumped back and darted away.

I watched as she approached a corner, stopping to turn around. She looked into my eyes before her little tail swished and she was gone. I realised I was late and had to run as well.

When school was over and another evening of drudgery beckoned, we began to return home. From the top of the hill, we watched the bobbing heads of eager school kids heading down to their waiting buses and mothers and fathers. We listened to their carefree conversations, discussing things that were alien to us.

"My Grandmother's coming to see us this weekend; she lives in Coventry, you know."

"After homework, we're all going to that new French restaurant in Pontcanna."

"We are going to see Jimi Hendrix, Pink Floyd, The Move and Amen Corner at Sophia Gardens tonight," Wendy Street broadcast loud enough for about forty or more children to hear.

Days out in the countryside, a park or at a concert were outsider pursuits. The only time we went to the park together was to pick up rubbish after the May Day celebrations. There were never any family outings to the cinema for us to see *Bambi* or *Snow White*. Some of our classmates would gleefully discuss the Saturday morning cinema for children, where they would throw things off the balcony onto the unsuspecting children below. There again, on the plus side, we were never left outside pubs with a packet of crisps and a bottle of cheap fizzy drink to become bloated and bored.

Of course, the significant difference between the outsider children and us was cultural, modern culture. What was that? What was modern? We lived in a time warp, in a relic run by nuns who looked at change as an anathema. We never had a radio or record player to listen too in the institution, never had a chance to keep up with the continually evolving pop music and the accompanying traditions. The only times we had heard music was in passing, in places like shops or passing houses on the way to school, listening to snatches of some tunes. A few pensioners had wireless sets, but their preferences were already hard-wired into them, be it classical music from their earlier lives. The nuns certainly didn't hum the latest hits. We envied every child who had access to a radio or television. Some even boasted that they had their own record player and TV in their bedrooms. We heard the televised news from children at school, so our second-hand playground ration arrived edited, filtered through minds that tended to omit the actualities.

I was too young to see the Beatles when they played in Cardiff's Capitol cinema in nineteen sixty-five. It was the last time they played together live on a stage in Great Britain. What with the limited access we had to a television set, I don't even remember seeing them, or seeing or hearing any news about the most popular band in the world. Well, a hoard of screaming girls was not an image the nuns would share with us.

We were obsolete in any conversations concerning current trends, especially fashion and hairstyles. It was if our version of pop culture was still forming in a petri dish. Music to us was old hymns, some of which we liked more than others. Questions like, who do you prefer, the Beatles or the Rolling Stones? Was similar to asking us if we preferred beetles or rolling stones, insects or marbles. They were irrelevant to us, compounding the view that the Nazis were stupid.

Even so, my passion for music was developing even with my limited access. Sister Sandra would hum a few songs, and one of the outsider kids had a transistor radio she'd play on the top deck of the bus where we would listen to the rebellious chart hits from the year-old Radio one with Tony Blackburn. A program that started in nineteen sixty-seven when I was twelve. I consider myself lucky to have listened to the sounds of the sixties and seventies, my devotion to popular music continues to this day.

The small dog was standing where we first met, away from the wall, intently scanning the passing school children's faces as they filed past her. She saw me and fixed her big brown eyes on my now beaming face until I stopped in front of her. Her tail moved tentatively, her long sloppy tongue licked her black button nose. Pat laughed, and like with the donkeys at Barry Island, went confidently towards the little black dog to stroke her rigid head. The dog was having none of that behaviour and scampered away, giving her no chance to complete her action. Pat gave me a look as if to say sorry, and we both laughed.

When we boarded the bus, I asked, "What do think of her?"

"She's beautiful," agreed Pat.

In the following days persuading the tiny giant to accept our proffered friendship proved impossible. However, she loitered in the same garden every day, giving me some hope for the future.

The answer to our dilemma came from neither Pat nor I but from a helper, Jasmin McCluskey, whose first job on leaving school was working in the kitchens of Nazareth House. She was a tall, tom-boyish, friendly girl who had short auburn dyed hair with a long fringe that almost concealed her black eyebrows.

We presented the problem to her while we waited for our evening meal of mashed potatoes and baked beans.

"Easy peasy," she said through her big teeth, teeth that were so large her lips couldn't cover them. Her permanent looking smile was always visible, making her appear perpetually joyful.

"The answer's in front of you."

I looked at her chirpy face questionably. I knew she was happy because her green eyes smiled back at us.

"Food." was her one-word explanation.

It transpired, the following morning that the little black dog waiting in the garden didn't like mashed potatoes or lumpy porridge. God knows we barely had enough food to eat anyway, without our rumbling bellies reminding us our sacrifice was in vain.

Our new friend Jasmin McCluskey was a lovely eye-catching Scottish girl with a female body of ample proportions, the only child of a family who had moved to Wales from Glasgow. She had a tendency to mumble through a mouth too full of teeth, though we learned to decipher and understand her through time and patience.

She told us in snatches about her family life. Her father was in the army and stationed at Maindy Barracks, a garrison about half a mile from the orphanage, one we never knew existed. During World War II it was home to thousands of American soldiers. She told us about her dogs that were the love of her life. One was an Alsatian, a sizeable powerful creature who had been an army dog until failing its final test, with friendliness, his ignominy. The other was a small brindle rescue dog, a bitch with big ears. We looked forward to our little snippets of conversation with Jasmin, though due to the circumstances, her short stories would sometimes take a week to come to fruition.

One day Jasmin tried unsuccessfully to include an extra egg on our Saturday evening plates. Saturday's dinnertime alternated between egg and soggy chips or powdered mash and baked beans, with every meal accompanied by a slice of bread and margarine. One scoop of chips, one egg, one slice of bread and one mug or a cup of tea was all everybody had. Even with my skinny frame, I was still hungry after mealtimes. I felt sorry for Pat, I used to impart a few of my chips when the overseeing nun was distracted. Jasmin slipped us an extra egg each from the large aluminium tray holding about twenty eggs floating in a sea of warm lard, she tried to hide one under the measured meagre portion of chips.

Jasmin was useless at subterfuge; she turned her smiling face around at least three times, ultimately attracting the attention of Sister Maguire, who was incensed when she noticed the two eggs on our small plates. The punishment she dished out was to take away our food. So we sat at our table watching the other children eating, our complaining bellies empty. Jasmin, who didn't look unhappy at all, just about kept her job and was demoted to dishwashing. To be fair to Sister Maguire, the retribution was judicious. She was one of the few who rarely used any form of corporal punishment.

Jasmin, who was more efficient than anyone at serving, soon had her old job back. She managed more successfully to give us extra chips now and then, and whenever she could, the crust from the loaf. She told us one of her other tasks was to feed the leftovers to the tramps who used to congregate in a small courtyard on the other side of the kitchen. The only access to this courtyard was through a narrow ornate cast-iron gate that the nuns would unlock for the hungry tramps. She informed us in her guttural Scottish accent that up to six tramps would be given a mug of tea and a baked beans sandwich. Sometimes a half-eaten sausage or bacon rind that the nuns had left would be made available for the famished fellows.

Leftovers? I pondered. What were leftovers? I never saw any food left except for uneaten fish bones. Most of the time, the plates were gleaming, even though if you were caught licking your plate, you were guaranteed to get a whack on the back of the head. But the temptation not to slurp the tomato sauce, the remnants from our beans and mash meal was too powerful to resist. The sounds of our frustration, the noisily scraping knives, proved futile. The trick was for every kid to lick the plates furiously in unison and then only a few of us would receive the misfortune of a throbbing skull.

There were always two choices at every mealtime take it or leave it, so food and sustenance was still the winner. Even the weak tea served from the giant teapot with the milk and sugar already added was always finished, we considered it a bonus to have a half-inch of tea leaves settled in the bottom of our mugs.

One evening, Jasmin whispered to us she had hidden a small parcel under the stone used to keep the door to the nursery playground open. She advised us to recover the package as quickly as possible; adding that inside it was the answer to the problem. She didn't have a chance to explain further as a nun was looming near. I managed to retrieve the paper parcel the next morning, after I'd prepared a breakfast of porridge for a dozen of us, washed the dishes, cleaned and polished, then readied the children for school. During that period, all the kids in the nursery attended school. I slipped away unseen to the door, and a few seconds later, the newspaper parcel was tucked safely away under my arm, hidden inside my scruffy old school blazer.

I sat impatiently next to Pat on the school bus, my curiosity in overdrive. We dared not open the top-secret bundle until the coast was clear. So after getting off the bus, we lagged behind the kids at the bottom of the hill, the location near to the elusive little black dog before opening the well-wrapped package. The curious little creature approached with caution stretching her slender neck sniffing loudly; she knew its contents before I even finished opening the paper bundle. Inside was half a dozen, golden cooked, delicious chipolata sausages.

Pat took one and started to eat it, "Scrumptious," she drooled, as I too bit into my mouth-watering fare.

I looked down to see pleading black eyes inside a little furry head, her pink waving tongue protruding under a black wet nose, her tail wagging so furiously it seemed she might just fly away. I offered the enthusiastic little girl a chipolata sausage; she approached cautiously, sniffed at it twice before she took the offering gently in her mouth, then scampered away to enjoy her gift. Two sausages and ten minutes later with our friendship almost sealed. She hesitantly allowed a couple of strokes to her little bony head on her third sausage. Realising we were late we dashed up the hill, turning at the top to see the dog was standing where we had left her; watching us, her tail wagging steadily.

After another uneventful school day with only the minimum amount of baiting and backbiting, we impatiently awaited the end of the day's bell. I had stuffed some cheese and tomato pie in the package containing a tempting flavoursome solitary sausage. We would have in general devoured our school dinners as the food was much better than in the orphanage, though there was a tendency to have mash with everything. The puddings were more varied, the tapioca pudding was one of my favourites, and confusingly called frogs spawn by the other kids.

At long last, the day was over. As always, we were mostly never overeager to return to the home, but we were keen to see the little dog. She recognised us as we approached and confirmed the fact by wagging her tail, but she refused to come closer, despite the proven alluring sausage, it seemed the confidence she had displayed in the morning had evaporated. She was a wary little creature, it was only when the procession of kids dwindled did she tentatively approach the opened paper parcel.

"Come on, you two," shouted the friendly bus conductor.

As soon as we boarded, he rang the bell, the bus jerked, and we were off. Looking back, we watched the dog, whose head remained buried in the paper until she was out of eyesight.

Jasmin was right, it seemed. Food was indeed the answer, though far more important, the food the dog liked. Jasmin had bought the chipolatas from her own purse and cooked them at home, our admiration towards the sympathetic Scottish lass deepened.

The Handyman

Remembering the initial success of the dawn crusade, I was keen to capitalise on my observations of the routines, strengths and weaknesses of my jailers, like a young Edmond Dantès plotting an escape. A situation made more manageable by my recently acquired freedom and virtual access to all areas.

I didn't enjoy going to the old people's wing as it always smelled musty. Though it was there, I eventually won around the grumpy Mr Noland or more likely wore him down with my persistent daily friendly disposition. After a few weeks, we became moderately affable, he'd smile warmly at me when I delivered his morning paper. Even with his crooked yellow teeth, it still broadcast his pleasure, for the smile suited his square face and brought to prominence his sparkling eyes that were as grey as his curly hair. He would always give me money. If I tried to refuse, he would become upset and insist, saying it was an insult to him if I didn't take the gift. To decline was an affront to him.

He would say, "Blue, I have plenty of money, so take it."

He had shortened his nickname for me, from 'Blue eyes, to Blue'. I liked the moniker, soon all the men and women in the old people's section called me Blue. Except for grumpy Mrs Gittings who continued to call me anything horrible she could think of, calling me a skinny, ugly brat was her favoured choice.

As a result of Mr Noland's financial kindness, I soon accumulated quite a sum of money. So much so my secondary hiding place, a small cavity behind the door of a big cupboard, was getting full. I decided I would need another hiding place for my cash cache soon.

The change in our relationship was a key factor to the plan I had been incubating, now we were friends, I decided the time had arrived to see if it could be hatched. One day I had a nasty cut on my knee after a session of catch. I had the inspiration; this could be the ideal opportunity to begin my plan's next stage.

I showed the injury to Mr Noland, who was naturally concerned, he asked me how it happened. I didn't enjoy lying. Though, I thought this situation warranted a detour from the truth. So I said the leg of my chair collapsed when I stood on it and I cut my knee when I fell. Sister Toms had repaired the chair, but the leg fell off again, so I propped it up with books. I could see him frowning as he stroked the grey bristle on his square chin.

Later that day, I went to see Mother Superior and outlined my plan to her. She listened intently, her sharp knowing eyes flashing sideways and upwards, her lips moving as if to say something but she didn't until I finished my brief dialogue.

"Milly you are indeed a Saint, you have my blessing."

The next day I walked with a pronounced limp as I approached and handed Mr Noland his newspaper. He watched my Oscar-winning performance with a questionable lift of his untidy grey eyebrows.

"The books I used to prop the chair leg slipped. Then I hurt my leg again," I whimpered.

"Right," he growled and stood up. "I'm going to sort this out. For once and for all."

“I know where the key for the tool shed is,” I said, perhaps a little too quickly, for he gave me a rapid sideward suspicious glance.

“Go and get the chair Blue and meet me there,” his voice authoritative, flicking off his slippers before turning to pick up his shoes.

In my excitement, I skipped to the door forgetting the limp; then slowed to spin around a moment before he looked up towards me.

“In five minutes,” he murmured.

I nodded and hobbled out into the whitewashed corridor smiling complacently.

Five minutes later, I was holding the chair and using the dismembered limb to point to where the key was. Once inside the shed, Mr Noland studied the dusty, cluttered contents, scratching at his bristles, intently scrutinising tools, broken chairs and cabinets. The change in him was subtle and steady, his sad face transformed, appearing more determined and confident. I could sense the energy as he stood up and straightened his back, gaining a full three inches to his stooped thin frame. With his preliminary inspection of the shed over he ushered me out of his new domain, promising that I would have a repaired chair later that day. I left him with a look of contentment on his grey face as he purposely started to organise the jumbled interior to his satisfaction.

I limped away to carry out my daily duties. To remind me, I placed a marble inside my left boot; the intense discomfort was a constant reminder of my idea’s success. A few hours later, my chair was no longer an object to be preceded by words such as rickety or old, it was now a sturdy, sanded, and wax polished chair. Within a week, Mr Noland would transform the old shed into a newly painted professional workshop, with sparkling clean windows and net curtains.

Mr Noland became a different man who now appeared to enjoy his life, revelling in his new position as the orphanage handyman. To the dismay of some nuns, he would often be seen humming or whistling quietly to himself as he contentedly went about his duties in the home, more often than not a freshly renovated item in his arms. The transformation was amazing. Now he was animated and enthusiastically waved whenever he saw me, which was practically every day. He rarely sat in his old chair by the window these days, where the wallpaper behind the seat still revealed the faint outline of his profile, a shadow etched by the sun surrounding his static body, a permanent reminder of how long the poor depressed man had sat aimlessly staring through the window.

I tried to refuse the money he gave me on an almost daily basis, to no avail. Luckily by then, I had found a new hiding place for all the coins. There was a narrow space near the wall of his new workshop, hidden by a vibrant fuchsia. I had almost forgotten about the hideaway little Heidi and Janice used. The one they emerged from, the first day of my incarceration. There was barely enough room to squeeze through, but once past the constricted gap, the breathing space opened up considerably with enough room for half a dozen kids. Fortunately, there were no traces of the previous visitors who were now long- gone. I doubted that many, if anybody, knew of its existence. Pat would never have squeezed through the narrow gap, not with her recently acquired curves and bumps.

I selected a secure place in the poorly lit space for my new money stash. There was a missing stone in the main wall that was high enough to be out of reach of small children should any of them be adventurous enough to enter this gap. I found that a stone of similar dimensions placed in the hole neatly concealed the large cavity behind. So this became my new stash. I was confident my secret hiding place would remain a secret.

I concluded that my first hiding place by the radiator that had remained a secret for many years should be kept for use, even though it was now full of money and confectionary for our secret banquets. Though, I felt I should move the money from my other secret stash, the not as secure hollow space behind the door to the big cupboard. So I began methodically transferring the coins to my new hiding place one or two handfuls at a time, each time counting the money before I deposited it in procured white socks. By my calculations, the cash, all in silver coins and secured snugly in the warm cotton socks, amounted to what an adult would earn in about a month. There was still half as much again in the big cupboard, and most likely the same amount behind the iron radiator. I was rich, guilty and filthy rich. My thoughts went briefly to bright coloured coats from Howells and disappearing duffle coats. I even considered new spectacles for Pat, but how can you achieve the impossible when you're in a cage?

After school one day, I was in the process of transferring more coins and had just put another handful in my tatty school blazer pocket, when I heard a noise behind me. I turned towards the porthole door, behind it stood Mrs Gittings, looking as if she hadn't noticed anything, pulling a trolley containing clean bedding and towels behind her.

She entered and nudged me out of the way aggressively while adding savagely, "Get lost you ugly, skinny brat."

Had she seen anything? I wondered as I fled. I dismissed it as unlikely. She couldn't get her big fat hands in the small gap, anyway.

Though, two things went through my mind on my way to my hiding place. First, was my secret hiding place in the cupboard still a secret? And second, I wished Mr Noland hadn't oiled all the noisy hinges in the home. The day before I had noticed him with an oilcan in his hand, squirting oil on the dormitory door hinges. The consequences of his actions were now as instantly recognisable as the nursery bell. The early warning system of creaking doors had now been disabled. Those noises, plus the click of a switch, a faint rattle of keys and moving shadows underneath doors had always successfully alerted us; other alternatives would have to be discovered.

Mrs Gittings confirmed my concerns the next afternoon when I tentatively stretched my hand into my secret hiding place to find it was no longer secret. It was empty. Not a single coin remained. I was 'pig sick', to quote my friend Pat after I had told her about the stolen money, though she didn't know the amount. Mrs Gittings had hoodwinked me. I was as angry with myself as I was with her.

To make matters worse, a few days later, I couldn't fail to notice her new expensive-looking hairstyle, her smart new shoes and clothes. Then Pat mentioned Mrs Gittings had had her nails shaped and varnished and was wearing new greasepaint that did not disguise her pockmarked face. I was livid, but I never showed her I knew it was her.

I told Mr Noland of the theft. At first, he was sympathetic and then became angry. After a little while, he smiled serenely. "I would have given her money, had she asked me. Still, I'll make sure you don't lose any more," he said and grinned, pondering how to achieve this as he scratched his stubble.

A few days later, when I was in the playground with the new kiddies, Mr Noland beckoned me to his workshop. The inside differed completely from my first visit there with Sister Toms. It was almost clutter-free, the walls lined with tools, the shelves filled with paint cans, workbenches held waiting pieces of furniture to mend. It was obvious he was proud of his labour. He smiled a pleasant yellow-toothed smile when I mentioned how impressed I was. "Now pay attention, Blue," he whispered as he closed the shed door. He removed a wooden crate from the middle shelf towards the back of the big shed.

"Press this one first, then this one, and remember to keep your fingers on both at the same time. It won't work unless you do it in that order," pointing at two screws out of a dozen innocuous-looking screws that fastened the shelf brackets to the wooden wall.

What won't work, I wondered? I did as instructed, pressing on the right-hand screw then I pushed another bony finger on the left-hand screw. There was a quiet click, then the whole shelf section sprung slowly away from the wall. He pulled it further to reveal the stone walls of my hiding place. It was an inspired piece of engineering, though I couldn't work out the purpose of a glassless window to my hideout.

"Pay attention," he said proudly, pressing one screw and then another on what was the outside wooden panel, both screws more or less opposite the inside screws, with another click, the outer section sprang open to reveal a four to five-inch space sandwiched between the internal shelf section and the outside. It was a shelved miniature cupboard with a magical door on either side.

"They won't find this," he said with a self-satisfied look on his face.

He demonstrated his work of genius a few times, explaining that if I became confused by all the other screws, the screws that required pushing were the only ones with the slot head pointing from the ground to the sky.

He closed the inside window while I went outside. I closed and opened the completely undetectable outside door with ease. I joined him in the shed workshop, his side of the compartment now closed and concealed. We both laughed conspiratorially together. My brand new hiding place gave me a great deal of confidence and satisfaction.

Mr Noland hadn't finished. From the bottom shelf he took out a small block of wood with attached metal pieces, it was a modified mousetrap with customised springs.

"Be careful with this," he warned, showing me how to set it, and what would happen if the release trap was touched. Metal snapped on wood with lightning speed the piece of wood used for the demonstration purpose boasted deep indents.

"I've cut it down so it will fit," he said guiltily. He didn't tell me what it was for, and I had the sense not to ask, thus alleviating him from any blame or consequences.

I felt no guilt whatsoever as I set the trap and slid it carefully into my old stash point in the big cupboard, wilfully ignoring the indoctrinated, 'turn the other cheek' from the Sermon on the Mount. It was a discourse I would ignore and disagree with all of my life. My cheeks were not for turning. Besides only prying, greedy stealing hands would be caught out, this was more of, 'An eye for an eye, a tooth for a tooth', I thought with satisfaction.

A month passed, and, I'd almost forgotten about the trap. The rest of my money was now safe and secure, sandwiched in-between the secret window doors, when, on Wednesday afternoon, a terrifying scream was heard echoing down the long corridors and throughout the orphanage of Nazareth house. It was said Mrs Gittings was seen running, screaming hysterically with a block of wood firmly attached to her hand, one Sister Toms had to release her fingers from.

Hopefully, her blackened nails and throbbing fingers disguised by her new nail varnish would remind her of her dishonesty and treachery for months to come. We passed each other in a corridor a few days later, each of us knowing we both knew who did what to whom and when. She nudged me violently with an elbow to my ribcage; despite the pain, I couldn't resist an ever so slight smug smirk.

The Mother Superior sent for me the next day, "It has come to my attention that Mr Noland has been giving you money. Milly this must stop; you must not accept any money from him," she insisted, making me promise I wouldn't.

"I have spoken to him and told him to stop," she added in a stern voice.

I speculated that Mrs Grass Gittings must have guessed where the money came from and told the Reverend Mother. Mr Noland never gave me any money after that day, whereas I never accepted any from him, though the amount of money stashed away increased weekly.

"Well, I'm not giving it to you, am I?" he reasoned.

He wouldn't listen to me when I endeavoured to get him to stop.

"You changed my life Blue, for which I am truly grateful. Amen. And that's that," he would insist.

The money in the concealed window cupboard accumulated reasonably quickly as he had more opportunity to increase my enforced income.

I opened the secret window one morning to take out a coin for a sausage roll treat for Roly, Pat and I. I christened the little black dog Roly because the now sociable dog would roll over and over when I tickled her belly. I stepped back in horror as the door opened to reveal two small stacks of lonely coins standing side by side. I fleetingly thought of Mrs Gittings. Then in the dim light, I noticed a little green booklet next to the pillars of coins; a glossy hardback with a picture of a black horse on the front cover. I cautiously picked it up and anxiously opened it, turning to the first page to read the top line above precise lines and spaces. *Milly Nash Savings Account*, it proclaimed in neat handwriting. Then I noticed in the top right-hand corner the sum of the missing money. Mr Noland had almost given me a heart attack. I had the idea my lifeless corpse would have remained undiscovered for weeks.

When I saw him later that afternoon, he said, "I thought it better and safer for you, Blue. Plus you'll get interest on it. It'll be safe there until you leave this place when it will be a good start for your future."

He explained Lloyds Bank was on Queen Street, Cardiff's main shopping street and I would need proof of my identity to access the money. No doubt, his words were pearls of wisdom, but I was confused. Proof of identity I mused, I didn't know who I was? When I told him I had nothing of the sort. He thought for a while, "I'll sort it Blue, don't you fret."

Friends Reunited

We were a few weeks into our new term. Pat, Natalie, Stacy and I were all in form 2C. Greta was now attending another Catholic school, St Joseph's, a short distance from the orphanage. I was initially shocked to discover that there were so many Catholic schools spread all over Cardiff, and it still puzzled me why Greta and I were in different schools.

The Saturday auction was in session. Pat and I, as was the norm at that time, were spectators with Sister Terry goading us with her usual whispered malice. Though what was not normal was Sister Sandra walking gracefully towards us, a radiant smile on her beautiful face.

"Come with me, you two. I have a surprise for you."

We happily, yet curiously walked with her towards the visitor room.

She opened the door and with a smile on her attractive young face and laughter in her eyes and said, "I'll be back in ten minutes."

Pat entered first and stopped, suddenly obscuring my view.

"Crikey Moses," she screeched and darted into the room.

I heard the sounds of gentle adult laughter and then the joyful shouting that followed. My eyes went to the child Pat was hugging. She had grown significantly and was almost as tall as me, but she was unmistakable.

"Lerina," I whispered in shock and ran to throw my arms around her.

"So you're the two angels who looked after my little girl," said the grown-up.

I've heard the same words before I thought to myself. I looked up to see a beautiful woman smiling radiantly.

"She's been pestering me nonstop to come to see you," the woman said, going on to explain that she'd tried for many long months, but had been told it was impossible as the home only allowed visits by relatives or those willing to foster or adopt.

As luck would have it, the parish priest of Saint Dyfrigs Catholic Church in Treforest, the village they lived in, was a very dear friend of the Mother Superior. It was him who had suggested and indeed organised Lerina's temporary stay in the home during a calamitous period.

Sister Sandra returned with two leather school satchels.

"Now girls, there are clothes and all you need for your overnight stay with Mrs Nairs," she said as we both grabbed the proffered items.

Three children squealing in delight must be relatively loud, for Sister Sandra gestured with a finger to her lips for quiet, which we instantly obeyed and joyful silence ensued. I was in total shock, my skinny knees doing the usual dance.

Sister Sandra said, "Mrs Nairs, there are clothes in their bags for Sunday Mass as well. Please, can you make sure you get the girls back by seven-thirty? Mother Superior will have my guts for garters if you don't."

Mrs Nairs replied in a distinct Italian accent, "Don't worry Sister. The train arrives at Queen Street at five-thirty, so that gives us plenty of time."

What a curious statement? Guts for garters, I thought puzzled.

We set off on another great exploration with Mrs Nairs holding Pat's hand and Lerina and me closely following. We all talked and laughed with every footstep. We walked a route I'd never been before, passing huge marble buildings she named as the National Museum of Wales and the law courts of justice, and then the magnificent Cardiff Castle.

I understood what Pat meant when she had said it was huge, with walls at least twice the height of the playground. Cardiff's impressive castle is set in five acres behind fortified walls, parts of it are said to be the remains of Roman fortification over two thousand years old. The fifth Marques of Bute owned the castle until he bequeathed it to the city of Cardiff in nineteen forty-seven. The inherited legacy and influence of the Bute family is indicative by the titles of areas in most of Cardiff, like Bute Park, Butetown, Mount Stuart Square and Mount Stuart House. Sophia Gardens is named after the wife of the second Marquis of Bute.

We went to a multitude of shops buying an assortment of produce. One shop, in particular, stands out as I remember an enticing aroma assailing my nostrils as soon as I entered the door. It was a charming shop in an arcade containing a plethora of sausages hanging on strings from the ceiling like meaty decorations, while others dropped down in long coils like snakes about to explore the ground. The only sausage I had seen previously was Roly's chipolatas and the odd tasty small solid slab on a plate. Mrs Nairs seemed to know exactly what she wanted, soon her shopping bag was filled to the brim.

Mine and Pat's first-ever train journey from Cardiff General Station to Treforest lasted about half an hour, the trip interrupted by six stops. The first stop was Queen Street, the station we were to alight from the next evening. I calculated we would next be here, after thirty-two hours of relative freedom. The journey was captivating; as we snaked over rivers and road bridges with the train's smoke wafting past the windows as the scenery flashed by. We rattled and chugged through woodlands following the course of the River Taff, with the hillsides gradually getting steeper by the mile before eventually becoming mountains.

The train finally stopped at our destination, Treforest, a small village in a valley a mile away from the town of Pontypridd. We disembarked and began the ten-minute walk to the public house the Nairs managed. Well, it should have taken that time, but it took nearly an hour as Lerina couldn't wait to show us the little park. This was a beautiful park built in a small dingle, surrounded by woodland. It contained four swings dangling on eight-foot chains that were a thrill to ride, a roundabout and a slide, each of which would shame the ones back at the orphanage. While a happy Pat was pushing an excited Lerina. Mrs Nairs explained to me the reason behind Lerina's stay in Nazareth House.

"It was the longest ten weeks of my life," beginning her heart-breaking tale, she told me how she met her husband Gordon in her native country of Italy as world war two was ending. She first set eyes on the dashing army sergeant on Venice train station, when he was on his way home to Wales. They actually physically bumped into each other while rushing for their respective trains. She, to the small village where she lived called Piazza Vecchia, a mere four miles journey, while his destination was Treforest station one thousand one hundred miles from her parent's country cottage.

"Scusami signorina," he said in perfect Italian as they glanced into each other's eyes.

"It was love at first sight, for both of us," she said, the love she felt showing in her dark brown eyes.

I noted her olive skin was only a shade darker than Lerina as I pondered her words. Love at first sight? I thought it was highly unlikely at first, and then I remembered Roly.

After a whirlwind romance, he caught his train six weeks later, his new bride at his side. On arriving back home, his family were initially elated and then outraged, as he had been reported missing in action, presumed dead, during the time of their brief courtship. Mrs Nairs knew only a few words of English but could hear the anger in their voices and see the angry faces of the family. The family consisted of three boys, three girls, his mother and father, all living in a two-bedroom house. Mrs Nairs was a little annoyed with them. After all, he had been away fighting a war for four years, and that's how they treated him.

Once things settled down, they lived comfortably in the downstairs front room. Within a short while, Gordon found unsuitable employment doing a work he didn't enjoy.

She said she used to sit for long hours waiting for him to come home from his new job, a horrible dirty occupation, crushing bones for use in the pharmaceutical industry. Although the wages were better than most, and within six months, they had saved enough money to move out. They went to live with an old woman, his auntie, who was the widow of his father's brother but not before a big confrontation.

Some family members resented her presence; his sisters were best friends with the girl he courted before being conscripted into the army. From the beginning, she suspected they talked about her, even when she was present. So unknown to them, she began to learn how to speak

English, picking up the language's rudiments with the help of an Italian family who owned a local fish and chip shop. With their help, plus tuition from her Italian-speaking husband, she soon became proficient in English without them realising. She could now understand their conversations, confirming her suspicions; they were talking about her.

She kept this knowledge to herself until they had packed their bags. They were going out the front door when she turned around to the family, and said in English with a slight accent, something similar to: "Thank you for letting me stay with you. I have listened to you for months talking about me, not once did you say anything pleasant. You never tried to teach me your language, and you laughed at me. I will not forget this. Goodbye."

She smiled as she finished this part of the personal account of her life. I wondered why she was telling me the story. I'm glad she did, though.

Five children and many happy years later, doctors confirmed the husband she adored had contracted tuberculosis of the lungs, a contagious disease. Gordon was hastily transported to the Sully isolation hospital. The hospital and grounds overlooked the Bristol Channel; regrettably, it was situated twenty-odd miles and three bus journeys from Treforest. Only she knew the severity of his illness, so at first, she hadn't told him his ailment was rather dire as she didn't want to worry him further.

As a precaution, she and her five children were x-rayed. Doctors found two of her children had mild forms of the disease called latent tuberculosis. They transferred her eldest son Lorenzo, fourteen, to another isolation hospital, a cottage hospital in Merthyr Tydfil, twelve miles from Treforest and in the opposite direction to Sully. Their eldest daughter Sandra, eleven, was conveyed to a different hospital in Treherbert, again twelve miles in the reverse direction from Sully but up a different valley from Merthyr. To traverse to each hospital, having changed buses took up to three hours, added to which, if visiting times were added, some trips lasted at least six hours.

The committee members of the Public house the Nairs managed were sympathetically supportive, so they hired a steward to assist her during her visits to different hospitals. She only just coped with all the visiting, the daily running of the pub and looking after her three other children, Duncan, who was then nine and a bit of a handful, Stephen her second oldest son was twelve, and Lerina six years old, before another calamity occurred.

Stupid Stephen, she said wryly, slipped off a chair in the kitchen while getting plates out of the cupboard for him and his sibling's meal. That's a coincidence, I thought, remembering the time I fell off my chair and broken plates. She left a broth simmering on the gas stove while the potatoes and cabbage were bubbling away on another two rings. She had only been away for a minute to attend to something in the bar across the hall from their living quarters.

"He was only trying to help; he's a good boy, really. Without his help, I wouldn't have been able to manage," she said.

Stupid Stephen had slipped off the chair dragging the saucepan of boiling cabbage water with him, scolding his arm from his shoulder to his fingers and part of his chest, suffering second-degree burns to parts of his arm. They rushed him to hospital by ambulance, this time to East Glamorgan hospital, in another direction from the other three Hospitals and six miles from the pub. She went with him to the hospital, where his wound was dressed, then he was admitted to the children's ward.

"Even with all the pain he was in, all he said, over and over was; I'm sorry mam," she said, smiling proudly.

Once the painkillers and medication had taken effect, and he was feeling drowsy, she left to catch the last bus. During the half-hour bus journey, she tried to find an answer to her newest challenge. Duncan, as young as he was, could look after himself up to a point, though he couldn't look after Lerina in the way Stephen did. Perhaps she could find someone to look after them when she was visiting the hospitals, but no one came readily to mind.

She still had not found a satisfactory answer when she arrived back at the pub at closing time, just as Bryn, the temporary steward, was shutting the big double doors. At once, he told her she had a visitor. She entered to find it was the Catholic parish priest, her friend Father Doyle. He was a slight man with high, rosy red cheekbones, a permanent smile on his face, enclosed within a disproportionate head that appeared much more substantial than his body. He was wearing a fixed smile when she entered the room. He routinely popped by on his way back to the Parish house expediently around closing time, saying he had been visiting a sick person.

The two children had gone to bed and were sound asleep, so over a large brandy, the real reason for his visits, Father Doyle talked with her about the latest setback. After her courageous confrontation with her husband's family, they had all come to admire and respect the no-nonsense attitude of the proud Italian woman and her happy-go-lucky lively children, even so, she was too proud to ask them for help for they had their own lives to live.

Not long into the conversation, Mrs Nairs was being persuaded to follow a possible resolution to her dilemma. He had suggested putting the youngster in Nazareth House until she was ready for her return, telling her Lerina would be well looked after by the Mother Superior, saying she was a dear friend. They talked for about three or four brandies, with him extolling the virtues of Nazareth House, the notion slowly making more sense to Mrs Nairs.

Two days later Lerina was on her way to Nazareth House after being sworn to secrecy. Here Lerina was processed in the same way as everyone else, they hacked off her long shiny dark hair and replaced her clothes with Nazareth House attire, following the conditions made by the Mother Superior who had reluctantly agreed to Father Doyle's request. The hefty cash donation to Nazareth House was the major contributing factor to offset any valid objection or red tape problems.

Everything she told me started to make sense. The pieces of the jigsaw were now all in place. Lerina was happy because she knew her mother was coming back for her. When she asked me when her mother was coming for her, it was only because she just didn't know exactly when. I wondered when my mother would come back for me and thought it would be a lot longer than the longest ten weeks of my life. I mostly ended my prayers with, "Please send my mummy and daddy back."

I was glad she told me the story, I felt very proud that she did.

Stephen was in the hospital for three weeks and in a sling for another five. Lorenzo had come home a month after Stephen's stay in the hospital. Sandra came back a week after that. With another two of her journeys now obsolete, Mrs Nairs life had become more comfortable, so she fetched her darling daughter from Nazareth House. She had nothing but praise for the nuns and Nazareth House. I said nothing to dispel her belief. Though she was angry about the ridiculous haircut, Mrs Nairs looked very embarrassed when she realised what she had said.

"I'm sorry Milly I wasn't thinking," she said apologetically.

I laughed and said, "I've had much worse than that."

"I'm sure you have," she said sadly before continuing more brightly, "Do you know what? You're a gorgeous young girl. Your blue eyes, those high cheekbones and your lovely teeth, along with your gentle personality, will make you very well-liked with all the boys. And I'm going to cut your hair before church tomorrow."

I was tremendously flattered. I had never been told anything like that before, except for Mr Noland, who had mentioned my smile and my blue eyes.

"Boys, why would I want to be popular with boys?" I wondered aloud.

Mrs Nairs laughed, "Milly, please try to understand. I think you and Pat are adorable, clever children. And I'm very grateful to both of you for looking after Lerina. I've told you this story, so you will understand that even when circumstances and situations seem hopeless, have faith and pray, trust in God. It will get better for you in time, I promise you. Be patient Milly and have faith. My door will always be open for the two of you." She grinned broadly, displaying a perfect set of white teeth.

Those words were spoken to me as if I'd known her for years, yet it was only a matter of hours. I tried to absorb her words, it all started to make sense to me. I liked her more by the minute.

Pat was pushing Lerina on a swing that was getting dangerously high. Each time it returned, she leapt from the floor and pushed with all her might. When the swing reached ninety degrees to the ground, the chain became slack, causing the swing to fall back towards the ground with a resounding crash and a rattle of chains. Sounds of laughter bounced off the steep slopes around the park.

"She told me to do it," Pat colourfully explained, probably expecting an admonishment like back in the home.

Mrs Nairs smiled patiently, "She always likes the thrill of that. Her brothers have to push her all the time. They call it the point of no return. Come on then, let's get home."

We left the little park with a promise we would return the next day, and I, for one, was looking forward to it. We walked by the side of the gurgling river, through dense trees hosting noisy ravens nesting high up within the canopy, before stopping at a gap between the trees. There we stopped to gaze across the tranquil river Taff towards a large stone building on the other side of the river. It was five stories tall with large windows on all floors overlooking the river, at one side stone steps spiralled downwards towards the river some thirty feet below. In the middle of its garden, a hefty tree stood proud and tall, its branches and leaves stretching over the river and garden like a giant parasol.

"That's my house," declared Lerina proudly as Mrs Nairs smiled affectionately down at her.

"Wow," Pat and I said in unison.

We traversed rows of trees and in due course climbed up steep stone steps to the main road where the spectacle of the Catholic Church of Saint Dyfrigs welcomed us as we went through an iron kissing gate. From the outside the church was breath-taking; the entrance consisted of two large archways either side of a central half-domed roof, with each access covered by a slate roof joining the dome twenty-five feet above. On the wall above the half, dome a carved stone statue of a semi-naked body of Jesus Christ, his hands and feet nailed to the cross; his head slumped towards his chest in a posture demonstrating his sacrifice, dominated the frontage high above the entrances.

To gain entrance, we had to open two solid oak doors on gothic-style hinges. We entered to stand for a few minutes admiring the interior of the one hundred feet long and forty feet high structure. Mrs Nairs said building work on the church finished in nineteen twenty-seven and improvements were made in the nineteen fifties that included a new free-standing altar. The Church congregation numbered over two hundred, there were going to be two extra parishioners the next day.

"Come on, girls, you must be hungry by now," said Mrs Nairs bringing our brief stay to a conclusion.

Outside we ambled across a road bridge over the river from where we could see the garden of the public house. It was a short journey around the corner, up to a slight gradient until we arrived at a gravel driveway. That sloped down twenty feet to the pub's main entrance enclosed within outsized bay windows. Nearer I noticed the bottom sections of these were obscured by opaque glass. Peculiarly, on this side of the house, there were only three floors to the frontage, the second floor had a single-window jutting out from under the roof.

Ten yards to the right was the Glamorganshire canal that once gently flowed the twelve miles to Cardiff, bypassing Nazareth House ten yards to the left of our dormitory.

The big pub doors were open, so we entered to walk silently down a wide hallway, passing a doorway on the right. Just inside the room was a machine with a shiny Indian's head above a small glass window. We slipped into the empty room for a closer look, seeing the window was full of sixpenny coins, and above the Indian, another glass window had three reels with pictures of fruit on them. Lemon, orange, melons, cherries, are the ones I can remember. There was also a tac on one reel and on the other a tic. One side of the machine had a handle with a knob on the end of it, adding to my inquisitiveness.

"That's a one-armed bandit. It's a tic-tac-toe machine. You have to put in a sixpence to play to try and win money. Mammy plays it all the time." Lerina announced.

Mammy said, "Come on chops. Show the girls the bedroom and come down after. Oh, and don't forget to wash your hands," she said as an afterthought.

The bedroom was spacious with two double beds in each corner, opposite were two large wardrobes, their doors wide open, revealing an abundance of children's clothing with shoes of different colours on shelves. More variations than I had seen in my life except for a clothes store. Between the wardrobes stood a big dressing table with a large oval swivelled mirror, with hairbrushes and various unidentifiable grooming objects scattered over its surface.

"That's my bed, and that's Sandra's," said Lerina pointing to the sizeable beds. "There are camp beds for you two, but mammy said we could all sleep in my bed if you want?"

We looked at each other, smiled, and nodded. On realising the symmetry, we both laughed, which had the effect of making us all laugh. Even though it had been almost two years since Lerina's abrupt disappearance, our mutual camaraderie confirmed our rock-solid friendship.

Laughter filled the bedroom for the next half an hour. The thick carpet muffled the sound of our heavy boots, unlike the constant thud of boots on wooden floors back the nursery. The bright curtains and decor were unerring as I imagined a child's bedroom to be. My bedroom, I thought.

The bathroom was white and bright and smelt like roses. A big mirror over the wash-hand basin reflected our images; three young girls smiled back, two girls in ill-fitting and bawdy attire and one girl with perfect clothes and hair. Embarrassed, I quickly glanced away to avoid my reflection. I washed my hands, I desperately tried to shake the strange feeling from my mind. I was excited, apprehensive and flummoxed all at the same time.

Love at first sight

The aroma that greeted my nostrils as we entered the living quarters for the first time was extraordinarily appetising and welcoming.

"Steve, here they are. Milly and Pat." Lerina said excitedly, pointing at us as she spoke our names.

I looked at the fourteen-year-old boy who smiled at us, I stared into the deep, bright brown eyes beneath long dark eyelashes, his looks hypnotised me. His glossy dark brown, almost black hair was slightly longer than mine, his tall frame and acquiescent demeanour was coupled with the healthy glow on his olive skin. The handsome boy with a striking kind face stared back as if amused.

There was a strange reaction to my very being. I felt what muscles I had in my body surge and contract brusquely. I felt numb and unresponsive as though I would swoon. The handsome face came into focus, then blurred like a camera lens, zooming in and out; my knees started involuntarily crashing into each other. I was tongue-tied and couldn't say a word, I sensed Pat's amusement.

"Hi, nice to meet you," she said, freeing me from what was getting an embarrassing situation. She knew me better than anyone in the world.

Thanks, I thought and knew she received the subtle message.

"Hello," was all I eventually came up with.

Later on, the six of us sat down for, tea. The first time I had heard the word being used.

With our heads bowed, and hands together, Mrs Nairs started the proceedings with an Italian delivery of grace.

"Bless us O Lord and these gifts we are about to receive. Amen."

I could barely speak during the most delicious meal I had ever tasted in my life. At intervals, I cast furtive glances at the boy admiring every little detail, his lovely voice, the beautiful accent, the gentle way he spoke, the way he ate his food, how he held his fork. Images of us together showered my imagination. What the heck is going on with me?

I could sense Pat's relief as I slowly regained some of my composure and conversed more sensibly than the monosyllabic nonsense of the preceding ten minutes.

The meal was indisputably fantastic, spaghetti bolognese with garlic bread, neither of which I had ever tried before nor tasted as good since. Lerina showed us how to eat it by twirling the spaghetti with a fork onto her spoon. The garlic bread was crunchy, with a rich taste that embraced my taste buds. They held the entire meal in a friendly atmosphere, with mild chiding and a pointing finger the only rebuke, followed with amiable laughter at any of our accidents. I instantly forgot any embarrassment in the relaxing atmosphere of the family table. When we were finished, there were red chins and slightly stained blouse casualties even though serviettes were used.

Mister Nairs was a quiet, polite man who still looked thin and frail; although he was well on the road to recovery and was working more or less full-time. Sandra was an amusing, intelligent-looking pretty girl who joined the friendly banter with warm enthusiasm, though she also looked pale and somewhat fragile. Tuberculosis is a debilitating infectious disease that can sometimes take years to recover from.

The delicious meal finished we sat on the settee watching television while drinking orangeade until Mrs Nairs said it was eight o'clock, the time for us to go to bed and for her to open the upstairs bar.

It was later than our regular bedtime, I was tired and feeling the after-effects of the long day. To our glee, Mrs Nairs handed Pat and me small bundles of clothes, each an assortment of clean cotton coloured garments.

"These were Sandra's they don't fit her any more. I hope you like them, now off you go to bed."

We climbed the stairs hearing sounds of a multitude of simultaneous conversations and laughter, as the pub was becoming busier, the acrid smell of cigarette smoke and beer following us. Lerina explained Saturday night was the concert and bingo night with dancing and singing.

"On the weekends, Mammy runs the upstairs bar and Daddy works the downstairs bar," she informed us like the perfect guide.

We changed into our nightshirts while Lerina put on an enviable cute red nightdress. All of a sudden, she pointed excitedly to our bundle of clothes with a twinkle in her almond eyes, a broad grin creasing her olive face. Investigating the clothes, I found a beautiful blue nightdress. Pat was equally delighted when she explored hers and was soon quickly changing into her pink nighty.

Minutes later, the three of us were sitting cross-legged on the clean, fragrant big comfortable bed, giggling, looking as I imagined typical preteens did, talking and enjoying life. I thought of the little ones back in the orphanage and the tales we'd tell them. I loved every single second of our brief sojourn into family life.

Tired as we were, we remained awake. Three heads peeped through a gap in the slightly open bedroom door watching the limited activity through the double doors. From our vantage point, we could see a throng of smiling people carrying trays of empty glasses and then returning with full, frothy beer filled ones. The accompanying sounds of cordial conversations and laughter made me feel happy and relaxed.

An amplified voice announced the bingo was about to start. The silence that ensued was instant, almost like when a nun would appear.

Later that night, through the now closed-door, after a muted telling off from Mrs Nairs, three contented little girls lay side by side in bed, listening to the tipsy valley folk thoroughly enjoying life. By now, Sandra was in a deep slumber in her bed. It was the last hour before closing time, the time when the customers would show off their musical prowess. Though some were less tuneful than they thought, making us laugh when a particularly tuneless participator performed.

Then when the amplified voice stated it was last orders please, there were chants of, Diana, Diana and Diana, followed by the sounds of stamping feet. A few moments later, there was rapturous applause, the loudest of the night, as a woman's voice began to echo through the loudspeakers singing *Goldfinger*, the theme song from the new James Bond film sung by Shirley Bassey. It was such a powerful and emotive performance it sent a shiver down my spine. The applause when the final tune had barely finished eclipsed the previous one by a hundred decibels it seemed.

"That was mammy," Lerina said nonchalantly, the pride on her face revealing her real emotions.

So Mrs Nairs first name was Diana, a beautiful name for an attractive person I thought.

The last song of the night, before the merry revellers departed to their homes, was a mass sing-along of *Pennies from Heaven*, accompanied by the sounds of tinkling penny coins landing on the floor after each chorus.

I had never ever slept in a bed with anyone before that night. I found it strange and was somewhat pleasantly uncomfortable. With the sudden silence and after a long day, sleep was not difficult to achieve. Though not before Mrs Nairs had poked her head around the door to check on us, only to find three tired girls in their pretty nightdresses kneeling at the side of the bed, their hands together to their faces thanking God for the day.

"Goodnight girls," she emphasised as we jumped into bed, she clicked the light switch off and closed the door.

I'd been thinking about Stephen on and off since our first encounter. I just couldn't get him out of my mind. I was pleasantly puzzled. I also had the thought that throughout the day, there had been no telling offs, to have such an admonishment free period was a refreshing feeling. I was asleep moments later.

I woke up at the first sign of daylight with the sound of birds welcoming the dawn and the sun chasing the darkness away through the curtains. I had had a restful invigorating night's sleep in the most comfortable bed in the world. I felt elated and energised. My mind went straight to Stupid Stephen. I smiled when I remembered I'd dreamt about him during the night, he was pushing me on a swing, I was laughing as he pushed me higher and higher.

"What are you smiling at?" Pat whispered at me. I hadn't noticed she was awake.

"I just remembered yesterday," I whispered.

"Best day of my life," Pat said in a hushed voice.

"Me too," I mouthed mutely.

We slipped out of bed, leaving Lerina and Sandra to their dream worlds, and silently said our prayers. I found myself inadvertently asking God to take care of Stephen. I shook my head vigorously in an attempt to get him out of my confused mind, I was getting worried I didn't know what was happening. I answered Pat's questioning expression with a scrunched up nose. We retrieved our toothbrushes, paste and beakers and went without a sound out towards the bathroom. The door suddenly opened, making us jump back.

"Good morning, ladies. The bathroom's free," the voice of Stephen quietly said.

My knees responded by osculating back and fore, thankfully unseen just above the hemline of my blue nightdress.

His bright liquid eyes looked down at us, slowly taking in the image before him, he sexily whispered, "Very nice, see you later." before walking away.

"You really, really like him, don't you?" Pat said as we looked at our frothy toothpaste selves in the bathroom mirror, my blushing face told both of us the answer.

Lerina was awake when we returned.

"It's only half-past six you nutters," she said affectionately.

"Stephen is up," we said simultaneously and defensively.

The three of us burst out laughing, comfortable in each other's company.

"He sweeps up, mops the floors and stocks up while mammy and daddy have a sleep in," Lerina explained.

Sandra said in a friendly sleepy voice, "That's what I want to do, so shut up."

Lerina put on a stylish, comfy looking woollen pink dressing gown. While she tied a bow around her middle; she slipped her bare feet inside elegant fluffy warm looking matching slippers. An image of boots and an oversized starched vest came to mind.

Downstairs in the empty kitchen, we watched as Lerina put half a dozen eggs in a large, water-filled saucepan, placing it on the gas stove. Amusingly, she struck a red ended piece of wood against the sandpapered matchbox, then tossed the lit match at the escaping hissing gas underneath the saucepan, immediately jumping back a step as the gas ignited with a decisive pop. Using the same method, the eye-level grill burst into flames, four slices of bread were gingerly slid under the fire. When the water started to boil, she turned over a glass egg timer, the little grains of sand filtered through a tapered neck to the other side. When all the sand is gone from the top, they are cooked she explained. Pat and I were astounded.

We ate soft-boiled eggs, with crispy toast she had cut into small strips or soldiers as she called them. We dipped the soldiers in the perfectly boiled eggs, they were delicious. Not only was it another first for both of us, but we also agreed later it was the best breakfast we had ever eaten, we only ever had tasteless hard-boiled eggs and soggy toast. Lerina said the breakfast was courtesy of their chickens.

Lerina went to get washed and changed, while on our insistence we washed and dried the dishes. We were almost back at the bedroom door when we heard muffled sounds emanating from the concert room. Intrigued, we walked cautiously to the open door and found Stephen there, busily cleaning the one hundred seat concert room. Evidence of the previous night's festivities was strewn over the twenty-something wooden tables and floors. The smell of stale cigarette smoke and beer filled the room.

My heart skipped a beat as my stomach did somersaults. My mind was totally in turmoil. My skinny knees joining in only added to my confusion. What was this boy doing to my being? Fortunately, I quickly regained some of my self-control.

Despite his protestations, we insisted on helping with the clean-up, after all, we were expert cleaners after our years of enforced practice. I noticed Stephen give an occasional frown when working. And when Pat playfully asked him if the work was too hard, he replied no, but he had injured his shoulder playing rugby the previous day. Both of us nodded sympathetically. Like we knew what rugby was?

We emptied butt-filled ashtrays into a cardboard box, but not before he had examined the cigarette packets.

"They sometimes leave a few," he explained as he retrieved a single cigarette from a discarded twenty pack. With a twinkle in his desirable eyes, and just like sister Sandra the day before, he put a finger to his lips, saying, "Shush." Quietly indicating he wanted closure on our secret.

Lips I wanted to kiss. What was I thinking? What's happening to me? I couldn't comprehend what was happening with my emotions; I was befuddled and elated.

Ashtrays washed, his pocket three cigarettes richer, we stacked chairs seat down on top of the clean tables, effectively clearing the floors for an obstacle-free sweep. While he went off to fill a galvanised mop bucket with warm soapy water, I had a chance to talk with Pat. We were in total agreement as to this being the best time of our lives, although she spoiled it a smidgen by saying, "What's with the knees? And stop staring at him like you're looking at a cute little puppy dog like you do with Roly."

We swept the floors of discarded losing bingo tickets and floor stubbed cigarette ends, while Stephen mopped the floors behind us, gradually progressing towards the raised stage containing all the paraphernalia required to entertain the customers. Coins littered the dance floor in front of the stage.

Stephen elucidated. "They do it every week; the last song is *pennies from heaven*. So they toss pennies in the air."

We all laughed, I looked from a beaming Pat to the shining olive-skinned handsome face of the boy smiling warmly back at me, an image etched in my mind forever. I was in Heaven, thinking it was indeed better than the near Hell I was used to. Lerina came in and helped in the final part of cleaning, stacking the coins on a table as we finished sweeping the last remnants away.

Stephen generously sorted the money into four equal piles. He stared at me and started to speak when I returned his gaze a warm, comfortable sensation engulfed my body.

"Dad always says, any money you find this side of the bar you can keep. So it's all right." Still eyeing me, he continued, "And to me, that means other things as well." He finished by giving me a right-eyed, you know what I mean, gorgeous wink.

In response, I made an involuntary incomprehensible gurgle. Pat howled with laughter at me. Thankfully Stephen thought it was his joke, which was funny. I joined in the laughter, feeling slightly embarrassed. I gave Pat an elbowed prod in the ribs, she smiled playfully in response.

Later that morning, we descended the stone steps to the cold cellars beneath the pub. Sounds of clucking chickens caught our ears as we passed through heavy transparent plastic curtains that sealed instantly behind us. To the right, through another set of curtains, I could see a spotlessly clean cellar. Inside was a multitude of wooden beer barrels resting on wooden trestles and rubber hoses trailing neatly across the flagstone floor. Further back, various stainless steel pieces of equipment were lined up neatly on a long wooden table.

"We are not allowed to go in there," Lerina said.

We went down more stone steps to the floor below, the clucking getting louder. Lerina handed Pat a small wicker basket which had a cane curved handle as we went through another set of curtains, to be met by a maze of doors and curtains. Lerina went through a door and returned with a wooden scoop full to the brim.

"Chicken feed," she said, handing me the surprisingly heavy object.

Out in the flagstone courtyard, clucking sounds were getting even louder. Lerina opened the top section of a stable door. We peered over the top and could see the nodding heads of chickens, which were excitedly dashing around as though impatient of waiting. She flung open the door with a flourish. The birds rushed crazily towards her. Pat and I took three steps backwards as the chickens rushed at us, flapping their wings clucking even more enthusiastically.

"Chic chic chic chic," Lerina chanted.

We looked at each other, laughing at the apparent ritual as she grabbed a handful of food from my scoop to scatter over the floor.

The birds darted towards the offerings, reminding me of the kids back in the orphanage, forming a queue for food. While it was frightening at first, Pat and I relished in tossing the feed, first one way then the other, the manic chickens following our every move. After they had eaten the final handful, we went into the barn and took still warm eggs out of the straw-filled nests scattered on shelves and bales, placing them carefully in the basket. Lerina started to clean the barn, raking the floor and shovelling bird droppings and straw into a galvanised bin.

"Daddy uses that in the garden," she said, finishing by throwing buckets of water from the outside tap over the floor and sweeping it away with a hard-bristled broom. I had wondered why she was wearing wellingtons. We, however, were in our everyday clothing complete with our clod hopper boots.

We continued down more spiralling stone steps towards the river where we explored the garden, especially the fenced-off vegetable patch containing table food that Lerina expertly identified, mindful of not stepping on the chickens who wandered freely around clucking contentedly as they pecked at the ground. They were as free as we were. I was so happy, I thought of Heaven and the Garden of Eden. His smiling winking face came to mind, my own smiling face caught Pat's eye. She tut-tutted looked skywards to the top of the big tree and walked away with a smirk.

Lerina pointed to a big speckled brown feathered chicken and said, "We are going to have that one today."

I was only half-listening, my thoughts elsewhere, and Stephen still in my mind's eye. From high up, Mrs Nairs shouted in a friendly tone; it was time to get ready for church.

Lerina bathed, while Pat and I sat at the dressing table in the bedroom, looking at our reflections as Mrs Nairs skilfully clipped away at our hair, subtly changing our appearance. I couldn't believe the transformation; finally, a pretty bow completed our almost unrecognisable images. We were little girls for now.

She returned our blouses now washed and bolognese free, we left for the bathroom and bathed. We shampooed our hair, later replacing the bows on our gleaming scented hair.

Feeling comfortable, confident and wearing some clothes borrowed from Sandra, who wasn't going to Mass, we strolled contentedly hand in hand to the church. This was simplicity even ordinary to them. To me, it was pure bliss. I knew nothing of comfort and love. I considered the previous two days abnormal. My life in the orphanage was normal.

Mrs Nairs introduced us as, Lerina's friends, to a few of the smartly dressed congregation before entering the church; in return, they acknowledged us warmly, of all the cheerful faces. There wasn't pity in any of the eyes, our clothes and hair made us appear as ordinary children, our boots were discreetly unnoticed. I liked the reaction, for the second time in my life, I experienced pride.

I glanced around the grandiose church from my pew location next to the aisle. In front of me was the majestic altar and above it, silver candelabras hung high above the crucifix and chalices. Father Doyle stood in his pristine gold and silver robes, surrounded by six altar boys wearing black or red cassocks, each one adorned by a crisp white crocheted surplice. I noticed one altar boy was looking directly at me with a slight smile on his face and hilarity in his familiar languid eyes. My whole body jolted, and the pew juddered.

Faces and eyes turned my way as my face turned red, feeling it could have lit Lerina's gas stove until Stephen turned away to concentrate. After that, I reminded myself I didn't need to be so furtive, and I watched him perform his saintly duties unnoticed. At the end of the hour-long Mass, we placed half of our pennies on the silver collection plate as it was passed from one person to another.

We met the eccentric Father Doyle after the service, a little later joined by Stephen, who was now dressed in his smart civilian clothes. After exchanging pleasantries, Mrs Nairs left to go back to cook the Sunday lunch, leaving Stephen to escort three happy girls to the little park.

Who says dreams don't come true? I thought ecstatically as the boy of my dreams pushed me on the swing next to my friends. I laughed, we all laughed. It was, indeed, heavenly.

Sunday lunch came and went in a flash as the hours tumbled by in a happy miasma. Duncan was staying with his best friend, and Lorenzo was playing cricket, so they missed a lunch, which was the most delicious I've ever experienced. It was a *Grande Festa*, Mrs Nairs declared as she served the carved meat and served vegetables from large oval tureens.

The chicken was delicious remarked Mr Nairs. Sandra, Stephen, Pat and I agreed it was indeed succulent. As was the entire Sunday lunch. Though strangely, Lerina appeared to be unhappy and was unusually quiet. It was only later as we were getting ready to leave she told us, the meat, the chicken we had eaten for Sunday lunch, was Gertrude, the speckled feathered chicken we had fed that morning. I was utterly traumatised, I never considered where meat came from before. Pat nearly retched. Nobody said a word for a long time as we digested her words and unfortunately, poor Gertrude.

Later we said an emotional farewell when we were dressed in our orphan clothing. Though this time we were wearing blouses that had never been so white before, our hair was coiffed and bowed, with new clothes filling our satchels. Mrs Nairs was taking us back alone as Lerina had school the next morning and hadn't done her homework yet.

"Besides, I want to see a friend in Cardiff," she added.

We hugged for an eternity, scared to be the first to loosen our grip, frightened, meaningful this might be our last meeting. We eventually untangled, Stephen said goodbye to Pat and pecked her cheek. Then he turned to me, his eyes on fire, he stooped down and kissed me, a gentle, tender kiss close to my mouth, so near I could feel his warm breath on my lips. My cheeks were like a furnace, it felt as though he could have charred his desirable lips on my scorching face.

"Take care. I hope to see you again," he gushed beaming.

I hope and pray we do, I thought, my knees knocked in concurrence.

As we walked to the train station, a tear escaped my eye and trickled past my nose, the first in a long time. Pat kept her face away from me. I suspected to hide her misty eyes.

The coincidences that recently occurred mystified me, like the children being named Duncan and Sandra. Mrs Nairs saying, so you're the two angels that looked after my little girl and then Stephen falling off a chair in the kitchen. It seemed almost otherworldly.

The reality of the situation between the outsiders and us abruptly came into a sharper focus during our brief stay. What they considered a regular routine was unnatural to us. A pure pleasure, like walking to a new church for a service on a Sunday was forbidden, as though we might make a break for it and claim sanctuary.

Wearing the same clothes and haircuts that made us look like outcasts from another world, stopped us evolving in a society that was changing daily. Wales was in the singing, swinging sixties, we were stuck in the stoic fifties. The gulf between our peers and us in Cardiff was widening. All the outsiders had to do was switch on a television or a radio to enhance their dreams of a better life, while we turned sheets, made beds and cleaned to ensure we had some sort of existence. And there was nothing we could do unless we were adopted or reunited with our families.

We both experienced a deep-seated depression after our visit to Treforest. The jubilation we had fleetingly felt soon dissipated once we were back to the reality of our dismal existence; the experiences we enjoyed on our trip to a Heaven were effortlessly overwhelmed by the hell we had to endure daily. It was as though we realised we never had the opportunity to become ordinary children, for in the nursery we were used as little mothers instead.

We never recovered, humdrum days slowly but surely passed. The clothes Mrs Nairs gave us were never seen again. I busied myself within the nursery, terrified I would become emotionally attached to any child. Though it was inevitable I did; my emotions were up and down like the rollercoaster at Barry Island, where we went each year, none more joyous than our first one. It was quite a few months before I settled down. Stephen was still on my mind. I became almost obsessed, but it wasn't torturous anymore.

I viewed the memories with affection and regret. Pat and I would imagine and chatter about living together in a big house or a castle with a mum and dad. We still both talked of the Nairs family with fondness, wondering when or if we would ever see them again, so our first choice of a family was always living at their big home, with Lerina and Stephen, our stepbrother and stepsister. My own thoughts regarding Stephen took another direction, I knew then I loved him, and that he would be forever in my heart. Pat and I both knew that a conclusion to a happy ending was unlikely, so we reverted to our original daydreams and imagined our father would be a famous actor; Errol Flynn was my choice, Pat's favourite was always Robert Taylor.

Freedom Beckons

This was my eighth year in Nazareth house and my second year back in the nursery. I was used to the tediousness now; it had been my home from the first day except for the short period when I was twelve.

Even though Pat and I didn't share a dormitory, we were still inseparable and as close as ever. We talked about living and working with each other when we were released. We had been the best of friends for eight years. Eight years of looking out for each other. She was like a sister to me, more so than my own sister. I couldn't imagine my life without Pat.

We both started counting down the days before our freedom from Nazareth House. We had decided to share a flat somewhere in the city. We planned to work together as waitresses and go out every night.

I celebrated my coming of age, for I was now a teenager. I say, celebrated. Sister Sandra smuggled a sponge jam and cream cake into the nursery after school. She, Pat and the eleven little ones sang happy birthday to me and we all shared the cake.

Sister Sandra by now was one of our best friends, we had mutual trust, she wasn't a 'them' anymore, and she would confide in us many secrets of the home.

Two weeks later we celebrated Pat's thirteenth birthday in the same fashion.

There were a few kiddies in the nursery who were vulnerable, unhappy children. I tried my best with them, it helped that Sister Sandra was a wonderful, caring nun. I did notice that after her arrival, we never had many kids younger than five. I don't know why, but it made my life more comfortable, and sometimes I felt as if I wasn't needed in the nursery.

The summer holiday trip to Barry Island, as usual, was fantastic, the freedom exciting and memorable. I asked Sister Sandra if Pat, Natalie, Stacy and Beryl who had a bed next to Pat, could help and join us on the first coach, she dutifully obliged, even organising for Mr Noland to join us. He made sure we had a great time. He must have spent a fortune, spoiling us with many treats, including ice cream and my first ever jam doughnut.

Now, we were both thirteen and attending class 2C. Pat was back to her natural cheery disposition, and she had developed into a shapely young woman. She was much taller and fuller than I, unlike me, she filled out her clothes. With her slim waist, her shapely legs and ample breasts, she became the envy of most of the girls.

Pat loved the reaction she was receiving from the boys at school and the home. It was probably because of this attention she started to become more aware of her looks. So it was no surprise she hated her National Health Service round glasses, vowing she would buy a new pair as soon as she escaped. I had the means to help fulfil her wishes, but I couldn't find a solution. I told Mr Noland of my intention.

He smiled and said, "I'll think of something Blue. Leave it to me."

I was still the skinny Nazi, as the Mostyn school crowd would call me, not five feet tall yet and weighing about six stone.

"You're as flat as a pancake," Pat would often chide.

A change to my routine occurred when Greta and I were selected by a family. We both went to Porthcawl, a seaside resort twenty-five miles from Nazareth House, to stay in a large static caravan for seven days with a Catholic family of five.

I felt genuinely sorry for Greta; she was tall and had high cheekbones like my own. With a decent cut to her blonde hair, she could easily be regarded as attractive. During the only seven full days and nights we ever had together, I noticed with some concern she had some strange traits and characteristics. She was miserable and unapproachable she appeared lost in her own world. I often had to drag her back to reality when she was preoccupied with some thought, standing with an open-mouthed expression that made her appear gormless. She hardly conversed with me or the narcissistic family.

I couldn't blame her for that because they were dreadful. We were treated like skivvies. We had to sleep on a hard sandy floor in our clothes, cook their breakfast, wash dishes, and in general, we were treated like slaves, we were expected to wait on them hand and foot. The whole experience was uncomfortable, unpleasant and stressful. The family did nothing but argue. They were a spiteful miserable family, both Greta and I disregarded them in the tense atmosphere with relative ease. We hardly spoke to each other for the entire week. Greta and I were really strangers to each other; on reflection, I suppose it was relatively sad.

We went to the funfair with them on three separate days, we watched as they went on all the thrilling-looking rides, each time callously not offering either of us the opportunity to accompany them. I didn't enjoy myself; I missed Pat and couldn't wait to get back.

Another occasion was just as miserable. I stayed with a family from Caerphilly, a town only six miles from Cardiff. A municipality famous for its cheese and a thirteenth-century medieval fortified castle and moat set within thirty acres of grassland and said to be the largest in Wales and the second largest in Britain.

I didn't like the family. The mother was condescending, the father had a look of insincerity he eventually confirmed. The couple had twin daughters who were a few years younger than me, both of whom completely ignored me at first. Natalie had warned me about them. She stayed with this family a few months before; she told me they were a bunch of ratbags, coming soon to the conclusion she was right. I only stayed with them for the one night; I don't think I made a great impression on them. I was back in the orphanage early on Sunday morning.

I explicitly remember entering their big beautiful home, where, unlike the enticing aroma that welcomed me to the Nairs house; a disgusting smell hit me like a brick. No sooner was I through the door, when they had me washing piles of dirty dishes stacked in the sink. After that, I had to clean the two girls' bedroom, picking up the toys and clothing scattered all over the messy room. I cleaned the bathroom, wiped the tide marks from the sides of the bath. I scrubbed the downstairs toilet. When I finished the polishing, the patronising Mr Ratbag inspected the results of my labour and declared the work satisfactory.

Mrs Ratbag said, "Mm the stew is almost ready, I hope you're hungry Milly."

We sat down for lunch, five unappetising bowls full of steaming stew in front of us. We all thanked God for thy bounty, ending with a truly grateful Amen. I stared at the offering without any gratitude whatsoever, it looked and smelt disgusting. I felt sick just looking at the messy mass seeing rainbows in the layer of fat floating on the surface. I watched them eating the food as if they had just come off an enforced diet. Mr Ratbag, with a mouthful of food still in his mouth, asked me if there was anything wrong. I shook my head and lifted a spoonful into my mouth. It was dreadful, worse than the worst food in the home, which incidentally, was our version of stew. I forced another mouthful and looked up to see them stuffing their faces. They ate like pigs, each of them displaying the contents in their open mouths as they chewed noisily. Try as I might I couldn't even swallow my second mouthful. Mr Ratbag asked me again if I was all right. I shook my head, jumped off the chair and rushed to the downstairs toilet where I was violently sick

Mrs Ratbag rapped on the door, "Are you ok in there, Milly?"

Being honest, "No, I've just been sick."

"Do you mean my stew is not to your liking?" she said pompously.

A lengthy strained, tense atmosphere continued until bedtime, the two girls hated me and said as much. I was used to listening to vile insults and successfully blotted out their venom with thoughts of Stephen, Lerina, the Nairs, mums, dads and castles.

They couldn't wait to get me back to the home the following morning, thankfully it was before breakfast, and I couldn't wait to eat half-decent food again.

Pat was due back the same day as me. To our mutual surprise, she had been picked out on auction day to stay with a lovely friendly family. Like me, she couldn't believe it when it happened after all those years of being overlooked. She had become hardened to accepting a full life within the confines of the home. The trip to

Treforest had been her only excursion into the outside world without a nun's supervision.

Pat moved again, she was now in another all-girl dormitory, most of them were two or three years younger than me. The girls were all mature, unlike me, most of them wore brassieres. Unluckily for Pat, it was managed by Sister Terry. Pat wasn't her usual rascally self. It was a period in which both nuns and inmates bullied her. Beryl had moved with her their beds were either side of a very affable girl called Maria. Pat related the most horrendous anecdotes, for she and Beryl were constant targets for abuse. Their chief persecutors were Sister Terry and the leader of the tormenters, Brenda, a violent blonde-haired thug. Brenda, with the vicious snarl and the nun with the merciless sneer, was a match made in hell.

Initially, Brenda's arrival about a year before was welcomed by all the girls including Pat, Natalie and one punch Gloria. Not long after her arrival, I delivered something to Sister Terry in the dormitory, I was chatting to Pat when we were distracted by a loud squabble between Brenda and Gloria. Brenda soon proved to be a match for Gloria and defeated her in the ugly brawl that followed, a fight witnessed by all of us, including the nun. Gloria had no opportunity to deliver her trademark punch. It was all over in a few seconds. A blow to her face and a punch to her stomach, left her lying defeated on the floor, a dribble of blood seeping from her nose.

Sister Terry could hardly contain her sadistic pleasure as she slithered down the now quiet dormitory, sounds of Gloria sobbing punctuating the tense atmosphere. She unbuckled the leather belt around her middle and in a frenzied assault proceeded to attack both fighters, firstly with the strap end and then the buckle end. Sister Terry became uncontrollably careless, and both girls were cut and bruised on the arms and legs. As a consequence, they needed to miss school until the cuts healed, and the bruises had faded.

Beryl was a timid, reserved girl, who had been in the home from the age of three. She was about two years older than me. Pat said that Beryl looked after her when she was first in the nursery, they were very much alike in stature and appearance as both wore National Health spectacles. Beryl was also slightly deaf, a disability the nuns and especially Brenda mocked. Children who were thought to be different were bullied by both kids and nuns. The nuns appeared to have the idea that a person's physical appearance determined their personality.

I'm sure the callous nuns initiated all the nicknames, like poor Conks who had a large nose, a tall skinny girl whose narrow face made the appendage appear much more extensive. Then there was Bugs, so-called after Bugs Bunny. She was another tall, slim girl with sallow cheeks who had a bony pointed nose, with two exceptional front teeth that hung over her bottom lip like two adjacent tombstones in a graveyard. She must have heard the phrase, "What's up, Doc?" a million times. They called Pat and Beryl four eyes and me skinny or goody two shoes.

Peggy was a quiet, introvert, attractive dark-haired girl who was in the home for only about a year. She looked uncannily like her twin brother, particularly when sporting a similar haircut. The trousers he wore and her gait were the only noticeable differences. Peggy, whose real name I've forgotten from lack of use, was knocked down by a car when she was three years old. The severity of the injury resulted in the amputation of her lower left leg, which was cut off just below her knee. We knew when she was in the vicinity, for the approaching sound of her prosthetic leg knocking on the polished parquet floor was like the metronomic sound of a ticking clock, announcing her imminent arrival. Her false limb resembled an upside-down sink plunger, the type used to unblock sinks. She was initially called Tic Toc or Peg Leg but this changed over time, to Peggy.

Another girl was Squinty who evidently needed spectacles. She would examine most objects through the tiny slits of her eyes. Most of the kids would look at her and not the television on telly days.

Marie Phillips, a girl who was a veracious intelligent dark-haired, lively young girl, almost a woman, had the bed next to Pat. She was coming to the end of her time after many years in the home and was being prepared for her release into the outside world. Employment and lodgings were already in place for her. She had complained of recurring headaches for months and months. In response, the nuns dispensed orange coloured junior aspirin for her. Pat would often whine to me about Maria disturbing her sleep.

Dramatic weight loss and a grey pallor finally alerted the ignorant nuns to the severity of her ailment. Eventually, a doctor was summoned. He immediately admitted Maria to the hospital where she died of a brain tumour haemorrhage three weeks beyond her release date. She was only fifteen. As far as I know, no one attended her funeral, for it was not conducted by Nazareth House as she was no longer their responsibility.

Pat told me that one day Sister Terry had beat Beryl with her belt because she thought she was being rude and had ignored her. The hateful nun didn't realise it was a result of her deafness. And, as though this was not enough punishment, she locked the terrified girl in a dark cupboard for an hour, after telling her there was a mouse in there that would crawl up her leg.

Beryl's beseeching muffled screams and sobs fell on deaf ears. On her release from the claustrophobic tomb, she collapsed to the floor, gasping for breath. Disparate wheezing noises accompanying her heaving chest. The nun's fearful face informed the witnesses that Beryl was in serious trouble. An ambulance arrived quickly, they rushed her to the Heath hospital a two-minute ride away. Sister Terry's actions had triggered a severe asthma attack that nearly killed Beryl, who had never suffered asthma before that day. Asthma and claustrophobia have plagued Beryl's life ever since. Sister Terry remained blameless and soon returned to performing her cruel ways.

I realised just how lucky I was, closeted away from the daily brutality, safely tucked away within the boundaries of the nursery. I was sometimes mistreated and occasionally suffered physical abuse like a pinch or nudge, though that was, in general, the only punishment I received. I never experienced any physical abuse when in the presence of Sister Sandra.

Pat, however, intermittently continued to suffer from the harassment. She wasn't a weakling by any means, was of the same proportions as her two chief tormentors Brenda and Gloria. Though, not having either the brutality or the experience of fisticuffs, she put up with the bullying, until one day.

I was passing the senior recreation section one evening when my attention was distracted by a loud commotion emanating from within. Inside Gloria, who loved her role as one of the home's bullies, was goading and pushing a slightly bored-looking Pat around, whilst in the background, the other girls were watching and waiting for the usual grand finale. I shouted to Gloria to stop. She instantly forgot her quarry and turned around to face me, then strode menacingly towards me, her fresh prey, clenching her right hand into a fist. My skinny knees danced. But I was ready for her, Pat and I were both prepared, we had trained long enough.

"I've had just about enough of you, you bitch," Pat suddenly shouted.

Gloria immediately stopped and turned around to confront Pat. Gloria's face contorted into pure evil. In a rage, she jumped the few steps towards Pat, who stood her ground looking unconcerned. Gloria was poised ready to strike, and typically, such was her speed, power and force she would have knocked Pat twenty feet away. However, Pat was prepared. Like with all our other triumphs, we had practised how to react to different situations. We knew about Gloria's methodical one punch and the warning signs. We held many practice bouts in the nursery playground, a couple of times, she didn't duck quickly enough, and I ended up clouting her temple, as she did to me, which was Gloria's ultimate target.

Pat dipped her shoulders and dodged the swinging fist, she straightened up and slammed her own clenched fist directly into the bully's solar plexus. The air whooshed out of her mouth. Everything was going to plan, Gloria instinctively doubled up. As an innovation, something not part of the script, Pat brought up her knee to meet the still sneering face of Gloria. The sickening sound of her nose cracking on Pat's knee brought about screams from the watching girls. Gloria went down like a dropped sack of potatoes, lying motionless for three or four seconds, an eternity for us.

It looked like Pat might have killed her. The amount of blood on Pat's leg, Gloria's nose and on the floor was horrifying. Pat looked from Gloria to me, then back to Gloria, the look of terror the same as when Linda cut her throat. Never were the words, to add insult to injury, more appropriate than when Pat projectile vomited over Gloria.

Gloria raised her bloodied, vomit speckled face from the floor, carelessly put her hand to her nose. A loud crunching noise and a wail of anguish from Gloria confirmed her nose was indeed broken. With a look of horror on her face, she turned towards Pat and cried, "Dou booke by dose."

By this time, the commotion had alerted the nuns, a posse of them quickly arrived, and they dragged the crying bloody bully away.

The next day the Reverend Mother sent for me. When I arrived, Pat was already waiting in her office, shaking like a leaf on a windy day.

"I have listened to Pat's version of the events of last evening, now I want to hear yours," her voice sounding unusually punitive.

What I told her was, in essence, the truth. I said Gloria was pushing Pat around. I asked Gloria to stop, then she turned on me. Pat was trying to protect me when Gloria swung her fist at her. Pat dodged the punch, but such was power and impetus of the girl she went straight into Pat's clenched hand. The girl doubled up and hit her face on Pat's knee as Pat tried to escape. What I didn't say was Pat gripped Gloria's hair just above her ears tugging her face into her knee.

My account must have tallied with Pat's version of the events, for the Mother Superior dismissed us with a serene, "May God bless you girls. You may go now."

My bosom buddy and I happily skipped up the corridor with our arms around each other's shoulder, smugly satisfied with the outcome of the event.

We never saw Gloria again. Sister Sandra told us later that Gloria was sent to a Doctor Bernardo's Home nearby, another charity that cared for vulnerable children and young people, and girls with broken noses. As a side effect, from then on, not much bullying occurred when Pat was around as her reputation had attained mammoth proportions after defeating Gloria.

Retribution

The chocolate lady visited us on Saturday with a woman that looked like a younger carbon copy of her. She introduced her as Auntie Doreen. When she said it, it sounded like, Doooorreeeen. She was actually the younger sister of my mother, I wondered if my mother looked like them. My grandmother Gretchen, Doreen, Greta and I walked into the big city for lunch. As luck would have it, it was an Italian restaurant. To the consternation and embarrassment of the two outsiders, Greta ordered bacon and eggs, even though it wasn't on the menu. I ordered spaghetti bolognese with garlic bread. My newly discovered Auntie Doreen asked for the same meal. The look of astonishment on their faces was amusing as I ate my lunch like a veteran Italian, with far superior etiquette than my auntie, who used a knife and spoon. I said nothing about the Nairs, and I finished my meal with no red stains on my clothes. Incidentally, the food paled in comparison to the fare on Mrs Nairs table.

I had often wondered what my mother's name was, throwing caution to the wind, I asked them outright. They both looked flustered, eventually, after a significant amount of consideration, my grandmother's one-word reply was, Jane. Their lack of enthusiasm regarding my parentage stopped me asking my father's name.

The remainder of the day was dreary, deficient in both entertainment and emotion. They went shopping, and we had to listen to them talk of their home, the highlight being when Chocolate Granny bought a very stylish table lamp for one of her guest bedrooms.

I knew, ultimately Greta and I were the responsibility of our parents, the parents who had abandoned us. Though I liked Gran, she was not responsible for us. My assumption is my grandmother must have hated my mother and father with such intensity, she could barely utter their names. Yet at the same time, she must have felt a modicum of pity and responsibility towards her granddaughters, for she occasionally visited us. So far her penance consisting of sweets, chocolate, a duffle coat and an Italian meal.

Not long after, Brenda and another bully, a fierce-looking plump girl who was new to the home, whose name eludes me, decided to escape. Early morning the two girls sneaked out over the wall towards the park heading towards the weir. Their ill-conceived plan included leaving two small bundles of clothes on the banks of the River Taff, while they took a shortcut to a girl friend's house in Ely, a few miles away.

The orphanage was soon in turmoil. They cancelled the Saturday cattle market. Frantic nuns wearing concerned faces searched the home. Sister Terry, her pale face a picture of unadulterated evil, was gliding up and down the great hall no doubt contemplating her revenge.

The search widened from the home's grounds to the fields and parks nearby. They selected four or five nuns, each was to lead four trusted children in search of a particular area. Sister Margarita singled out Pat, Beryl and Natalie and I. We crossed the busy main road heading towards the playing fields and river, shouting out the girl's names every minute or so, not that we really cared one way or another about finding the bullies. Our walk took us across the footbridge hanging on metal ropes above the still waters of the River Taff, situated just before the placid river plunged down the weir into the turbulence below.

Pat spotted them first, pointing at the clothes on the bank high above the swirling water.

"That looks like one of ours," Pat screeched, pointing at a blue woollen jumper.

"That looks like one of ours," Beryl repeated, picking up a blue skirt.

Sister Margarita assuming they had drowned, no doubt remembering poor Paul from years earlier, squealed, "Mother of God."

The police were informed, and they searched the river, then a telephone call from the girl friend's mother notified the relieved Mother Superior of the escapee's whereabouts.

I imagined the headlines in the Evening Echo, its front page proclaiming: '*Two Nazareth House girls feared drowned in the river.*'

It was mandatory, for every child in the orphanage to witness the retribution for betrayal after Sunday Mass. Three nun's, one of whom was Sister Terry, stood in the centre of the great hall with the two terrified girls sitting on chairs. A few more nuns and eighty or more children watched the proceedings.

The two nuns held bamboo canes in their hands. One nun had a full staff about the thickness of an adult thumb and around a forearm in length. The other nun's rod was twice the length of the other and tapered to a thin point. When she flexed her arm and swished it through the air, the bamboo bent with an audible crack. She continued slashing; liking the sound, especially the effect it was having on the gasping audience.

They went about their business systematically. Forced the two girls to take off their boots and kneel on the chairs with the soles of the feet bare, waiting for punishment. Sister Terry theatrically unbuckled her fabled belt, the diminutive nun directed the action like a gifted entertainer. Her beady eyes flashed and her thin lips pursed into an unambiguous look of pleasure before she gestured to the nun with the long cane and shrilled, "Five," in a playful happy tone.

The nun instantly lifted the cane high above her head, taking time to aim carefully at the exposed sole. It whooshed down with a thwack, forcing a pitiful yowl to emanate from the bully Brenda. Undoubtedly a few spectators felt no pity, involuntary oohs and ah's escaped from the captive audience at the swish of each stroke. Five strikes to each girl on both feet followed. The other girl winced but bravely made neither sound nor cried tears. Next, they were made to stand, hands outstretched with their palms up.

Sister Terry nodded so vigorously towards the other nun that her glasses almost fell off her pointy nose. Again, "Five."

The nuns then slashed down five times to each hand of both girls.

Then it was the merciless Sister Terry's turn. She could barely contain her excitement as she bent the girls over their respective chairs and swung her belt, whacking each girl soundly on their backsides.

Brenda yelped, cried and pleaded for mercy, the other girl never uttered a sound. The girls were dragged to their feet and repeatedly struck on the shoulders, back and backside by the three ogres. The onslaught lasted a full five minutes and still, the girl never made a sound.

Sister Terry finally went berserk when the girl had the temerity to smile at her. She was in a frenzy hitting the girl with the buckle end and had to be restrained by the other two nuns before they could take away the belt.

Home Alone

We hadn't really noticed or missed the blustering Linda; she disappeared over the weekend. Sister Sandra, who was probably only six or seven years older than us, couldn't hide her enthusiasm when she excitingly said Linda was going to be fostered. She was genuinely pleased for the braggart.

A righteous Catholic family who lived a few miles from Cardiff fostered the noisy boastful girl with a superior attitude and vivid scar on her neck. They already had five children who were all boys, they desperately wanted a girl, so they decided to adopt. Sister Sandra said it was unusual that they specifically requested a teenage girl; adding light-heartedly that it was probably to do all the cleaning. Like Sister Sandra, I was happy for Linda. However, I was delighted she was finally gone. Our mutual dislike had intensified after her near decapitation.

About a week after, Sister Sandra told us Linda was returning to the orphanage. It didn't shock me when she confided the family didn't take kindly to her and she didn't like them. The short journey from fostering to adoption had fallen at the first hurdle. I wasn't looking forward to renewing our war of attrition or seeing her familiar form strutting through the corridors like one of Lerina's chickens.

The following Saturday's cattle market was in full swing with Pat, Greta and I sitting in our usual place watching the ritual to which we were usually only spectators. Before us, prospective substitute parents were studying the keen, overeager faces of children who were almost pleading for attention in their desperation to escape the turmoil of the institution. In the background, Sister Margarita, with a serene, contented smile on her face was escorting a pleasant-looking man and woman through the busy hall. She stopped suddenly scanning the room through her squinting eyes until satisfied she had found her quarry, then abruptly pointed in our direction and said something to the couple. In response, they strode purposefully towards us as we shuffled submissively on our bench.

"This is Pat," Sister Margarita said, and in less keen tone added, "And these are her friends Greta and Milly." She gestured in a sweeping motion towards the smiling duo, who both wore spectacles. "Pat, Mr and Mrs Gilbert want you to stay with them tonight. Your clothes are waiting for you in the visitor room."

Pat, a cheeky grin on her happy face, tagged along with them with a slight skip in her step indicating she was pleased to go, stopping at the big doors to turn and wave a cheerful goodbye.

I didn't see Pat the next day, which was unusual but not alarming, what gave me cause for concern though was her absence on the school bus on Monday. Linda, who had returned to the orphanage a few weeks before, said loudly enough for me to hear, that Pat hadn't slept in dorm two the previous night. The statement left me perplexed, my anxious curiosity imagining hospitals and illnesses.

Little Roly was waiting by the wall for us. She gave a precursory glance around for Pat and looked up towards my face. Her tail stopped wagging straight away. Roly knew. Sensed instantly, something was amiss. Tilting her little furry head slowly from side to side as if to say, what's up Milly? There was no need to. I could see the question in her bright eyes. She asked the same questions seven long hours later, when I sat on the wall with her, stroking her head and neck while she placidly licked my other hand.

As was usual, I went straight to the nursery to help with the little ones. Sister Sandra was alone in the kitchen. She beckoned me in, and without trying to gloss over her story, told me Pat had gone to live with the family she had stayed with on Saturday, adding, that if Pat didn't like the family, she could come back.

So I waited for Pat, thinking she would come back, for there was no way she wouldn't want to return. I was confident she would come strolling into the nursery, her cheeky impish face beaming.

Sister Sandra, who I suspected knew a lot more about the mysterious circumstances regarding the whereabouts of my soulmate, remained unusually tight-lipped for quite a few days. With a certain amount of guilt, I began to feel resentful towards the kindly nun, until a few days later, days that seemed to last forever, she finally broke her silence on the matter.

"Milly," she said soothingly. "I've heard Mother Superior say that Pat doesn't like it where she is and is desperate to return."

Delighted with the news bulletin, I later spread the classified information to a few of my own confidants. It was especially unusual to receive any intelligence, and I was enormously grateful to Sister Sandra, who, without a doubt, had taken a risk informing me. However, my unreliable intimates were a bunch of tell tales, soon the news spread through the voluminous mansion like wildfire.

The next day stories about Pat were rife in the institution. I personally heard Pat was being held prisoner by a family of fifteen who lived in the countryside just outside Cardiff. Though, apparently, she escaped, by running away through a dense forest, but was captured very quickly by detectives who had followed her trail. Another girl told me the police apprehended Pat after she fell asleep on one of the beds while hiding in a bungalow. They hastily returned her to her new family's cottage. She was being forced to clean and cook for the entire family of a mum, dad, eleven boys and two girls. She has to wear rags, while the evil mother and the two girls treated her like a slave. Pat, they said, made numerous escape attempts, the latest arrest occurred only the previous evening when she was dragged screaming from her bicycle at the gates of Nazareth House and taken back in handcuffs.

I was amused by the transformation of the information and grateful it held little resemblance to the original message. I couldn't wait to ask Pat when she had learned to ride a bike or quiz her about the Hansel and Gretel, Cinderella and Goldilocks-like experiences, she suffered; or more so, hear about her police records and her criminal activities. I chuckled to myself as I thought of Chinese whispers and the imaginative young minds as the story travelled from one ear to another. I concluded I had learned another lesson. Don't betray a confidence.

I waited as patiently as I could, on tenterhooks, eagerly watching every opening door. I looked up at every footstep, imagining Pat's happy freckled face would soon be poking around the nursery door.

"If Pat doesn't like it there, she can come back," Sister Sandra repeated, when, I impatiently asked her, probably for the thousandth time, for an update.

"The Reverend Mother will arrange her return as soon as possible,"

I recalled the words of the Mother Superior the first day I met her. When she told me my mother would return as soon as she could arrange it. Well, that was more than eight years before. Was this a pack of lies invented to pacify me?

I became disillusioned and depressed. I couldn't eat or sleep, my mind tossing and turning in tandem with my emotions. Despite all the pleading words and sermons from Sister Sandra, I began to think of her as a two-faced liar and a traitor. I became very angry and aggressive, refusing point-blank to speak to anyone, even the understanding Mr Noland.

"I'm here when you want me Blue, take care," he said, confusingly adding. "You have three to go."

I carried out my duties in moody silence. My one and only source of comfort was my silent pal Roly. The intelligent tiny dog even started walking me to school. We would saunter the steep hill, her encouragingly nudging my skinny calves with her cold, wet nose, herding me towards the iron school gate as some mothers did with their own children, and once there, standing at the gates and waving me a comforting goodbye with her magic wand wagging appendage. She waited for me at lunchtime, when we would share a packet of crisps purchased from the tuck shop at the bottom of the hill. I skipped the school dinners, not wanting to be in the company of another human being. I resented the world and everyone in it. To compound my grief, all traces of Pat seemed to be obliterated. Natalie Ward, who thankfully left me alone now occupied Pat's old school chair and left me to my mourning, sometimes placing a comforting understanding hand on mine.

I experienced a morbid-like heartache as the time progressed and Pat did not return. My sleepless nights, along with my erratic behaviour, became a significant concern for the nuns. My refusal to eat coupled with the ever-increasing dark shadows growing under my eyes meant I became even more skeletal looking by the day, an appearance that even my teacher the kindly Mr Jones commented on.

When my anguish became unbearable. I tried to escape from the living hell, I irrationally decided to feign an illness, by frantically scrubbing my face with a dry towel, consequently creating startling red raw skin which left my high cheekbones dry and flaking. My actions had the desired effect. They transferred me to one of the spare beds in the nursery with a nun in constant attendance. Encompassing the bed was a partial metal grill and a metal canopy, with a plastic curtain that could surround and totally obscure the patient. On either side of the bed were chairs. One occupied by a sequence of nonplussed nuns, who sat on guard twenty-four hours a day, most likely with orders to prevent me from killing myself. I lay there curled up in the foetal position for hours on end, being force-fed Horlicks with a raw egg every few hours. This lasted about a week or more before I felt I wanted to live again.

The news about my return to sanity began to percolate throughout the orphanage. The cheeky faces of the kiddies Daisy, Susan and Garan, a chirpy young boy whose name in Welsh means Heron, peaking through the curtains helped me to cope. I missed Roly and Mr Noland, and I grieved for my constant companion.

When I finally returned to school, a furious little black dog reprimanded me. Roly was in her usual place examining the faces of the bus passengers. When she saw me, she ran towards me barking angrily; her bark sounded different to her normal I want to play, hello and goodbye barks. I found it decidedly amusing and consoling. We sat on the wall together scoffing the chipolatas Jasmin gave me that morning, not caring about time or consequences. I stayed with the calming Roly for ages. She had the desired effect on me. When she chaperoned me to the school gates, I was relaxed and relatively assured, albeit excessively late.

A concerned looking, Mr Jones jumped up from his chair when he saw me hesitating at the classroom door. He rushed forward to escort me to my desk next to Natalie, his kindly hand resting gently on my bony shoulder, asking if I was well and whispered,

"We are all glad to have you back."

I shuddered when I saw my reflection in the mirror of the girl's toilet. My cheekbones were like the knuckle of a clenched fist, the dark puffy shadows under my dry, lifeless eyes were frightening even to me. No wonder Roly had barked at me, I thought. I downed a hearty rushed meal at dinner time before joining a waiting Roly to enjoy two packets of plain crisps. Feeling better, I returned to class on time, with the small, blue salt-filled, twirled package, in my pocket. Roly didn't like salt and would try to spit the small grains out of her mouth.

As the weeks progressed, I concentrated on my chores and school, gradually becoming to feel more alive again. I hoped and prayed Pat was happy. I forced myself to believe she was. What else could I do?

Before I knew it the end of term and Christmas was upon us. That year my nursery pals and I had one of the best Christmases ever. From what I remember our Christmas dinner consisted of three boiled potatoes, five Brussels sprouts, three slices of stuffing, a small strip of chicken and a dollop of lumpy gravy. We all thought it delicious and enjoyed our meagre meal with elation.

I thoroughly enjoyed that Christmas despite my continuing distracting thoughts. Memories concerning Pat, Lerina, Janice and Heidi washed over me in waves like the tide rushing over the golden sand at Barry Island. I remembered all the children who never came back. I reminisced about meeting the red-lipped Heidi and Lerina. I had a strong feeling that Pat was doing well and was now over her hasty departure. I finally come to the conclusion my inspirational best friend wasn't coming back. I knew we both wished each other well, and I hoped with all my heart we would meet each other again. After all, we had both promised we would.

Money Crisps and Sausage Rolls

My fourteenth birthday was only about a week away. I thought of Pat and the long months since her disappearance, as her birthday was soon after mine. I had forgiven Sister Sandra, though, in reality, I had nothing to forgive her for. She was a totally innocent bystander. The saintly nun had totally and absolutely absolved me of all my hateful accusations and thoughts.

Now I had a new quandary to consider. The stash of money in my secret window and my little green book had vanished, leaving me with just two columns of coins; sufficient for a few weeks' worth of crisps and sausage rolls. Though, I was not perturbed. I had no doubt Mr Noland knew where they were. He advised me to transfer all the coins from my other hiding places to our secret window a few days earlier. I expected he was planning something. My hiding place in the nursery was now free of coins, the window seemed empty with only a few sweets and chocolates to occupy the space.

The mystery was solved the following Saturday morning. The cattle market was flowing smoothly when Sister Sandra, accompanied by Mr Noland, who was wearing his best suit, unexpectedly approached me. Sister Sandra carried a duffle coat that resembled, or in fact, was the one that kept going missing. Later I noticed with some surprise that my grandmother was right, it may have taken three years, but I did grow into the duffle coat. By the looks of the fraying cuffs, it was highly probable quite a few of us did.

"Come on. We're going to the big city. Mother Superior and Sister Sandra said it was all right for me to buy you a birthday present," Mr Noland winked.

We walked a different route to the city, strolling along a tree-lined gravel path surrounded by football pitches. Every twenty yards, there were wooden benches, which proved to be convenient as Mr Noland became breathless. The handles of the holdall he carried, stretched taut under its weight. Every so often, we stopped when he would inevitably light up a filter-less cigarette, spitting out any loose strands of tobacco. He would sit puffing contentedly with his hands on his knees, until his breathing became steady, identifying the passing birds, mentioning their nesting and feeding habits. And when a distant squirrel hopped onto the path, he informed me about hibernation. He pointed out and named the different leafless and evergreen trees, saying that the oak tree was his and most carpenters favourite. I felt I learned more from him during the leisurely walk through Bute Park than a month at school.

In the city centre, we entered a large building through a heavy glass door. Once inside the imposing space, he led us to join a small queue formed before a glass barricade, behind which sat two prim and proper women, each wearing a white blouse and black neckties.

"Good morning. I'm Clive Noland, this is Miss Nash. We've come to see the bank manager, Mr Holmes. And Miss Nash would like to make a deposit," he eloquently said.

He produced my little green book and my missing bags of money from the holdall. I noticed the black stallion design on its cover was like those on the posters adorning the walls. Moments later, we were ushered into an office.

The goatee bearded bank manager behind the desk stood up to his full height. A broad grin creased his face as he said warmly, “Hello, Clive.” He looked down at me, still smiling broadly. “You must be Miss Nash. I’m very pleased to meet you. Seeing as you can’t find your birth certificate, I’ll need you and Mr Noland to sign a few papers to safeguard your new account.”

In my neatest handwriting, I signed my name on various forms and in my new green book.

“Miss Nash,” he said respectably. “Just ask for Mr Holmes whenever you come in again. It’s been a pleasure meeting you at last young lady.”

Mr Noland and Mr Holmes were demonstrably good friends for they parted company with a hug. He shook my hand, warmly with a pleasant smile on his kind face. I experienced a proud, warm feeling flow through my body.

After a hot cup of tea and a glass of pop, my first ever soft drink in a smoky cafe, we ambled back to the home. Mr Noland said he had only left Nazareth House a few times in the ten years he’d been there, adding with a smile, apart from the necessary visits to the pub and shop across the road. It transpired that a shop and a public house were situated to the left of Nazareth House. I realised that in the nine years I’d been here I had only ever walked to the right. In a few months a man would walk on the moon yet I’d never turned left, leaving Nazareth House.

We speculated as to Pat’s fate, concluding that she was most likely living the life of a little princess.

I smiled when he said, "That's the last one Blue. Acceptance. Do you remember when I said you have three to go? In life, we all experience grief. And we generally deal with grief in five stages. Learning these make us better equipped to deal with the loss of someone. As you did after Pat suddenly went away. The five stages are denial, anger, and you were an outraged young woman," he stressed in a slightly louder voice before continuing, "depression, bargaining and the last one, acceptance."

I mulled over his words, understood and nodded. I realised that mingled between his wise words, were the words, a young woman. I was always little Milly, little Blue, Blue eyes or Blue. I am a young woman now, I thought proudly. Two months earlier, two little fried eggs had grown on my pancake-like chest. At long last, they had decided to take a small incursion into the outside world. Though stubborn and defiant, they refused to gain satisfactory proportions. The thought reminded me of Pat, who was most definitely a young woman.

I thoroughly enjoyed my little educational jaunt to the big city. I've no doubt that Mr Noland did too, despite the breathless interludes. He was grinning broadly when we promised each other we would do it again.

My part-time duffle coat and I parted company as soon as we entered the big doors. We watched as Sister Margarita drifted off with it.

Gretchen, the chocolate lady, told me on one of her visits it shocked her to see one of the other girls wearing my overcoat. Initially, she thought it was me. She was outraged and told the Reverend Mother in no uncertain terms that the duffle coats were an expensive gift for the exclusive use of her granddaughters.

I had few thoughts of material objects except for my green book and its money I owned nothing. I didn't consider my boots, tatty blazer, dress or jumper my property. Other girls had probably worn my secondary school underwear, socks, and dresses a thousand times before. We had no choice in the matter. They selected every item of clothing for us and laid them out on our chairs.

My little green book and small paper bags full of sweets were tucked safely away in Mr Noland's holdall. He would transport and transfer them to the secret window a little later. I had selected the kiddie's favourites: Gobstoppers, Blackjacks, Sherbet Flying Saucers, Lollypops, Jelly Babies and Love Hearts. All of which would soon be on the shelves inside the secret window. It would resemble the sweet shop we had visited earlier that day.

Corpus Christi

It was time for another batch of children to be prepared for Holy Communion. I watched in admiration as Sister Sandra and Sister Margarita fitted the veils and adjusted the clothing of my charges. At one point, I even thought I recognised my old dress and shoes; attire that had been locked away until required, now being worn by different girls and boys for another special event. I reflected back tenderly to seven years earlier, recalling how Pat and I went through the same routine, smiling as I remembered how excited we were.

After Holy Communion day another special event on the social calendar occurred, this was the annual May Day parade, culminating in a fete and sports day held in Blackwier, Bute Park. The fete was a yearly fundraising extravaganza organised by Nazareth House and local Catholic schools. The weekend-long festival's permanent location was a cordoned-off corner of the park's vast grounds, sandwiched between the River Taff and the old Glamorganshire canal. At the only access point to this area, a smiling young nun standing near a small tent guarded the fare-paying entrance; another nun, Sister Margarita, sat behind a paper pasting table distributing ticket stubs and counting the money.

Marquees and tents of differing sizes, with their canvases billowing in the gentle breeze, formed a systematic line that stretched as far as the eye could see. Strategically positioned between were a variety of hot dog and beef burger vans, toffee apple sellers and sweets stalls. In all, there must have been a dozen colourful ice cream vans, each one playing their pied piper-like enticing tunes. There was a coconut shy, a traditional game at fairs and fetes, which consisted of throwing three wooden balls at a row of coconuts balanced on posts like golf balls on tees. The player winning each coconut he or she successfully dislodges. I have watched as patron after patron attempted the seemingly possible achievement, and nearly all of them found it futile.

Practically everyone from Nazareth House attended this grand money-making opportunity. Sister Norma, a small, grim-faced well-organised nun, who played the church's majestic organ, also doubled as the sports nun. Though why she held this position baffled me. Her minuscule, hunchbacked frail body made her an unlikely candidate. Though, she had a knack for whittling out a suitable talent for the individual events. During the cold winter months, she selected her competitors, making the reluctant kids practice sack races, relay races, long jumps and hundred-yard dashes until she chose the best possible,

"As champions for the good name of Nazareth House." It wasn't difficult to be added to her list; for the wiser kids performed their trials at an uninspiring snail's pace, knowing from experience they would have more fun at the fair without the interruption of competitions. Two nuns were designated to escort any unruly or misbehaving child back to the home, the nun's innocent-looking hand on the arm of the child disguising the vice-like nuns' pinch.

This year I was competing in the under twelve's races that included the sack race, the hundred-yard dash, egg and spoon race and discus throwing. The fact that I was fourteen was totally irrelevant.

"But you look like you're eleven my child," Sister Norma replied to my protestations.

The choir all enjoyed watching her dynamic performance as she played the organ, happily stooped over her beloved keyboard beneath the ranks of giant brass penny whistles that stretched towards the domed ceiling. Her flying fingers resembling jumping spiders as she exaggeratedly tugged the organ stops and stamped down on peddles; a performance that mostly went unobserved, unless a parishioner took a sneaky glance over their shoulder.

This was the same enthusiasm she exhibited at the May sports day. Fortunately for Nazareth House and me, at the last minute, Sister Sandra persuaded Sister Norma to change her mind regarding my illegal-under twelve entries. Reluctantly she agreed, knowing I had little chance of success against my age group. I didn't mind, as long as I beat Linda. I did, however, have an ace up my sleeve for the sack race.

During summer, usually on bright sunny mornings, a corner of the nursery playground becomes an extension of the kitchen. Sacks of potatoes, carrots, peas, onions or any other vegetables are laid out on a stacker-truck, alongside buckets of cold water and two strategically placed three-legged wooden stools. On each, a small metal potato scraper, the tough grind for the morning intrinsically distinctive. Ahead of us lay a few hours of tiresome toil. In pairs, we would prepare the vegetables for the kitchen, with the two peelers changing when tired, until the last of the water and potato-filled buckets were successfully ferried to the kitchens. The buckets containing peelings and gauged out black eyes, along with any other inedible waste, were sold to a man who bred pigs, to make the swill. Only when the stools and the rest of the paraphernalia were all safely tucked away, could we congregate into our sunny play area, where our wet hands and wrinkled fingers would slowly dry out and regain their natural shape.

It was during one potato peeling session, I managed to snaffle away an empty hessian container to practise for the forthcoming race. Quite by accident, I discovered that if I placed my feet in each corner of the sack, I could actually trot, rather than hop. I could almost run as fast as a woman might in a tight skirt. Consequently, that sunny afternoon, I won the sack race at a canter. But more importantly, I beat Linda Evans, who was as usual too confident of her own success. She was always determined to better me at everything.

The race was witnessed by at least a hundred cheering, whistling, smiling or laughing people. Amongst them were the little ones, jumping up and down excitedly and beaming. After the race, there was a lot of head-scratching and discussions regarding the legitimacy of my victory, with Sister Norma in the middle, her dour face darting from one referee to another.

"Well, Milly was in a sack, she came first, and, she won the sack race?" she proclaimed loudly.

The crowd cheered as a shiny winner-medal dangling on a blue ribbon was slipped over my ridiculous haircut.

"Winner of the sack race, Milly Nash of Nazareth House," boomed a voice over the loudspeaker. My Nursery comrades, the Nazareth House boys, and girls, the crowd cheered even louder.

Bolstered by my victory, I came second in the egg and spoon race, again beating Linda, who was a distant third. After the result, as an excuse for her being well beaten, she complained that something was in her eye.

"Yes, the back of me," I chided.

Nazareth House did reasonably well that year, better than any of the previous bank holidays I could remember. The smug looks on the nuns' faces suggested all was well, though we all lacked the hugs of congratulations and back-slapping experienced by the other victors. We were envious of the warmth and happiness displayed by their proud parents.

Another memory I have is that in all the years of competitions it never ever rained. The May bank holiday weekends were always bathed in bright sunshine.

On the final day of the fete, we were all tucked up in bed by seven-thirty, with Sister Sandra praising all the nursery inmates for their exceptional conduct and success. I remember thinking fondly of Pat and how we always looked forward to the following day.

Early the next day, the procession of kids and nuns followed the course of the previous two days. For the duration of the May bank holiday, there was none of the usual scrubbing and polishing, only the standard bed making, for we had other tasks to perform. Nuns and kids alike were equipped with plastic bags, shovels and brushes. Two nuns pushed noisy two-wheeled stacker-trucks; one piled high with rattling bottles of soft drinks in wooden crates, the other with three cardboard boxes that had previously held potato crisps.

Once through the now unguarded entrance, we were assigned to various sections of the litter-strewn lawns. All the vans and caravans had disappeared, leaving a few empty tents and marquees, each with the entrance flaps securely fastened. The small army of specialist cleaners filled bag after bag of the carelessly dropped rubbish. Unusually, some nuns helped by picking up discarded empty bottles. The rationale behind this seemingly supportive act was that shops charged a refundable deposit on bottles. I visualised the nuns queuing up with an armful of bottles, buying sweets with the proceeds and scoffing them in their cells at night. The clever nuns never missed a trick.

When we finished, our stern-faced sweaty guards, who despite the searing sun were clad head to toe in their heavy woollen garments, marched across acres of immaculate terrain inspecting every blade of grass for any hidden debris. Evidence of our efforts lay buried in a multitude of bags waiting for collection. Our reward for three to four hours of donkey work was on the ground under a shady oak tree, in open crisp boxes revealing their full sandwich laden contents. A regimented line of hungry kids formed in front of the crates and boxes where a nun handed out sandwiches and a bottle of pop to each worker. We wolfed down the cheese and onion sandwiches and drank the fizzy drinks while watching inquisitive squirrels and birds. I passed on the knowledge learned from Mr Noland to my little pals as we shared some of our food with a few of God's creatures.

To be entirely fair, the nuns allowed us to play, even producing skipping ropes. I had the idea Sister Sandra was the mastermind behind this. Though soon, the harsh tone of a pea whistle stopped our play, beckoning us towards the tents and marquees. These were then opened, to reveal even more rubbish on the trampled flattened grass.

I was delighted when my nursery chums and I were assigned to one of the roomier marquees. I had told everyone in the nursery beforehand to look out for dropped money, and if they found any to hide it immediately without making a sound. Prior experience had proved it to be profitable. Out of sight of any supervising nuns, a dozen jovial, children each armed with the required tools and sacks proceeded to clear the vast interior. Almost immediately one of the little ones found a shiny silver coin, quickly concealing it without any sound or display of excitement. One of the new boys Garan, who was about eight years old, found a pristine green coloured pound note, a relative fortune back then. Even though he had been counselled, he whooped in delight, ultimately attracting the attention of the overseeing nun outside, who just happened to be Sister Terry. She came in and grabbed the note out of his hand then walked away without uttering a word, leaving poor Garan dumbfounded with twitching eyes and a quivering bottom lip.

That evening we counted the spoils of the day which were on a par with the snatched note. We laughed off the incident with Garan and the nasty nun, especially when recalling the look on his face when the evil nun grabbed the bill. The dormitory ambience and camaraderie was palpable as I took the orders for their favourite sweets and chocolates. I had the idea Pat would have loved that beautiful, unforgettable holiday.

You're Going Now

My friend Mr Noland stumbled and broke his wrist. In the few months before his accident, he had a lingering heavy cold and flu, which left him weak and shaky, resulting in him getting more unsteady on his feet. Now with his arm in a plaster cast, he appeared depressed and frail, showing signs of ageing. He wasn't as active as he used to be, and for a while, he returned to his previous existence in the chair by the window. Now it was my turn to cheer him up.

I reminded him of the five stages of grief. The words I'd learned from him. He laughed when I said, "You have two to go."

"I think I'll have a chat with the Mother Superior," he said, looking as if he was considering his options.

The consequence of his conversation with the Mother Superior was unparalleled in the home when I was allowed to walk with him to the public house or the boozer as he called it and stay with him for an hour. I enjoyed going to the pub with him. The smell reminded me of the Nairs and more especially of Stephen and Lerina. I would sit with him while he guzzled two or three of pints of frothy brown ale, listening intently as he told me tales of his life before the home, all the while sipping my lemonade as he tried to educate me. He wanted to prepare me for the outside world; he'd say if he thought I was getting bored. Pat would have loved the boozer and the mystery trips to the left.

My last year in the orphanage provided me with a freedom I had never experienced. I thought perhaps the Reverend Mother still believed that I would take my Holy Orders and become a nun. I even seriously fleetingly considered it during my brief bout of depression. The cattle market days were no longer part of my routine. I suspected to prepare me for a life of chastity and religious fervour. She even let me visit Jasmin and her lovely mum and dad. They chatted amiably while I patted the friendly dogs. Like when I first met Ruth and Kate, I could hardly understand a word they said.

Greta, Jasmin and I even went to the cinema together one Saturday afternoon. Jasmin was a touchy-feely young woman, who always held my hand or had an arm affectionately around my shoulder, but never in the home or in front of the nuns.

Greta lived in a bedsitter not far away from Nazareth house, she left the home weeks before. Sister Gabriel found her the bedsit and employment working in a cafe run by a Greek couple. Greta didn't like the job, she left after one day.

Her hair was now stylish and a little longer. Strangely and bizarrely she always dressed the same, every item of clothing, white, even her shoes. For an unemployed person, she seemed to have a considerable amount of money. Without saying as such, I knew Mr Noland disliked Greta, and I assumed he didn't give anyone else money. So I didn't ask any questions, I quietly speculated.

My little doggie friend waited each day. In the morning, when I alighted from the school bus, she would be sitting patiently on the wall or the pavement next to the bus stop sign. Most of the kids would greet her with a jovial good morning, or a 'Hiya Roly.' At dinner time, she would be outside the school gates waiting for me to play with her. She was a bundle of energy and would fetch a tennis ball a hundred times or more, displaying the same enthusiasm each time. Apart from her namesake trick, rolling over, I taught her countless more. Her wet tongue always enthusiastically lolling and slurping at her black shiny button nose, her big bright brown eyes never leaving my face, the enthusiasm never waned. It was akin to mine and Pat's ball practice sessions.

About three or four months after Pat left me, my little black curly-haired friend taught me a trick. One morning I was the last getting off the bus, busy opening the package Jasmin concealed the evening before. Roly and I shared many chipolatas, sausage rolls and crisps. Sausages were our once a week treat. I'd slip Jasmin the money for her to buy and cook them. By the time I stepped off the bus, little Roly must have assumed I wasn't on it, for she was sadly sauntering away her head down, her tail motionless.

I shouted my name for her, she snapped her head around and glanced towards me; her little furry face immediately transforming from dejected to delighted, her tongue popped out, the big eyes brightened, her thin, scraggly tail began to wag energetically, and she started bounding towards me. It seemed like she was going too fast to stop. Then, when she was about two paces from me, she leapt straight into my arms and proceeded to lick my ecstatically beaming face. It was the most fabulous greeting anyone in the world would love to receive. I was overwhelmed. She had the confidence and trust to know I would catch her, although she was going fast enough to bowl me over, she seemed to stop and then leap up into my arms. It was a trick we would perform many times for the school kids, most of whom loved the adorable little dog. On quite a few occasions, she would follow me into school and try to hide under a chair or a bench. I have to say the teachers were terrific, even so, they would shoo my friend away, while wearing a sympathetic smile.

Mr Noland had his plaster cast removed and was able to work. Now that he had a purpose in life, he returned to his happy self. We usually spent at least two or three hours in the boozer most Saturdays, where he'd smoke cigarettes and drink a few glasses of ale.

Thanks to Mr Noland, the pub sessions and our educational jaunts to the city, my knowledge improved. He helped me with my homework, explaining in great detail each and every problem, which ultimately had a profound effect on my schooling. My end of term exam results surprised everyone, none more so than me. I came top of my class, first out of thirty-five boys and girls. As a result, I leapfrogged the next level when I was transferred to form 4A. Only the lovely Lorna from Nazareth House had ever attained the giddy heights of class A.

Initially, there was a downside to this, for Wendy Street and her entourage were also in that class. There always seemed to be one obstacle in my way, for every up there was forever a down. On the plus side, Lucy was also in the class. We were still friends, but as time passed, we were never as close as we were nine long years before. To be honest, we both tried, but such was the class divide between us any real camaraderie was predestined to fail. I was still one of us. Sorrowfully Lucy was now more an outsider, than one of us. She mostly congregated with them, I would join Natalie and the Nazareth House gang at playtime.

Dinner time was always mine and Roly time. One day I was sitting on a wall eating crisps with my little pal when Wendy, who was utterly stunning and had the looks and shape of an aspiring model, strode purposely towards me.

"Hiya Milly, hiya Roly." She bent down to stroke her little head, Roly moved away, reacting just as she first did with my missing friend Pat.

"Sorry, sorry," her tone was quiet and pitiful. "You've a clever little dog there. I wish mine were as clever."

I nodded, suspicious of her intentions.

She turned to me and quietly said, "I know I should have said this before. But I'm really very, very sorry for being such a bitch and a spoilt brat towards you and Pat."

I had taken little notice, but on reflection, the hate had left her piercing blue eyes sometime before. I accepted the olive branch and shook her hand warmly. We looked into each other's blue eyes, both of us grinning, then she nodded to her loitering band of surly followers. Each, in turn, nodded back as if showing their acceptance of me. Even little Roly joined in; perhaps she sensed or smelt a change of mood, she allowed the attractive blonde the privilege of a tickle under her chin. I told her Roly wasn't my dog, and Roly was not her name. She never wore a collar so, with nothing to call her, I had christened her Roly. We both laughed. I could tell the warmth was genuine, I thought perhaps the pretty girl may have had an epiphany moment in her life. While we would never be bosom butties, we would remain respectful towards each other for the rest of our school days.

I often wondered if Roly waited for me on non-school days and holidays. I know she did during my short visit to insanity, because of the telling off she gave me. She returned the favour one Monday morning. I arrived at the school bus stop, she wasn't in her usual place, nor was she there a lunchtime or at the going home time, or the next day. I became more worried by the day. By the time Friday came and went, it had been five solid days without a sign of her. This meant I had the entire weekend to contend with, giving me more time to think irrational thoughts.

I didn't know how old she was; though I knew, she was getting old. I had noticed the signs a short time after our first meeting. There were little flecks of grey on her curly coat; her eyebrows, eyelashes, the fur on her small chin was even whiter. My pal was unique. She obviously had an owner or owners who cared for her, for every few months she would trot towards me holding her head high, showing off her new haircut. Some of her summer grooms were so severe, she looked like a little black rat.

Mr Noland and I speculated as to the fate of Roly during our Saturday booze-up. During his second pint, and after a lot of grey bristle scratching, his not mine, he assured me that Roly had probably gone on holidays with her owners. On that logical assumption, I placed an order for chipolatas with Jasmin for Monday morning.

As the bus pulled up, I could see her in her usual spot by the wall. She wiggled her tail when she eventually saw me, for her vision was partially obscured by what can only be described as a lampshade around her neck. She licked my hand, her head just peeping out of the funnel.

"What have they done to you little girl?" I said soothingly.

The intelligent little dog rolled to one side to show me. Roly's belly was shaved. A vivid red scar was in the middle of the bald patch, held together by a multitude of untidy stitches, making it look like a zipper. The weeping wound where the sutures entered her flesh appeared excruciating.

I walked alone to school, feeling very sorry for my pal. However, she was there at dinnertime, waiting at the school gates. She soon proved there was nothing wrong with her appetite when we shared a bag of salt-free crisps and the chipolatas I'd forgotten to give her in the morning. My hopes were raised even more when she was there at home time. She wagged me a very encouraging vigorous goodbye as I boarded the bus.

During the next few days, my anxieties waned as Roly proved she was a tough little cookie, though it was understandable she didn't like the funnel. Mr Noland explained that its purpose was to prevent her licking or biting her stitches.

Days later, she appeared one morning without the contraption around her neck. The stitches were out, and her owner or owners had given her a groom. The skinny little creature wanted to jump up into my arms, but couldn't. I gingerly picked her up and cuddled her. I could tell straight away she had lost weight. I had a chance to examine the rapidly healing scar on her tummy. When I described the position of the wound to Mr Noland, he assured me it was a routine operation for a girl dog saying she would very likely recover quickly. After a short while, she did, with the scar was no longer visible under her newly grown fur.

Mr Noland continued to top up the green book and my chocolate store. On alternate Saturdays, we would walk into the city, or take the tram if it was raining, mostly to see his mate, Mr Holmes. Then we would leave for a public house as he always liked to have a beer or two while educating me as to the ways of the world. I was like a sponge in water, absorbing his words, I adored listening to his eloquent voice as he regaled me with stories and snippets of information designed to educate me.

During the return journey, I would often stop and admire clothes in the store windows, even though I knew it was pointless. I now had the resources to buy beautiful clothes like those worn by my ex-enemy Wendy, but what would happen to them if I did? Like the clothes Diana Nairs gave us, they would probably vanish.

Roly made a steady recovery, but not total recovery. When she felt well enough, she would walk me to the school gates. But more often than not, she'd wag a happy goodbye from the bottom of the hill, as though she didn't have the energy. I never experienced the thrill and joy of her jumping into my arms again. I was dreading the time when I left school and started employment. I would probably have to say goodbye to her. And was already making plans to visit her on weekends. I briefly thought of attaching a note to her collar.

So I could spend more time with her, I stopped having free school dinners. I'd give Jasmin enough money for us to have chipolatas nearly every day. Jasmin didn't mind in the slightest, she'd say yes every time I asked. I looked to her as a friend, mentor and role model and trusted her implicitly.

As the months flew by the irony of the situation became clear to me, I honestly didn't want to leave Nazareth House or Mostyn. I loved Mr Noland, school and meeting Roly; it was as if I was becoming more insecure each day. I was worried about Mr Noland, who was also getting slower and seemed to have aged considerably during the past two years. We no longer walked to the city and went by bus instead. Little Roly showed similar signs of ageing; she was becoming lethargic, had lost her sparkle and one of her eyes now looked misty, comparable to the last drop of milk in the bottom of a glass. Though encouragingly, she was in her usual place in the mornings and at home time, though she missed some of our lunchtime sessions.

My black furry haired friend chose the Monday of my last week in school to disappear. By the Thursday she still hadn't shown up. I knew all was not well, but I was powerless to do anything. I only had one day left. I sought the advice of my other fragile pal. He suggested we should take a taxi there on Saturday, to ask some locals where she lived, something I would never have considered as we rarely talked to outsiders.

My heart missed a beat when I saw her by the wall on Friday morning. My joy was short-lived for I immediately recognised she was critically ill. I picked her up and cuddled her. She licked my hands and face, even though the poor little girl barely had the energy. I could tell she had used up every ounce, just get here. She curled up in a small ball, breathing shallowly. I stroked her head and tickled her tummy until her little tail twitched to show me she was content. I gave no thought to going to school. I talked to her, I pleaded to her, and I begged her to get better. More importantly, I prayed to God for her.

Roly sniffed the air, raised her head and looked towards an old woman who was standing a short distance away. My little pal uncurled herself from my lap and stood up unsteadily, looked up at me through half-closed hooded eyes, eyes that wanted to sleep, she stretched her face towards mine and licked my mouth like a kiss, a goodbye kiss. She staggered towards the old woman and stopped at her feet, before turning to look towards me, wagging her tail. It was still swishing as the woman picked her up. I knew I would never see her again. Her breath smelt of death, similar to the smell that emanated from Paul's coffin before the lid was closed.

I sat on the wall crying until dinner time had passed, and it was time for the afternoon session. Nobody asked me why I'd missed the morning. Nobody cared, as most of us were leaving; some were going to college, some to higher education. I said a sad goodbye to various other friends and teachers that afternoon.

"Stay on in school Milly. Take your A levels. Then you can apply to universities. Milly, the progress you've made in the last two years is remarkable. You're sure to get a scholarship," Mr Jones, repeated what he'd said to me a dozen times. He gave me a letter, exam reports and a personal reference saying as much.

It mattered little, for I was starting work two weeks later. Sister Gabriel had found me a job as a live-in nanny to two small children. Though the Mother Superior still held the belief, I would take Holy Orders.

I walked with my friend Natalie, who understood what I was going through, on our last walk down the hill to the waiting school buses, underneath my fried eggs, my heart actually physically hurt. My thoughts were of Roly and the cherished times we had together. The old woman was standing alone in the spot Roly, and I had occupied in the morning. I instinctively knew she wanted to talk to me.

I turned sombrely to Natalie, "Tell Sister Sandra I missed the bus."

The old woman gestured me towards her. She was no taller than me and just as slim. She had an attractive kind face, with pale grey eyes, her slightly smiling expression held a look of grief and sadness. She didn't have to say anything; her face told me my worst fears had come true.

She said in a soft Cardiff accent, "I knew she met someone from school because, like clockwork, she'd be scratching on the door for me to let her out on school days. She always had a look of happiness on her face after meeting you. She couldn't wait to show me the tricks you taught her. She was a clever little dog because she never came here on weekends or school holidays. It's been about three years, hasn't it?"

"Four years," said a croaky voice that didn't sound like me, "It's my last day in school today," I added.

"She's been unwell for months, she had an operation to remove the melanoma. I hoped it was successful, but unfortunately, it returned. She's been crying all week at the usual times she met you, begging to go out. I had to carry her here to meet you this morning. She so desperately wanted to say a last goodbye to you. She died shortly after we went home,"

Even though I was expecting it, I started crying as I've never cried before. I howled and sobbed for what seemed an eternity, tears flowed, and my nose was full and running. I could hardly breathe. She put a comforting arm around my heaving shoulders. She had come prepared and passed me a folded freshly ironed cotton handkerchief. I wiped my eyes and without thinking blew my nose.

"Sorry," I spluttered.

She smiled softly and said, "Oh, you can keep the hankie, I have something else for you. She held a small leather collar with a little round metal name tag hanging on it,

"She didn't enjoy wearing it much. But I thought you might like it, to remind you of her."

I looked at the tag.

"That's my phone number if you want to speak to me," the old woman said when she saw me looking at one side of the shiny metal tag.

I turned it over and started sobbing again. On the other side, engraved into the metal disc was, Millicent.

"I called her Roly." I sobbed.

"Oh, dear. I think you've missed another bus," the old lady said concerned, paused and asked. "What's your name?"

"Milly," I whimpered.

She replied in a shocked quiet voice. "I called her Millicent after an actress named Millicent Martin. I used to call her Milly when I thought she was naughty or particularly mischievous."

I caught a few buses back to the home. While I was on the second bus, feeling as though an anvil was on my chest, it occurred to me why little Roly always seemed to make an appearance. Pat's squeaky high-pitched voice calling my name on the walk to school four years before must have attracted her attention, by calling an abbreviation of the intelligent dog's name.

I arrived back at the institution at least two hours late, and I didn't give a damn. I had only ever been late once before, that was after taking the cute little collie sheepdog puppy to the police station. Sister Terry had answered the door then, and I was fully expecting her to do the same now. She opened the big oak door on my third knock. The look of pure evil on her face should have been frightening, but this time, it wasn't. After the traumas of the day, I wasn't in the mood to suffer meekly or to compromise. This time I was ready for her, I'd held enough practice sessions in my mind's eye. We were about the same height, I probably weighed less, but I had my youthful vigour, flexible arms from years of cleaning and the shadow and strength of a lost friend at my side.

She drew back her fist to strike me, I was too quick for her. I reacted swiftly, completely surprising the monster, displaying an attitude she did not suspect I had. I shot out my bony hand and clasped it around her throat, holding her windpipe beneath her wimple firm within my grasp. She tried to struggle, so I intensified my grip.

I pushed the terrified nun, who was struggling to breathe, against the wall, and I put my face close to hers. I whispered to her through gritted teeth. "If you ever touch me again, I'll rip this out," emphasising what I meant by tightening my grip on her gulping trachea. "I can repeat this before you can blink an eye. Do you understand?" I hissed.

When she didn't answer, I squeezed harder.

"Do you understand?" I repeated menacingly and a little louder.

She nodded weakly; her eyes told me I had broken her. She was the one who now looked frightened. Brenda had achieved the same results with Raymond, a six-foot hulk from the school when he tried to thump her. The thought of a bloody windpipe on the ground and a gasping body in the throes of death lying next to it had the desired effect. I acted out and repeated Brenda's words and actions. I loosened my grip and pushed her away, observing her carefully as she turned and skulked sheepishly away. I couldn't help myself. I thought about Pat and all the kids whose lives she had made a misery. I ran up behind her and kicked her soundly up the backside.

Hope Springs Eternal

I had nothing to look forward to, the pleasure of meeting my little friend each day was now gone forever. I walked around in a daze, with constant thoughts of Roly curled up on my lap.

Final preparations were in place for my move into the outside world. Mr Noland and I went to the city on the two Saturdays before I started my first job. I emptied out my two secret stores, using the money to buy a bright red handbag and a silver purse. The first item to enter the bag was the collar that belonged to my beloved friend. Inside a zippered side pocket, I secured my precious black horse booklet, folded up inside, was a pink piece of paper the Mother Superior had given me the day before. Now effectively, all my worldly goods were in one red handbag.

The pink sheet of paper assured me I was Milly Catherine Nash. In the centre in bigger letters than the rest of the document, it stated Certificate of Birth. I studied the handwritten text. My father was Horace William Nash, a landowner who lived in St Mellons, a suburb of Cardiff, and my mother was Jane Isabella Thomas, a beautician. After living for fifteen years and five months, I now had a name to put on the imaginary face of the man I had so wanted to love me. Throughout all my years in the orphanage, I didn't wish for much, all I ever wanted was a mum and dad. It wasn't until I stayed with Lerina, that I could add a bedroom like hers. Now I had proof of my identity.

I thought long and hard about the word identity. After all, in reality, I didn't know who I was, as I had no mother or father.

I had only experienced an existence of fear, trepidation and solitude, living in an institution run by motiveless God-fearing robots, whose routine had remained unchanged for decades. Did I really have proof of my true identity?

I should have felt glad to be leaving, I wasn't. I was terrified. The two weeks after the death of Roly was almost unbearable. Mr Noland, God bless him was outstanding. He assured me that little Roly was in doggie heaven looking down on me, her eyes and cancer cured and her vitality restored.

During his attempt to console and help me come to terms with life's inevitable conclusion, death. He gave me a poem to read. *An Essay on Man. Born but to die* and *Hope Springs Eternal*, are but two of my personal choice lines. I think when he gave it to me, he may have been a little too ambitious, I still have the poem now, each time I read a verse I understand a little more and realise the genius of *Alexander Pope* and Mr Noland.

Mr and Mrs Mitchell collected me and my black plastic bag from Nazareth House. I was waiting for them by the gates I'd entered ten years earlier, feeling the same trepidation and terror as I had then.

Mr and Mrs Mitchell, "call me Dave, and this is my wife, Sharon," were a pleasant enough couple who had two daughters, of five and six years old. Joyce seemed a timid little girl. She had long jet black hair and was the image of her father. Sherry, the younger daughter, had the same green eyes and dark brown hair as her mother. Though, as on many previous occasions, I found out that looks can be deceiving.

When we arrived at their house, Sharon didn't appear overly friendly, informing me informally that my measly income was to be paid in cash each Friday, she showed me around her home, and supplied me with a sheet of paper. The white A4 page with the heading stating DAILY, underneath in columns on the left-hand side were the numbers one to ten and next to them an assigned task. Below this and again central was the written word, WEEKLY, with more numbers descending to the bottom of the page. I didn't need a list to tell me what to do or in which order; it was more or less a repetition of the last ten years. Sharon showed me my simple bed in the corner of the big bedroom, opposite the luxurious beds of Joyce and Sherry; a bedroom jam-packed full of toys, with wardrobes full of clothes.

I started to have reservations about the situation I was being forced into. They expected me to cook for, look after and sleep in the same bedroom as the two kids. The youngest of whom was the same age as I was when I first entered the wrought-iron gates of Nazareth House. From the beginning, the children behaved appallingly. They were undoubtedly spoilt. I was in no mood for it. I decided there and then to leave. To be entirely fair to 'call me Dave and Sharon,' I was far from being in the right frame of mind, and it was more than likely, the nuns had provided them with the lists.

The next morning, before breakfast, number five on the DAILY list. Cook a full breakfast for us unless stated, cereal for you and the girls. I slung the bag over my shoulder and said goodbye.

Mr Noland had foreseen this result, insisting I should have been given more time to grieve. He had personally tried to intervene, even pleading with Sister Gabriel who had been appointed my guardian. She was the nun who arranged all the adoptions, fostering and visits. Her other task was to help during the transitional period. From institutionalism to slavery, was my considered opinion. I telephoned the home and informed her I had resigned.

"Come back then," was all she said.

I walked the two miles back to the orphanage.

When I returned, I told the Reverend Mother superior I was finally prepared to become a nun, though thankfully she informed me I couldn't become a novice nun until I was sixteen. More than likely, my decision made her relent, and in an unprecedented move, she granted me a special dispensation to stay in the nursery and my old bed for a final month. Sister Sandra comforted me, I busied myself with the vulnerable unspoilt kiddies. So over the next few weeks, I gradually climbed down a few rungs from the brink of madness. I must have been almost there, because of the briefly considered option of becoming a novice nun.

Sister Sandra allowed me to have some space on the top shelf in the big cupboard. With the help of the kind man who was the closest thing I ever had to a father, we bought the clothes that would transform me into a young woman. Armed with a wad of money we went to the best stores and shops. Where, aided by enthusiastic shop assistants, who were undoubtedly on commission, I selected some tan leather boots with three and a half-inch heels, a pair of slightly darker corduroy tight-fitting trousers, and a V-neck white cotton top. While Mr Noland waited in the pub, I had my hair styled, my nails manicured and varnished.

When he saw me, Mr Noland told me I looked beautiful. He reduced me to tears when he gave me two gold bracelets and a gold ring that had belonged to his darling wife.

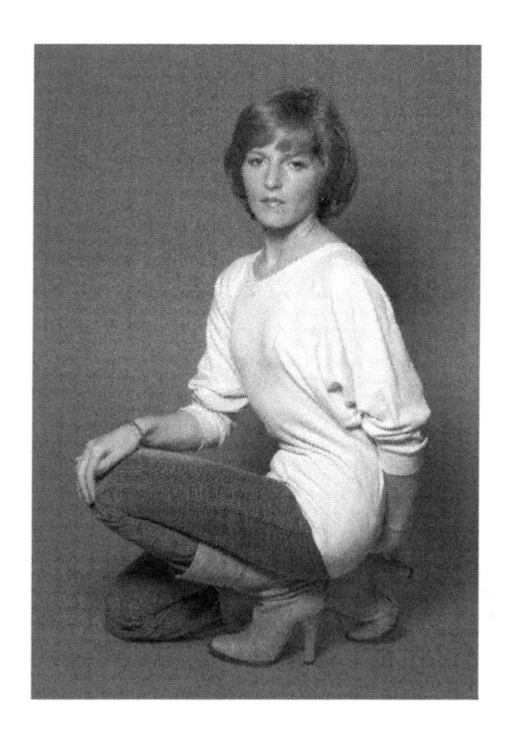

With the help of Mr Noland, I found employment working as a dishwasher in the kitchens of Cardiff's Heath hospital. The position came with accommodation provided. I actually quite liked the job. Whilst I relished the freedom with no kids to look after, I found I had too much time in the evenings to reminisce; the isolation only compounded my heartache.

"I'll see you on Friday evening at the pub opening time. Then you can tell me all about it," Mr Noland said, smiling, displaying a set of tobacco-stained teeth. Thankfully his zest for life looked like it had returned. I wondered when my own passion for life would return.

"You can buy me a pint out of your first pay packet," he added playfully.

I duly met Mr Noland as arranged in the boozer and dutifully bought the first round from my first week's wages; my silver purse was bulging with money.

Lately, I had noticed with some surprise I was getting quite a lot of attention from boys and men alike at the hospital. I was used to looks of pity, now it was most definitely looks of admiration. I wasn't interested in the slightest; I turned down the almost daily requests for dates. After years of being in the institution, living life as constricted as a nun's, my conviction was still, them, the outsiders and us. I felt embarrassed, fending off their interest by making up feeble excuses like I was washing my hair or visiting my Grandmother, eventually coming up with a more permanent solution when I invented a fiancé called Stephen. I'd point to the ring that belonged to Mr Noland's wife and say I was engaged to be married. All the time wishing it was true.

"Time is a great healer," my proxy parent would say.

He was right to a certain extent, but the scars, though not visible, were still there.

I enjoyed working in the hospital; the wages were reasonable and the conditions excellent. I even managed to save a little money. After a while, I settled down to a routine I found gratifying. I'd made a few friends, but I didn't feel confident. I was known as a shy girl. I wasn't shy. I was just reluctant to speak. After years of living with nuns, I was finally conditioned to remain meek and silent. My upbringing contrasted completely from theirs. Coming from poles apart evolution, similar to Tarzan and the apes, and the differences seemed to become more apparent by the day.

I'd spend the rest of my time reading. Four or five times a week, I'd meet Mr Noland for a drink even though I was underage. My tipple had graduated from lemonade to vodka and lime. The barman, the owner's son, had taken a fancy to me and wouldn't charge me on my round.

The man whom I thought of as a surrogate father would laugh and say, "I told you so.

I recalled Mrs Nairs predicting I would be well-liked by all the boys. As it transpired, it would be girls as well. Jasmin and I returned to her house after a night out, we'd had an exciting girly night out and were both a bit tipsy, but not drunk. Her parents were in bed, we were whispering snuggled up on the settee in front of the dying embers of a once roaring fire. She asked me why I never went out with any of the men or boys who asked. I told my nineteen-year-old cute confidante, I didn't want to, I didn't know what to do, or what to expect, and besides, I've never been kissed, and I don't even know how to kiss.

Without looking at me "I can teach you if you like."

Assuming she was doing me a favour, I nodded. Jasmin surprised me by leaning towards me, she kissed me with her mouth open, I didn't think she would teach me this way, but I allowed her to continue, we kissed for a few minutes before she stopped and said, beaming more broadly than usual,

"You're supposed to close your eyes, you know. Now, Milly, you do the same to me,"

I did, and over the next five minutes, she taught me how to expertly French kiss. I found the familiarity of kissing particularly enjoyable. She wanted me to practice more, but I said no. For by then the proverbial penny had dropped.

The Important Man

I was sweet sixteen and a few months and never been kissed by a man when I first went to a night club with Jasmin, my first kisser and the still unemployed Greta. While Jasmin and I huddled uncomfortably in one corner, Greta who was dressed head to toe in white, moseyed around the nightclub like she owned it, showing off and making it blatant she was well known. A group of smartly dressed men she was flirting with looked in our direction. They said something to Greta before two of them came over to where Jasmin and I were standing.

"Hi, I'm John, and this is Dan," said the second most gorgeous male I'd ever seen.

My knees did a slight jig, but nowhere near the energetic tango, they performed for Stephen. Underneath his immaculate, luxurious locks, his dark brown eyes sparkled. When a broad grin lined his handsome face, there was a glimpse of a perfect white-toothed smile reminiscent of Errol Flynn's. We talked or to be precise, I listened, to the charismatic man who was about two inches taller than my five foot two and a half. I quickly returned questions with a question and hopefully nodded in all the right places. I was acutely aware of my inadequacies; my lack of confidence made my ability to converse intelligently complicated. He was a millionaire and lived on the island of Jersey, he'd said, staring at me intently waiting for a reaction. Not getting the required response he tried his coup de grass.

"I'm flying my Piper Cherokee six-seat aeroplane to Jersey tomorrow. I have a business meeting before lunch, then I'm flying straight back to Cardiff. Would you like to come with me?"

"No thanks, I'm washing my hair."

The look on the boastful man's face was priceless.

Dan was getting nowhere with Jasmin and gave up after a short while.

Jasmin, I and Greta of the queen of clubs, as she called herself, returned each week, mainly because it was a free night. I was undoubtedly much friendlier with Jasmin. Jasmin was an intelligent, confident, caring, and quick-witted young woman. That's not to say Greta wasn't. She had her attributes, but I knew Jasmin better.

"John's paid for the drinks, ladies," the barman would say.

John considered a returned smile an invitation to join us. Greta liked him and made it blatantly obvious. When someone else was paying, Greta's drink was a large vodka and orange juice, one she'd request in an accent she must have borrowed from someone living in the north of England. When she paid, which wasn't often, it would be an orange juice.

Five weeks after our first meeting, John who knew nothing of our lives and more importantly, Nazareth House, shocked me to the core by asking me to live with him in his house in Jersey, even though he was forty-five years old. That made him twenty-nine years older than me and mature enough to be my father. I considered it bizarre and said no. I hardly knew him. I'd only met him five times and then for barely a few short hours, though I was still attracted to him only because he reminded me of Errol Flynn.

A week later, he asked me again, this time using different tactics.

"Come and live with me. It's a big four-bedroom beach house; the sand and sea are my gardens. You can go swimming every day, I'll take you to the finest restaurants in Jersey. I can fly you back to Cardiff anytime you like," he almost pleaded.

I tried to let him down gently and explained, I was only sixteen, and I had never been with a man before. But when I did, he would be my husband. I told him I liked him very much, but not in that way. I thought I may have been harsh, but he beamed his Errol Flynn smile.

"Don't worry, I'm an important man, I promise I won't touch you," he whispered close to my ear, so close I could smell the Jimmy Savile cigar smoke on his breath.

"Please come. All my friends will be jealous of me if they think I'm living with a beauty like you. You can have your own room, and I'll employ and pay you as a housekeeper. Just pretend I'm your boyfriend. It will be our secret."

I was flattered but declined.

"Think about it. The offer is still there," John whispered.

Kevin, the pub owners' son, plonked down Mr Noland's full pint glass on the snug serving hatch and picked up my empty glass. I casually glanced towards the men-only bar as a tallish lad walked in. I admired the smart blue denim shirt ornately decorated with pearl coloured buttons he was wearing. My gaze went up slowly to the face of the handsome young man, his own gaze meeting my eyes. The same languid, liquid smile and eyes of nearly five years before in St Dyfrigs church looked at me. I felt so much pleasure, my tummy lurched, and my heart raced. I smiled a smile so broad my lips hurt. I raised my hand and waved furiously. Stupid Stephen looked over his shoulder to see who I was waving at.

Kevin chose that moment to return with my free vodka. He turned to serve Stephen, his new customer, in the process obscuring my view. A few moments later, Kevin returned to resume our chat as I watched the denim shirt going out of the door.

When Kevin noticed me looking, he said,

"He only came in for cigarettes."

I ran to the door. You're not getting away that easy, I said to myself as I skipped onto the pavement. My state of exhilaration immediately evaporated. Stupid Stephen had his arm affectionately around the shoulder of a beautiful girl wearing black-framed spectacles who looked like the Greek singer Nana Mouskouri. The slim young woman with long dark hair was rocking a pram containing a crying baby. Stephen handed the proud-eyed girl the cigarettes and picked up the tiny sobbing child who immediately stopped crying. Stephen and the slim girl both laughed. It was at that point I noticed the third finger on their left hands bore the gold bands that proclaimed hands-off, we're married.

My heart sank. Not a day went by, without me thinking of him. He was even more handsome than I remembered if that could be possible. He had matured gracefully; his dark blue stubble accentuated his features. I added the fresh image of him laughing to my memory, trying unsuccessfully to obliterate the good-looking young woman. He's only eighteen, what's he doing getting married so young? I thought angrily. I supposed the crying baby answered that question.

That evening I had more vodka than I should have. I always shared most of my inner thoughts with Mr Noland and poured out my heart to him. While Kevin poured out the drinks, Mr Noland listened attentively, "Milly," he started to say but coughed instead. His coughing fits had increased in intensity over the previous months. He automatically pulled out a handkerchief and coughed into it, then opened the hankie to have a quick peek. A worried frown appeared but quickly faded. He put the hankie swiftly back in his jacket pocket. Mr Noland didn't think I noticed it was bloodstained.

He continued casually where he left off, "Milly, it's better to have loved and lost than never to have loved at all."

At about ten o'clock, two hours later than our usual departure, Mr Noland asked Kevin to phone for a taxi for a tipsy Milly Nash. I woke up the next morning with a thumping headache, vowing never to drink so much again. Joining the pounding was the image of the pretty girl. Get out of my mind, Nana.

My pal, Clive Noland, came up with another stratagem when we discussed the next stage of my life. He'd asked me dozens of times to call him Clive. I tried and failed; to me, he would always be Mr Noland.

"We're on a level playing field now, Milly, call me Clive."

With his help, I began to study even more. He called it; Clive's University of life. He selected more of the books he wanted me to read and would quiz me afterwards. We started off with Ladybird books on nature; regrettably, we only did this for a few short months as his health deteriorated rapidly. Even though he was in considerable pain, we would still laugh. His sense of humour and dry wit are, thankfully, my legacies. The next time I saw him, he was upbeat and in fine form. I told him I had trouble getting Stephen out of my mind. He knew about the millionaire and advised against it.

"He's much too old for you Milly," he said, shaking his head.

I said to him. "It's better to have loved a short man than never to have loved a tall."

He pondered this for a second then we both howled with laughter at my deliberate faux pas. I'm glad that's my last memory of him because he was killed two days later.

"Run over by a bus right outside the gates," Mother Superior told me in a practical, matter-of-fact way when I went to find out why he wasn't in the pub.

"Tripped and fell under the wheels. Mr Noland died instantly. Didn't feel a thing, thank God," she said in cool imperturbable, emotionless tones.

I was in a state of shock. I realised he was ill, like with Roly I was preparing myself for the worst. I called in sick at work and locked myself in my room for three full days and cried. I stared at the wall for hours. I thought of the good times, as he'd taught me to do in times of grief, though it didn't help. I eventually unlocked my door to attend his funeral. His favourite tree, the oak was his choice of wood for his coffin. He'd told me he wasn't fearful of death. He even said he was looking forward to being reunited with his darling wife.

When little Roly died, he said, "When I go Milly, I'll find Roly and take her for walks for you."

I thought warmly of him during the service, even so, tears trickled down the front of the black dress onto the shoes I was wearing. Attire I had purchased in part with his money. In silence, I thanked him for being a part of my life, making it more bearable, helping me to cope with living in the outside world. I selfishly wondered how I would survive without him.

All the home's residents attended his requiem mass. I had the strange impression that to all extents and purposes, I was the only outsider there, as he had no surviving relatives. The sombre choir, my friends up in their lofty perches, sang *The Old Rugged Cross*, with Sister Norma performing less animatedly for the slow hymn. I only recently discovered why Sister Norma only reprimanded the group to her right and said nothing to the octet on her left. When she was a teenager, she lost her eye in an accident and wore a false glass eye, so in effect, was blind to her left-hand side.

Mr Noland had paid for and planned his own funeral down to the last details. The culmination of which was when his body was finally reunited with his wife in the same grave. And I have no doubt whatsoever, that his soul was with her in Heaven.

Left or Right

I was absolutely petrified as I glanced at the ground ten thousand feet below me, the *Piper Cherokee* bounced and lurched towards the island of Jersey, a hundred and sixty-mile flight from Cardiff. John had lied to me. It wasn't his plane but Dan's, who was at the controls.

I felt sad I hadn't heeded the words of Mr Noland. I was in no condition to make any rational decisions and was regretting them at the airport. I packed in my job and was on my way within a week.

I had no one to advise me, the only person that did was dead, and even his last advice I'd ignored. I was stupid, and I knew it.

I had laid out the conditions as to my move to Jersey. John had agreed to all of them. My actions were born out of misery. John's only requirement for me was that I would have to pretend to be his girlfriend when we were in the company of others. Of course, he expected me to cook and clean.

When we arrived at the house, I found my dense carpeted bedroom was a decent size with a three-quarter bed, a large wardrobe and a dressing table with a big bay window that overlooked the sea. I didn't sleep well and was bitterly regretting my decisions. At least John didn't lie about his house. It was as he described. I listened to the colliding waves throughout the night. When I awoke, the view was as beautiful as Barry Island's beach.

I knocked on his bedroom door situated across the landing from mine. I thought he said, come in, so I did. The two things I noticed first was his gorgeous pearly white smile and his unruffled shinning hair. Unfortunately, the teeth were in a glass of water and his wig on a hat stand on the dressing table.

The old, toothless, bald man shouted. "I dold u dot do cubin."

I closed his door and went to my room thinking, what the bloody hell have I done? Then I started giggling. I was still intermittently sniggering when he knocked on my door an hour later. I resisted the urge to mimic his voice and repeat his words, wiped the grin off my face and said come in. Neither of us said a word about the incident.

I weighed up my options as the days passed, deciding to leave as soon as was possible. This time I was more a slave than a skivvy. I cooked, cleaned, scrubbed, polished and angrily regretted my rash judgement.

He soon showed his true colours the first time we went out to a pub in the island's capital St Helier, a twenty-minute walk by road from his beach house. Mr Noland had taught me to answer a question with a question if I was unsure. He said people like to talk about themselves, when they do, they end up warming to you, because in general people believe they've had an inspiring, stimulating conversation. When in reality, they've been doing most of the talking? It proved to be invaluable advice.

I was talking to Dan or I should say, listening to him, as he discussed the attributes of his aircraft.

"That's an amazing plane you have. It must be challenging to learn how to fly," I mentioned.

"I'll take you up and show you the island from a thousand feet if you like," Danny, as he asked me to call him, replied.

John's timing was impeccable. Neither of us had noticed him until he leaned in so close I could smell his usual cigar and whisky breath, to say menacingly in a wavering voice.

"No, you bloody well won't."

John kept me away from Dan for the remainder of the evening, informing the others I was his property, by kissing me and putting on a show. He tried to put his tongue in my mouth, but I kept my teeth well clenched, I shuddered repulsed each time. John introduced me to a few people but gave me no opportunity to mingle. He wanted them to be jealous, yet he was the jealous one. The atmosphere was tense, climaxing in a scuffle between the two, now former friends.

Back in John's house, he shouted at me as soon as the door was closed. He called me a slut for flirting and screamed, inadvertently spitting into my face. He said that I had shown him up in front of his friends. I remained calm and explained that he had made a fool of himself and told him Dan was just trying to be friendly. Then I reminded him not to kiss me again, and to stick to our deal.

John walloped me so hard I was knocked backwards. I fell to the floor and stared up at the drunken beast standing over me. I watched his Adam's apple move up and down as he swallowed hard. I had a fleeting thought of retaliating. Sister Terry had deserved hers and kept out of my way afterwards. Tonight he had shown how deceiving he had been and confirmed I now had another misery to escape from.

We ate breakfast the next morning as if nothing happened. A little while later, the name-calling started. John called me a stupid little urchin because I didn't know what an electric toaster was. I never said it at the time, but then I was uncertain what an urchin was. The only decent parts of our agreement were his trips away, though; while his relationship with Dan remained sour, he was prevented from taking flights to Cardiff. I had hoped to escape from John on one of his promised trips. As it was, I was stuck on my Island prison. After a short while, I began to recognise the reality of my situation. In the home I was locked up for most of the time, dependent on the institution for sustenance, warmth, clothing of sorts and a bed, all my life I relied on others for every physical and emotional want. Here in Jersey, my shackles were invisible, at first, I was desperate to escape. I had very little money, definitely not enough for a plane ticket, not that I knew how to acquire one. Where to flee to was another problem.

Jersey is situated nearer France than England. France is less than fifteen miles away. The currency was the same, yet the coins were of different designs. If the kiddies cleaning out a tent in Blackwier Field found one, they would have at first been elated and then confused as to their worth. This would have been confounded even more by the recent introduction of decimal currency. The coins were as alien and different as St Helier was to Cardiff.

The house, one of a hundred that lined the beachfront, was in one of the most affluent areas of Jersey. It was a big detached white building set in its own walled grounds. It had four en-suite bedrooms and downstairs were two reception rooms plus a large open plan lounge, the modern kitchen had French windows that faced the sea, and France. His den as he called it was off-limits to me and locked, which was a shame, as the shelves lining the room were full of books.

A routine developed where we watched television on separate loungers, with him continually puffing on a smelly cigar. Then one evening, while we were watching a TV program, he threw the book at me he became bored with after reading a few pages.

"Have a go at reading this," he sneered.

The book was *The Count of Monte Cristo* by *Alexander Dumas*. I devoured the pages with gusto; recognising the similarities between the young Edmond and myself, realising John had inadvertently helped me. Thanks to his book, I now thought of him as my jailer. From then on, I decided to better myself in every way I could, as Mr Noland had instigated. I was well aware of my failings.

John surprised me one day by buying me a gorgeous red dress with matching shoes. I wore the gifts, with my red handbag to a birthday party being held at a posh hotel in Saint Helier, the capital of Jersey named after a hermit who died in 555AD. The party was for Margie, the woman who owned the twenty-bed hotel.

She was a glamorous forty-year-old kind friendly lady, whom I had initially met at the pub where the friendship of John and Dan had ended. The attractive, graceful woman looked elegant in her pale yellow knee-length dress with matching heeled shoes, holding her red-lipped smile steady as she greeted her guests, her blue eyes reflecting the smile. She came over to us and went to shake my hand, changed her mind and kissed me on both cheeks.

"I knew the dress would fit you. You should smile more often, you look absolutely divine darling," she said emphasising, darling, by adding at least five more A's and a couple of I's. "You and I must have a chat later."

We began to circulate with John wearing the same disingenuous smile that first attracted me to him. He kept his arm around my shoulder and introduced me to his suited and ball-gowned friends, using the same words every time.

"This is Milly, my girlfriend. She's from Cardiff."

He might as well have put a sign around my neck, saying she's mine. I noticed Dan was at the party; I smiled and nodded to him.

John saw me and hissed through his teeth, well the teeth that were manufactured for him. "Don't ever do that again."

Again, I embarrassed John at dinner. I looked at all the knives, forks and spoons bordering the napkin covered plate and asked what they were all for. "That's a soup spoon, a dessert spoon, a knife for this and a fork for that," he hissed impatiently, embellishing this with depraved swear words he often used for emphasis, though quietly enough so no one else could hear.

Margie saw him, she knew instantly something was amiss. I saw her eyes narrow with one eye almost closing as a frown appeared on her brow. She noticed me looking at her and winked. I saved further embarrassment by following the actions of my fellow diners.

After the exquisite banquet, Margie came over, took hold of my hand and said to John as we walked away,

"I want to show your beautiful girlfriend something in my lounge. You don't mind, do you, darling?"

He had no option than to watch me being gently guided away. We sat on wooden stools facing each other, either side of a breakfast bar in her living quarters. I felt uncomfortable in the strained silence. I could tell she was deliberating, thinking about what she would say. I took the opportunity to look around at the trappings of success. Oil paintings adorned the walls, vases and ornaments were lined up in glass cabinets, the furniture and décor were tasteful and expensive-looking.

Finally, she said, "Run, run for your life, Milly. Get as far away from him as fast as you can. I've known him for a long time. He's not for you. I saw what the nasty bugger said, and I noticed the disquiet in your eyes."

My instinct was to trust the straightforward woman even though she was an outsider. I said quietly and without meaning too, almost pathetically. “I have nobody to run to and nowhere to run.”

She stared at me for a few moments; her blue eyes wide open as if in shock. “You have now,” she said, pulling me forward for a warm embrace.

Afterwards, John asked what Margie wanted, I sidestepped the question. He warned me to keep my urchin gob shut. I subserviently obeyed my master. I had no intention of telling him what had occurred. Margie, the perfect hostess, returned with fresh drinks for us, a double whiskey and ginger for him, vodka and lime for me. I thanked her and took a sip, there was no vodka. John didn’t see her wink. She plied us with glass after glass, John’s glass always holding more whisky than ginger.

“John, you and Milly, will have to stay here tonight,” Margie said as John’s words and movements became more erratic.

He managed to slur something that sounded affirmative. By eleven o’clock, he was paralytic, he had to be carried to a vacant room on the first floor, where he passed out.

We returned to sitting on the same stools as before. I looked at Margie as she poured me a real vodka and lime. She was about five foot eight, slim, had loosely curled jet black hair and had the air and confidence of a successful businesswoman.

“That worked, didn’t it?” she said and laughed.

I chuckled feeling incredibly comfortable in the company of the crafty woman.

She echoed my thoughts by saying. “I think you and I are going to get on. You should smile more often, you lit up the room when you walked in and smiled at me. Didn’t you notice all eyes were on you?”

We rejoined her other guests, and during the final two hours, I stayed by her side.

"Smile," she'd whisper now and then.

When the last guest had left, which happened to be Dan, he shook my hand. Looking directly at me, he said. "Goodnight both. And good luck."

Back in her lounge, she poured out two glasses of wine. Except for the vodka earlier we had only drunk lime juice. I liked Margie; she knew John would get drunk and pass out. She clearly had a plan, but what was it?

"It's not ladylike to get drunk, especially at your own party," she explained.

"And I've made sure you're sober as well, so I can talk to you, tell me to mind my own business if you like and I'll stop. You made me laugh when you twigged what I was up to. I could see the amusement in those lovely eyes. Ok then Milly, tell me all about yourself."

So I did, I partially unburdened myself of sixteen years of existence. I told Margie I was brought up by nuns, was in an orphanage from a baby until less than a year before.

"I did wonder for now, and again your striking eyes look as if you've experienced things other people couldn't imagine," she intuitively stated.

"John doesn't know about the orphanage, and I don't want anyone else to know," I told her as an afterthought.

She told me my secret was safe with her. I knew it would be as I trusted her implicitly already.

We both cried when I told her of Pat. We shed tears when I talked of Roly. Margie's tears streamed when I told her of Mr Noland and his intention to prepare me for the outside world.

"Clive Noland's University of life. He sounds like a lovely man."

"He was the father I never had," I replied sadly.

She looked at the smart shoes I was wearing, "Do they fit you all right?"

I smiled, recalling her earlier remark when she said she knew the dress would fit me, "You have good taste." I said.

"You'd look great wearing a sack darling," she shot back.

I remembered the sack race and grinned. I told Margie of the boy I fell in love with when I was twelve. I told her of Lerina and Mrs Nairs and love at first sight.

"Why, oh why did you come here with him?"

"Mr Noland died soon after I saw Stephen with his wife. I felt I couldn't cope. John said he had a big house, was a millionaire, had his own aeroplane and said he'd look after me."

I continued to give Margie a précis of my life. We talked until daylight, by which time the alcohol had taken effect. The empty wine bottles served as evidence. Though, it wasn't a one-sided conversation by any means. I felt Margie was releasing some pent-up emotions herself, for her own millionaire husband had died of a heart attack three years before.

"I came over here for a two week holiday, with two girlfriends seventeen years ago. I met Colin at this hotel. He was forty-three and worked on the reception desk. Days later, I was spending nearly every night with him. My friends didn't mind. They were happy. I was happy. He was a handsome divorcee who had two grown-up children. By the end of the holiday, he asked me to stay. He told me he had a house not far away but stayed at the hotel because he was lonely. Even though I had just graduated from Cambridge University and had a decent job waiting for me, I said yes without question or hesitation.

We were so in love. I didn't care; he was a receptionist. I could find work. What I didn't know, though Milly," she told me, her eyes shining, and a proud look on her face. "Was that he, in fact, owned this hotel; he was only on the desk covering for an employee. He told me he only pretended to be the receptionist so he could see me every day. So, I moved into his wonderful home on the beachfront. Our bedroom overlooked the channel. We would spend hours curled up, watching the tide coming in and out. We had a new kitchen and French windows installed. We were so very, very happy."

"It sounds just like where I'm living with John," I interrupted.

She stared at me, paused for a second while she thought of an answer, and said, "It sounds like it is because it was and still is my house. All the furniture, fixtures and fittings are mine."

I gawked at her, shocked, but not really surprised it was her house and not John's. He had lured me to Jersey with a pack of lies. I knew I was naïve, immature and foolhardy. I scanned her charming face, immediately becoming conscious I had never had an in-depth conversation with an adult woman before in my entire life.

"Yes, Milly. He lied again. It's my house. I loved living there at first, but I couldn't get the image of Colin and his wife living there out of my mind. So we converted this part of the hotel into living quarters and moved here. Your little John was a lazy, drunken womaniser; regrettably, he was a good friend of Colin's. John recently lost his business and had to sell his house to pay off obligations. He asked if he could rent the house, so Colin let him have it at a peppercorn friendship rate. I hated the little bugger. I still don't like him much now, I'm just starting to hate him again, for the way he's treating you." Her face inflamed with anger.

“When Colin died,” she said, as her ire faded. “I reluctantly let him stay. He asked me to buy you your outfit just after he received my birthday invitation. I couldn’t understand why. He said he wanted to surprise you, the lying little show off toad. What really confuses me Milly is why you came here with him in the first place? I know you said, he told you he’d look after you. But,” she floundered.

I said shyly. “I told John I’d never had a relationship with a man. And when I did, it would be with my husband. John said he was an important man and promised he wouldn’t touch me. He told me all he wanted was to make his friends jealous.”

“He painted a masterpiece of life for you here, didn’t he?” she sat up straight, took a deep breath and said, “Milly, do you think Mr Noland would like me to take over as your tutor? You could become my first pupil.”

Smiling broadly, I nodded.

“Milly you really are an enigma, you know?” she said, laughing as she topped up our glasses with the remnants of the third bottle.

I looked into her sparkly blue eyes feeling more comfortable than I’d been for a long while. Maybe it was the wine. Perhaps it was the drink that made Margie’s eyes shine, or conceivably the result of the tears we shed together. Undoubtedly, mine was the fleeting thoughts of the last time I’d felt almost as peaceful when the nun with the shiny eyes plaited my beautiful blonde hair. I recalled her last words to me when she said, “May God bless you, Milly.”

Margie was gazing at me quizzically when I snapped out of my daydream.

“Penny for them,” she giggled.

I looked back at her, imitating her expression.

She smiled, "A penny for them, or a penny for your thoughts, means. What are you thinking about?"

"Your reminded me of when I was five years old."

"Go on. I know you're tired, but I'm dying to know."

So for the second time that morning, I bared my heart and soul and shared some more of my inner thoughts with the woman, who by now was most definitely my firm friend. I told her about the kind nun and my braided hair. She shed more tears when I told her about Greta and I having the plaits chopped off. I talked about the black-clad nun, Sister Anna and Pat as I recalled the events leading up to my first night in the home. I skipped a lot of the particulars.

"Oh, my God. Your life was so full of sadness, misery and mystery."

"It still is," I corrected. "And you don't know the half of it. Though, I will tell you all in time. I promise."

"This is going to be as difficult for me, as it will be for you," she said, pausing to consider her next words. "So please be patient with me as this is my first day as a teacher. Anything I say is not a contradiction, it's designed to educate you. To get you ready for your return to Cardiff."

I had already told her I felt my destiny was back in Cardiff, I had a premonition my mother and father were still there. Furthermore, I needed to bond more with what little family I had.

"When you thought John said he was an important man, in actuality he said, he was an impotent man," slowly emphasising the syllables.

She waited for a reaction for a few moments, not getting any for I must have looked vague. Getting the hang of her new job, she began again. "The literal meaning of impotent is powerless, ineffective or even helpless"? She waited, with her mouth slightly open, anxiously waiting for a response, before adding, "Unable?"

"Don't tell me they didn't teach you about the birds and bees? Before you say anything, Milly." She stopped again, looked to the ceiling and shook her black curls. "Oh my God Milly, you're such a sweet innocent child."

She patiently told me without any embarrassment whatsoever, what the eventual and inevitable outcome is between a man and woman when they love each other, explaining in great detail about courtship, love, marriage, sex and babies, in the process giving me the biggest shock of my short life.

She must have realised the enormity of the mission in front of her, as I sat squirming, dumbfounded in front of her, she picked up the telephone pressed a button, spoke in a sober professional manner "Good morning Doris. Can I have two coffees and two breakfasts? Yes, the full works, please. Oh, and could you bring a dressing gown with you?" She looked at me and answered the muted question with, "Small, please. That's one of the perks of the trade, that's what comes with owning a five-star hotel," she said proudly.

The breakfasts from the hotel's kitchen arrived almost as soon as the phone was back in the receiver. There was a quiet tap, tap on the door.

"Come in, Doris," Margie said.

A smiling woman of about fifty entered pushing a silver trolley. On her head was a small white cotton tiara, she had flat black shoes, a black knee-length skirt and a white pinafore with little pockets by her middle. On the top shelf of the trolley were two gleaming silver domes, with handles on top, covering two large round plates. Two steaming cups of coffee, a bowl containing white square cubes of sugar and another plate with toast and marmalade sat on a silver tray on the middle shelf. While the bottom shelf held a white fluffy towelling dressing gown as white as the blouses returned to Pat and me by Mrs Nairs.

"You don't miss a thing, do you? I watched you take in every little detail," my new teacher said.

We ate the breakfast, which was delicious, finishing with the strongest coffee I'd ever tasted. John liked a cup of the instant at least eight times a day. This was much richer.

"Percolated coffee my darling, it's made from freshly roasted and ground Blue Mountain coffee beans."

I nodded slowly and then anxiously glanced at the clock.

"Oh, don't worry about him," she said and laughed. "Grab yourself a nice shower, put the gown on then come back here. I have a few things I need to say before I forget. I'm just popping up to see how little John is getting on."

She handed me the warm looking dressing gown with a pair of slippers on the top, before walking to the door and pointing down the hallway.

"The guest room is the second door on the right. You're sleeping here today," she winked as she closed the door.

I thought of winking Stephen as I showered. Refreshed, I then walked back to the waiting, amused and glamorous Margie who showed no sign of weariness. I was wearing the fluffy dressing gown and fleecy white slippers.

"He was awake and waiting for you when I knocked on his door. I gave him a bollocking for getting drunk and leaving you alone. I told him I looked after you, and you were in my guest room sleeping. I said to come back this evening. I'm sure he had his wig on back the front, silly little bugger," she snorted.

I laughed.

I awoke to feel refreshed and happier than I'd been since I stayed with the Nairs. I slipped on the dressing gown and slippers and walked out of the bedroom, heading towards the sounds of a discussion. I entered the room arriving at the tail end of their conversation. John was sitting with his back to me, a glass of whiskey in his hand.

Margie noticed me walking towards them but continued talking, "So that's settled then. If Milly wants the job, she can start on Monday. Ah, here she is now. Milly, I was just saying to John, I'm looking for a new receptionist. Karen is leaving the island to get married. I think you would be perfect for the job. What do you think?"

I looked from her to John, who could barely suppress his displeasure. I thought quickly, and putting him on the back foot, said, "Would that be all right with you, John?"

My lord and master replied sullenly, "If you want to, I suppose so."

"I'd love too. Thanks very much," I said graciously, sealing the contract by shaking Margie's hand.

Both of us looked happy, we were trying to not overdo the smiles. Margie caught me by surprise. Inside I was bursting with joy. I very much felt like hugging her.

And so began my two lives; the miserable existence with John and the exhilarating, elucidating one with Margie.

"If you don't understand a word Milly, just ask? That's what these sessions will be all about. I'll teach you posture and deportment, and how to use that beautiful smile of yours."

After years of being told to stop asking stupid questions, to shut up or you'll get a slap, or keep quiet you ugly charity case. I felt invigorated. "There are a few words I don't understand," I mentioned.

"What are they?"

"Well, you could start with peppercorn," I suggested.

Margie and I soon became the best of friends, my job was easy. Moreover, I loved the friendly atmosphere; it wasn't anything like work. I was unbelievably relaxed, though I still occasionally jumped like a startled rabbit at the click of a door. The only cleaning I did was when I was back at my prison beach house, I decided to stay in Jersey for as long as I needed after all this life was much better than the institution.

After about a year, John and I settled into a routine suited to our way of life. His lifestyle was perfect; he had it made; the need to work didn't exist, I was his housekeeper. To pacify him, I even paid him lodging money. He pursued his pleasures in life drinking whiskey, smoking cigars, giving me a dig in my ribs and reading westerns. I must admit, I found his short story cowboy paperbacks rather entertaining; even if the gore and the ultimate, forty-five gunshot to the head, was somewhat disturbing.

For three years, come rain or shine, I walked, ran or happily sauntered, the beach journey to the Galaxy Hotel. Margie took on the role of a tutor with unbridled enthusiasm, but it was challenging for me to break the habits of sixteen years. I had been brought up to be subservient, to be meek and silent around the nuns. When talking to someone, I didn't realise I automatically looked downwards as if submitting to their will.

"Smile, relax Milly. Talk to people like you're talking to me. Look into their eyes. Pull your shoulders back and think happy thoughts. Don't say good morning. Sing it. Goood Moorniing, Galaxy Hotellll, can I heelpp youuu," she exemplified. "Don't look at the floor Milly. Please don't slouch. That's better, now try to show your teeth when you speak. It's almost similar to snarling, darling; please believe me it works. Not that much of a swagger love. Don't mumble. Emphasise the vowels, but not too much. Try not to be a show off. But most importantly, try to be yourself. I know you think I'm trying to make you a different person but this is to bring out the real Milly Nash."

She'd give me books to read when I finished, we would dissect and analyse the fundamentals. We played a vigorous cut-throat three sets of tennis at least once a week. On the odd occasion, I even won a game, with Margie informing me of the significance of exercise and competitiveness. We went on long hikes together, all the time, her parenting me.

Throughout this period, John continued to treat me like a slave. I cooked, cleaned and washed his clothes. I always sniggered when folding up his initial-embroidered shirts, Y- fronts and socks. The showman continued to convince people I was his girlfriend, even though nothing could be further from the truth. I never told Margie, but he started behaving like a nun. He criticised practically everything I did, laughed at any mistake I made and would often give me a slap. I found it deeply disconcerting. It was behaviour I grew up with. I started to make mistakes deliberately, as I didn't want him to know the progress I was making with Margie. I hated him with a vengeance.

We went out together about twice a month. Thankfully, Margie would usually be there as well as Dan. I soon came to realise that nobody, in the close-knit community of Saint Helier Parish, liked the boastful, show off of a man I was once infatuated with.

Margie, my surrogate mother, had a racing-green open-top MGB sports car. During the tourist off-season, we would often have lunch in one of the more excellent restaurants in Jersey. The ones John promised we'd go to, but never did. She took tremendous pleasure in inviting John, insisting almost pleading with him to join us, knowing damn well he wouldn't.

"It would blow his bloody wig off, we would have to stop every five minutes to rescue the bloody thing from the road," we would roar with laughter every time.

Impetuous Urges

I stared with pride at the delightful looking nineteen-year-old young woman with a makeup-free face. A face that possibly could be mistaken for being made-up, for the face definition and cerise lips enhanced the gleaming white teeth smiling warmly back at me. I admired the feminine figure, the long sun-tainted strawberry blonde hair. Her sky-blue eyes twinkled above high cheekbones, her flawless complexion held a healthy glow. I nodded approval at my cheerful reflection.

Only now, I thought, after all these years, had I started to like myself, to think I was more than just a thing. The daily beach runs or walks to and from the Galaxy, along with the nourishing food Margie provided, had taught me to cook changed me without me really noticing. I still didn't like mirrors. For years I had been called ugly and worthless, jibes and name-calling that was meant to demean and ultimately humiliate me, to this day I can't fathom out why?

I was content and happy enough with the life I was living, but I felt something was missing. I could have left John a long time before and lived at the Galaxy, but I didn't want to burden Margie. Even so, I thought my time in Jersey was at an end.

A perfect opportunity had arisen for my escape from John; he was going away for two weeks on what he called a business trip. I had enough money from the accumulated tips Margie kept for me to pay for my fare back to Wales, once there, I had my money in the bank back in Cardiff. But I wondered if it was too soon to return. My wise friend advised me not to leave just yet, saying I still had a lot to learn. My impulsive juvenile urge to abscond was too strong, so after a tearful goodbye and with a return ticket Margie had unceasingly badgered me to buy clutched in my hand, I boarded the plane to Cardiff without a clue what my objectives were.

I had no intention of going to Nazareth House until I was settled. I wanted to avoid the painful reminders of my past, so I thought my first stop should be with an old friend.

Jasmin McCluskey smiled her cheesy smile when she answered the door and ushered me inside. For an hour, we talked, swopping recent anecdotes, partially catching up with what had happened after I left. Her main revelations were that she had left Nazareth House and was now working in a night club in Caerphilly, on her nights off she sometimes met up with Greta who still lived in Cardiff.

When we went to visit Greta, I was quite surprised she wasn't overly enamoured by my presence, but she reluctantly granted that I could sleep on the settee of her one-bedroom flat until I found somewhere else to stay.

Greta and Jasmin had entered a beauty competition that was being held the next evening at a nightclub in Newport, a town twelve miles from Cardiff. They spent over five hours getting ready for the competition. I thought Greta had overdone the makeup but said nothing; she had her hair her in a ponytail that was pulled back so tight she appeared almost Chinese. Jasmin told me Greta had persuaded her to enter, she was very nervous, and under no illusion of her chances of winning a beauty competition so hadn't gone to any extremes. Personally, I thought Jasmin looked attractive and stylish, especially in the beautiful red evening gown. Greta looked like the queen of clubs; her face paint was thick and generous, her eyebrows enhanced by black and blue eyeliner resembled Elizabeth Taylor in *Cleopatra*, she reminded me of a nursery nun in her white gown.

Jasmin's father drove us to the lavish nightclub in Newport. The car park was crammed with vehicles, ultimately giving us an insight to the attendance. Jasmin had a panic attack, stage fright more like it, even though we had a few vodka courage appetisers. To the chagrin of Greta, Jasmin managed to persuade me to take her place. I was uncertain and only agreed because Greta couldn't disguise her covetousness.

Jasmin dragged me into the dressing room and put a bright red lipstick on my pouting lips and expertly applied a little blue eyeliner. She went into the adjoining toilet and returned with her brassiere and about half a roll of toilet tissue, she didn't need to explain as she moulded the mass into a perfectly shaped, respectable thirty-two cup size. I slipped on Jasmin's red gown, which was too big for me. It instantly reminded me of dressing for school at Nazareth House. Such was the tissue padding I glanced down to look at my shoes and couldn't see my feet. In my hazy state, I wondered how Margie managed. She could have been wearing odd shoes for all she knew.

If it hadn't been for the large vodkas, I wouldn't have entertained parading in front of a couple of hundred people for one second. I shook my head vigorously to thicken out my hair.

One by one, the competitors were eliminated until they announced the Chinese Cleopatra, and I was part of the final ten of the forty hopeful contenders. I never expected to progress any further or reach that stage. Greta was excluded before the next round, leaving me in the final five.

Between the heats, we drank copious amounts of vodka. I thought I could handle my drinks, but Greta appeared to be stone-cold sober, though she didn't say much, while poor Jasmin, who was now drinking gin-based cocktails laced with fresh strawberries, was wholly sloshed. As I stood with the four beautiful women on the stage, I could hear Jasmin in the audience shouting.

"Come on, Milly. Come on, Milly, go get them."

I didn't understand what that meant; nevertheless, it made me laugh. To my shock, the consternation of the other competitors and the utter jubilation of the drunken Jasmin I came second. It transpired this was a qualifying heat, with the first two going through to the Miss Wales finals to be held a week later in the Caerphilly nightclub where Jasmin worked.

I soon found out Greta's lifestyle was not for me. She woke at about three o'clock in the afternoon, cooked bacon and eggs, then slouched around until evening, taking up to four hours to get ready to go out. In the club, she would flirt outrageously with nightclub men, who were after only one thing, as Margie would say. All Greta wanted though was attention, to be plied with drinks, get sozzled then return home at four am, only to start the routine over again. On the second night, she tried unsuccessfully to persuade me to become friendly with the friend of a man she liked. I had no interest whatsoever and refused. In the early morning, when we returned to her flat, she refused to speak to me.

I felt unwanted and only stayed with Greta for another night before I went to stopover with Jasmin and her mum and dad. By then, though, I was already determined to return to Jersey. I was missing Margie and my life with her. My sage was right as usual. However, the just in case, return ticket she insisted I bought was dated the day after the Miss Wales beauty competition. Luckily I also had enough money to tide me over until then.

That night I shared Jasmin's bed. For only the second time in my life, I shared a bed with somebody, though this time there was a pillow barricade between us. Jasmin laughed when I did it, but she gave me a goodnight kiss on the cheek.

On the night before the finals, we went to the pub near Nazareth House. Kevin the barman's reaction when we walked in was flattering; he made it evident he fancied both of us. I wasn't interested and knew Jasmin wasn't. Margie had explained same-sex relationships to me, leaving me mildly embarrassed and somewhat curious. Kevin, bless him, gave us loads to drink, that ultimately his father paid for until we were all roaring drunk. At one point, I apologised to the absent Margie.

Back at the house when we went to bed, Jasmin tried to kiss me.

“Jasmin,” I said seriously with a slight frown on my face, “Please don’t,”

“But you enjoyed it last time,”

“I was sixteen and naïve then. I’m nineteen now and probably just as naïve. I’m still a virgin and inexperienced, the only man that’s kissed my lips is an old beast. The kiss with you was nice, but the kiss with Steve, even though it was only close to my lips was out of this world. Sorry, Jasmin,” I said, trying not to look at her.

Jasmin stared at me for a few seconds, smiled her lovely smile and whispered, “I never thought you were interested in girls, anyway. Even though you’ve been away for three years, you’re still my best friend. But if ever you change your mind?”

“I’ll let you know,” I said.

We both laughed.

She placed the pillow barricade between us, whispered seductively, “Goodnight sexy.”

I sensed she was smiling.

I wondered how many girls faced the same conundrum. I guessed it to be plenty, though I thought most would be reluctant to admit as such. I was asleep within a minute.

Can’t walk the Catwalk

Jasmin and her mum cajoled me into going to Caerphilly for the finals. I was unsure and somewhat reluctant to appear; I was also a little proud and excited. On the day of the finals, the eleventh of June nineteen seventy-four, it again reminded me of dressing in Nazareth House Cardiff as I prepared for the pageant. My green evening gown, borrowed from Jasmin’s mum, was slightly too big. I could only fit into Jasmin’s four-inch red platform and stiletto shoes with tissue paper stuffed in the toes. I probably looked similar to a tottering child when walking with the borrowed stiletto heels. I would wear them with a blue swimming costume on loan from Jasmin, one that was only a slightly better fit. I had no thoughts of winning and expected to go out in the first heat, going along with Jasmin just because it promised to be a good night out. I didn’t like foundation, though; hesitantly I did use the same lipstick and blue eyeliner as the previous week in Caerphilly. Greta didn’t come with us. Her excuse was she was washing her hair. After witnessing the time spent by her on preparations for just an evening out, I believed her.

The Double Diamond nightclub Caerphilly eclipsed the Newport Mecca ballroom, there must have been a thousand people attending. Beauty pageants were particularly popular during this period with Julia and Eric Morley managing most of the competitions.

Jasmin wasn’t working that night. She was more nervous than me and had come prepared. She had brought with her a bottle of Pernod, a drink neither of us had drunk before. I stood left of the stage, five feet above the floor of the auditorium, with twenty-nine of the purportedly most beautiful women in Wales. The Pernod was taking effect, I was almost drunk but also a little chuffed with myself. My fellow contestants, all of whom were taller than me, attentively listened as the severe-looking dickey-bowed organiser explained what actions we should take when we presented ourselves to the judges and the audience. He then repeated the words directly to me, probably because of the vacant expression on my face.

"Walk," he said, licking his lips and pointing to the right of the stage, "to that artificial tree over there. Return and pause centre stage, where the judges are seated facing the audience. Turn to the audience look to the left, then right and then show the judges your profile, remember to smile and then walk back here."

I waited with the experienced girls who were all practising their smiles. The room was spinning, it took every reserve of concentration to stop myself wobbling. I watched as one by one they walked gracefully towards the artificial tree, turned and walked to centre stage, where they turned to the cheering crowd, smiling warmly at the judges, before returning to where I waited.

Before starting my journey, I tried to shake the numbness out of my head. I was well and truly smashed. I set off in the direction of the green blur in the distance, over the polite applause of the audience I heard Jasmin shout with a distinct slur, the same words she used in Newport, "Come on Milly. Come on, Milly, go get them."

I couldn't help myself and burst out laughing. In my confusion, I looked to see where Jasmin was, but it was dark, and my vision was blurred, the spotlights followed me as I walked to the far tree and turned ungraciously. Jasmin shouted again. I tried very hard to suppress my laughter, so much so, I walked straight past the judges and back to the other sniggering contestants.

I was still half-cut when we all paraded in our one-piece bathing costumes. I had a tiny bit of trouble with the toilet tissue and ended up with one boob more prominent than the other. Again Jasmin distracted me, shouting my name and whistling. It felt like I tottered and wobbled in my oversize stilettos over to the tree, turned around, then walked to where the judges were sitting. I was laughing so much at Jasmin; I gave the judges a precursory glance and walked by them once again.

The very gorgeous Helen Morgan deservedly won the Miss Wales title that evening. Five months after, on the twenty-second of November, she became Miss World, her reign lasted four days before she resigned. The tabloids were about to expose the fact she was an unmarried mother. She was stripped of her Miss World title, though she was still allowed to keep her Miss Wales title. Had Helen Morgan been stripped of that title too; I would have been promoted to third place because incredibly I came fourth. I was as shocked as my fellow beauty queens and almost missed the bow-tied announcer proclaiming I was the fourth-placed runner up. The audience cheered and applauded.

Jasmin however, was silent, for she was in the ladies restroom being violently sick. My one brief interlude into the beauty industry was over. I had neither sash nor cash for my efforts, only a vague sporadic memory and occasional flashbacks of the event.

Two hours later that evening, at nine twenty-five pm, while I was in bed nursing a hangover from hell, with the lingering taste of aniseed in my mouth, BBC Wales broadcast the highlights of the pageant. Jasmin, who said she watched the program with one eye closed, told me she never saw me at all. It appeared I was designated to the cutting room floor. I never even noticed any cameras, in fact, the time passed as if it was all a dream.

When I returned to Jersey, the next day, Margie was delighted to see me but wasn't the least bit surprised. And little John never knew I had even left the island. Except for my time with John, I lived a very pleasurable, educational and comfortable few more years on the island of Jersey. Until one day, Margie grabbed hold of both my arms, looked into my eyes, and sounding like a ninja master, said, "It's time for you to go now, Milly. You are ready now."

I'd already felt my second calling some time before, I was frantically trying to think of a way to tell her. She wasn't my friend anymore, she was the mother I never had, and we had a mother-daughter relationship. I knew her thoughts echoed my own, for she told me at least ten times a week. I owed her so very much, and I loved her unconditionally. I didn't want to leave, but I knew deep down within my heart and soul I had to go.

Margie handed me a slip of paper in the departure lounge; it was a cheque with enough noughts on it to start my knees dancing.

"Please take this money Milly; I have plenty and no one to leave it to."

She reminded me of Mr Noland. I showed her my last secret, my little black horse book.

"You had all this money all the time, why, oh why didn't you go back earlier?" she said flabbergasted.

"I came here knowing my limitations," I said, as I handed the cheque back to her. "I knew who I was, but realised I was lacking.

Clive and I talked about my insecurities and restrictions. We both knew I needed someone I could trust to guide me into adulthood. Not that I knew it then. You, my darling were the answer to both our prayers. I only stayed here because of you."

She just stared at me with her mouth slightly open, and then said with a chuckle,

"I told you, you were an enigma, didn't I?"

Margie held my two wrists in her hands, swinging them side to side. "You look the same, but you're not. You have an aura surrounding you, a look of contentment and confidence, the like I've never seen before. You're beautiful in both looks and personality. Don't you dare go jumping into bed with the first good-looking man you meet, or you'll feel my wrath."

I was pretty much the same height as when I first arrived, five foot four. I was seven pounds heavier than my original seven and a half stone. Thanks to Margie, I was a young woman who knew who I was, and what I was. Not only did I study life and living. I learned about myself and my own emotions. My skin glowed and even after my brief interlude into the beauty business, there was still a subtle womanly change to my body. My hair that was once originally short and lifeless was now shoulder-length with a healthy shine.

Besides the arduous mental stimulation, Margie taught me, how to eat, what to eat and when to eat; at the same time making me aware of the importance of healthy eating and all its benefits. “These contain vitamins A and B darling and are high in Vitamin C. Essential for you as you’re still a growing girl. They’re good for the hair and skin.” She’d say during our twice-weekly, kipper, kidney and fresh orange juice breakfasts.

The only downside was our passion for fine wine and vodka.

“Never drink too much in the company of others, not even acquaintances.” She always advised, “Only with some close friends, those you know and trust, and of course the ones you love. Know your limitations and stop when you feel you’ve reached them.”

I thought of Jasmin, gin with strawberries and the Pernod.

I left John a letter on the mantelpiece before I silently crept out of the house that morning. I thought long and hard about what to say to the brute. In the time I had been there, he probably hit me a dozen times. He had beaten me up on two occasions, leaving me unable to work. The second time this occurred Margie told him if he laid another finger on me, she would have him out of her house quicker than he could say, Jack Robinson. She had to explain who Jack Robinson was to me. He never hit me again, but the mental torture continued. I carefully worded my goodbye, Dear John letter. I wrote.

Dear John,

Goodbye.

Milly.

I left behind a wardrobe full of the clothes. The clothes John selected or wanted me to wear. In a leather suitcase, Margie gave me were the possessions I took. They were the boots, trousers and top that Mr Noland liked, plus the black jacket, blouse, skirt and shoes I wore to his funeral. I also kept the red dress, shoes and a few other things Margie had bought for me. I left everything else behind.

My last image of Margie, my lasting memory of Jersey, was of her laughing and ripping up the cheque into tiny pieces and flinging them into the air like confetti. I boarded the six-thirty morning flight to Cardiff, from Saint Peter port airport Jersey, four short months after my twenty-first birthday party. Which everybody except Margie thought was my twenty-second birthday; because John wanted no one to know I was only sixteen when he dragged me to Fantasy Island.

I shed a tear or two on the forty-five-minute plane journey to Cardiff.

Welcome Back

It wasn't really my want, but the first place I visited was Nazareth House. The taxi from the airport dropped me off at the uninviting entrance where I stared at the gates, recalling sixteen years earlier. The weather was exactly the same as then. The sun was shining, the shadows appeared ominous, the birds were singing. A shocked Sister Terry darted away after opening the door. I walked alone to the Mother Superior's office.

She mentioned nothing about the five years I'd been away and wasted no time by immediately asking me if I was ready to take Holy Orders.

I avoided the question by saying I'd let her know soon. Greta and Natalie told me they would supply a forwarding address for me to contact them on my return. I asked her if any messages had been left for me. Natalie did, Greta apparently didn't. The Mother Superior passed me a sealed envelope that had unashamedly been steamed open. In Natalie's spidery scrawl, were the words Natalie O'Grady and a local telephone number. So my friend married Keith O'Grady, after all, I thought happily.

She handed me another envelope, this one had a stamp and was franked the date I left Cardiff. The gummed seal showed clear signs of tampering. In neat handwriting it said,

To Miss Milly Nash, C/O, Nazareth House, Colum Road, Cardiff.

She looked at me warily as I opened it.

The plain single A4 sheet stated;

Dear Milly, I wonder if you could come to see me at your earliest convenience. Kind regards. Steve Holmes.

I wondered why the bank manager hadn't used headed paper and was curious as to what he wanted.

Mother Superior confirmed she invaded my privacy by adding casually and somewhat carelessly.

"Who is Steve Holmes, Milly?"

"A friend of Mr Noland's," I said and stared confidently into her feline eyes.

She squirmed uncomfortably under my knowing gaze and said quietly,

"Sister Sandra would love to see you. Go to the nursery. I'll also tell Sister Mary to meet you there."

Sister Sandra and Sister Mary looked at me as if I was another person, which I was, I suppose. They kept glancing at me, trying to work out what was different. The new inmates eyed me suspiciously; their timid faces, their wary eyes and stupid haircuts brought back painful memories. To them, I was an outsider. I realised that the majority of the kids I knew would be long gone by now. I decided there and then it would be a long time before I returned, if ever again. It was time to cut the umbilical cord.

I related a brief synopsis of the previous years to the two nuns. Sister Mary kept on looking from me to Sister Sandra, as if asking her a question, hiding the vivid scar on her thunderstruck face on each turn. Sister Sandra was staring at me, her bright eyes under her audacious spectacles displaying evident pride. She asked,

"So you went to University after all then Milly, where did you go?"

"I've just graduated from the Clive Noland University of life," I said beaming proudly.

"Holy Mother of God," Sister Mary said in a slightly higher voice than I remembered, jogging my mind back to the misunderstanding between God and the Bishop.

They told me that Sister Margarita had sadly passed only the year before. I loved her and the two nuns I was talking with. I would grieve for Sister Margarita and remember her with affection. I had no doubt she was in heaven with Mr Noland and Roly.

I called to visit Jasmin, a stranger at the door told me they had moved and he didn't have a forwarding address. The same thing happened when I went to Greta's flat.

I phoned my friend, Natalie, after a bit of happy catch-up chattering we arranged to meet the next day. Greta, it seemed, had moved to Blackpool. At least the accent she put on might now fit in, I thought, amused.

"Miss Nash to see Mr Holmes," I said to the woman guarding the door that said Bank Manager.

Mr Holmes afforded me the same bear hug he gave Mr Noland saying, "Where have you been Milly? I was getting anxious about you."

I told him about Jersey, my life there and how I was trying to save enough money to come back to Cardiff.

He listened intently, "Why didn't you use our branch in Saint Helier to access your finances?"

His words stunned me, I hadn't realised I could reclaim my money at other branches. I didn't want to have anyone feeling pity for me ever again, so I lied,

"I left my book safe in Cardiff." I still have a lot to learn, I mused.

"Have you your savings book with you now?" I nodded and handed him the book.

He said "Good. It needs updating," and went out the door.

He came back with the book and an envelope which held the unmistakable handwriting of Mr Noland. He handed me the open book. I was flabbergasted to see the total amount had jumped by at least a quarter.

"The extra money is interest. Your money is being held in a high-interest account with accumulating compound interest," explained Mr Holmes. He handed me the sealed envelope, the first one today that had not been tampered with.

"I'll get us a nice cup of tea whilst you read it," he said as he departed and closed the door behind him.

To Milly Nash, it stated in Mr Noland's neat calligraphic writing. My hands were shaking as I opened the envelope. The letter was dated about six months before his accident.

My Dearest Milly, it began. I could hear his voice. I visualised him talking, and I started to sob. *As you are reading this, I have finally succumbed to this damnation disease. That is cancer.*

Milly, you changed me; you made my life bearable when I thought it unbearable. I watched you the first day you came to Nazareth House. You plucked at my heartstrings immediately. You were literally scared of your own shadow.

On your first day at school, I could see how frightened you were by your shaking legs. Milly, your beautiful smile when you returned told me how happy you were.

During the next three years, I watched you grow up very quickly. I so very much wanted to smile back. But I was stuck at stage three, in the bottomless pit of despair and depression. My reason for living had died. I could see no way out, except for my own death.

I never told you this, but I asked Mother Superior if I could go to Barry Island with the Nursery group. You aroused my curiosity; I wanted to find out what made you tick. I wanted to know more about the pretty smiling little girl with the brightest blue eyes I'd ever seen. Without realising it then, it was my first steps out of depression and into stage four bargaining. You were, and still, are, the most unselfish, kindest, and understanding girl in the whole world.

When you gave Mrs Thomas Goldie, I smiled for the first time in years.

The Reverend Mother told me of your plan with the chair. I went along with it and surprised myself by reigniting my passion for carpentry, ultimately dragging myself out of the quagmire. Blue, I owe you so much. I had to force you to accept money; I foolishly thought that was the only thing I had to give you. What you really needed was someone to love you and guide you into adulthood. I know Mrs Noland would have loved you as much as I do.

Please don't be sad, please don't grieve for me, not the way you did for Pat and Roly. It broke my heart to see you suffer like that. I'm so very proud to see you develop into the sweet, intelligent, witty, caring person you are.

I loved working in my workshop and seeing you look after the youngsters, making them laugh, making me laugh. I'm glad your zest and passion for living and learning returned. I would love you to achieve your dream of attending University. Please don't be mad at me, but I have made provision in my will for you to realise your dream. Don't worry about The Reverend Mother or Nazareth House. I have bequeathed them adequate funds. I was paying and donating weekly, anyway. I estimate it will be about five years before you graduate; there are more than sufficient funds for you. Spend it wisely, Blue. Remember what I've taught you, don't tell anyone how much money you have. The friends you have should like you for being you, not for the money you have.

My dear friend Steve Holmes is my executor, he has my instructions. I have distributed all my worldly goods to various benefactors. I'm glad I gave you Doris's bracelets and gold band, you looked so happy.

He had never mentioned his wife's first name before, always referring to her as, my darling wife. I thought of Doris, the waitress and yet more coincidences.

There is one more thing, I'd like you to have the money to remind you of the old man you made so very, very happy. Milly, Blue, take care and enjoy the rest of your life, I love you.

Clive.

I looked at the letter and reread a few sentences. I could feel the corners of my mouth rise into an involuntary smile when I read Mr Noland knew of my plan with the chair.

He left me enough money to attend University. I felt a tad sad but regretted nothing. Margie, my surrogate mother, was a talented teacher. I may not have a diploma, but I was more than satisfied with the conclusion. As I know, Mr Noland would have been.

Steve Holmes knocked on his own door and came in. He had come equipped. In one hand was a cup of tea, in the other a large brown envelope and a white handkerchief he handed me.

"I thought you might need this," he said with a grimace-like smile on his face.

I dabbed my eyes, collected myself and politely thanked him, allowing Mr Holmes to complete his business.

"This is the preliminary cheque. The residue of Mr Noland's estate, after all, deductions and expenses," he said in his business voice.

I stared in amazement at the piece of paper, trying hard to put in order the line of numbers on the page. Before I could quantify the figure, he side-tracked me by extracting a green book, similar to my own green book, from the brown envelope.

"Following Clive's instructions, I placed the money in this high-interest investment account."

He handed me the booklet, whose figures bore little representation of the cheque's sum.

"That's the total after five years of compound interest," he said in an attempt to answer my confused expression. "Clive was a shrewd man and a clever investor." He smiled broadly when he said the words.

During the next half an hour, we talked of Clive. Each of us taking turns in regaling the man we both cherished. Then he abruptly stopped talking in mid-sentence and gaped at me his eyes widened.

"I hope you don't mind me saying, Milly. It's like…" He paused, considering his words and said, "I can't really put my finger on it. You look the same. Yes. A little older, I admit. But you looked like you floated in here. You look refined and poised, you walk with grace and elegance. You have a presence and assured confidence. You speak eloquently, reminiscent of Clive. And if you don't mind me saying so, you look absolutely beautiful. Clive told me some of what was in the letter to you. I know he was keen for you to go to University, but how did this transformation occur?"

I told him about Margie. I skipped the brute, not mentioning him once. He laughed a very pleasurable laugh when I revealed she was a Cambridge graduate. How she wanted to be a tutor at the Clive Noland University of life.

"Of course, I should have known. I should have recognised your perfect, accentless annunciation," he almost shouted, laughing enthusiastically. "My wife attended Cambridge. I must say, Margie and you have done a first-class job. Clive Noland will be as proud as Punch," he looked up to heaven, beyond the ceiling and laughed again.

I left the bank with some interest accrued from my savings account in cash, an amount tucked safely in my handbag. I still had enough money left in my investment account to buy a lovely house. Though, Mr Holmes had advised me against buying one; saying he would give me a mortgage at the drop of a hat.

I scanned the window of an estate agent, looking at the houses and flats to rent. One stood out in particular. There was a serviced flat to rent in Pontcanna. I always liked the name of the area, so I arranged a viewing.

"I'll meet you there in three hours," a tall, thin man in a suit a size too small for him, said, as he handed me a slip of paper with the address.

After leaving my suitcase with the polite concierge, I strolled around the duffle coat store, filled up a few shopping bags with skirts, dresses, blouses, jumpers and underwear but unfortunately no bra, as the store didn't sell any egg cup sizes. As a treat, I bought a pair of Wrangler jeans. I had already selected two pairs of shoes and was trying on some sensible flat shoes when a well-dressed woman approached me.

"Good morning Miss, I'm the assistant manager Mrs Barnes, may I help you with all the bags?"

"Yes please," I smiled at the lightly made-up attractive face.

She smiled a perfect professional smile back, then she beckoned to a man in a concierge uniform who looked uncomfortable standing by the lingerie.

"Fred, can you take?" She paused, looked down to where I was sitting.

"Nash. Milly Nash," I said, sounding like James Bond. I felt I should add; Martini, shaken, not stirred, but didn't.

"Can you take the bags down to your office? Miss Nash will pick them up later.

Taking out the slip of paper, I showed her the address. "How far away is Conway Road?"

"Not far, about ten minutes by taxi," said the extremely amiable woman.

For the next two hours, I continued shopping, buying a stylish, but not garish overcoat, cosmetics and a small faced gold plated dress watch,

"It's a seventeen jewelled Seconda, madam," the sombre grey-haired male assistant, assured me. My friendly guide who was sticking to her free-spending customer like glue, giggled like a little schoolgirl, then roared with laughter when I said out of his earshot and somewhat unintentionally, sarcastically. "First time I've ever been called a madam."

On a whim, I had my nails manicured and my hair plaited.

In the grand foyer of the Howells department store while I was waiting for my taxi, Verity, as I now called Mrs Barnes, asked me where I lived. I told her I had just arrived from Jersey. The address I had shown her was hopefully my new home in Cardiff.

"Just arrived? Are you looking for employment Milly? We have a vacancy in the cosmetic department."

I needed less than a second to reply. "When can I have an interview?"

"You've just had it. Can you start next Monday morning at nine?"

Single Life

My next stop was the address I had shown Verity. It was a fully furnished service flat on Conway Road, on the ground floor of a large three-story semi-detached terrace house. Flat three had a side entrance overlooking a large garden lawn. The man with the ill-fitting suit had barely shown me the impressive one-bedroom flat when I knew it was for me. It had a spacious bedroom, a decent sized lounge and a shared kitchen. Included in the weekly rent was a service charge for a cooked breakfast every morning. Hence the words, service flat. He informed me a woman cooked a breakfast, Monday to Friday between seven-thirty and eight-thirty for the four tenants.

"I'll take it," I said and paid the beaming tight suited chap three months in advance plus the requisite bond.

I went outside and paid the waiting taxi driver, thanks to my generous tip, we soon bundled my suitcase and shopping bags into my fancy first abode.

Fortunately, the flat had a communal payphone. Unfortunately, it gobbled up money at an alarming pace. I phoned Natalie again and asked if she and Keith would like to meet me for a reunion meal the next evening. When this was successfully arranged, I telephoned Margie at the Galaxy.

"Galaxy Hotel may I help you," she sang on the second ring.

"You already have a million times over," I sang back, mimicking her.

When I told her of my new employment and my new home. She chortled, "My God, you didn't waste any time. You probably don't care but, John came in about three hours ago, demanding to know where you were. I told him you were in Addis Ababa. Digging water ditches for the inhabitants."

That evening I sat in my lounge admiring my unfamiliar surroundings; my growling tummy reminding me I hadn't eaten since the evening before. I left my new flat and turned left. After not turning left at Nazareth House for nine years, I considered the left was right. I ambled down the sun shaded tree-lined road to a tee junction, keeping left until I came across a smart restaurant set back off the road, occupying the space of four terraced houses. The static neon sign spelt out *Gilbertson's French Restaurant.* I remembered a girl at school who had mentioned Pontcanna and a French restaurant. I walked in without pausing.

An attractive young girl with a smile that reminded me of Jasmin welcomed me, I was soon ensconced at a table with a large glass of Chardonnay. I sat recalling the wisdom of Margie, the time she advised me to never show off and only speak when you are totally confident of what you are about to say. To illustrate this, she told me the story of a beautiful woman in her hotel's restaurant, who asked for a glass of Chardon B. Saying she wanted to try the lesser version. Margie said she didn't say a word and gave her a glass of Pinot Grigio instead.

There were a few other diners scattered on various tables, they were easily overlooked. I enjoyed eating alone. I was comfortable in my own company, yet I still felt mildly insecure about my new surroundings and meeting my new housemates.

After I paid for my meal, the waitress sat and joined me. We chatted amiably over a glass of Chardonnay she had insisted on paying for, while the other satisfied customers gradually left, leaving us alone in the fifteen table restaurant. Amanda was easy to talk to. I liked her and her brother Mathew, who joined us when he finished his shift in the dungeon kitchens below. I found out she was the daughter of the owners of the restaurant; her brother, the head chef, had cooked the delicious meal I had just enjoyed.

That night or should I say morning, I slept reasonably well on top of the bare mattress. It soon became blatantly obvious, I needed more than clothes. I had no bedding, toothbrush, soap, towels and a dozen other things. I had a wash without using soap and dried myself with a cotton top. Thankfully my plaited hair showed no signs of disturbance. I could smell breakfast cooking as I made a mental list of everything I needed. On top of the list were a pen and paper. The two hands on my new watch showed me it was eight-thirty.

I opened my adjoining door to the kitchen to find what service I received for my service charge.

"Morning love, you must be Milly," said a smiling woman of about fifty. "I'm Vi. Enjoy," She lifted a plate off the top of another that held bacon, sausage, egg and beans.

"There's coffee in the pot. Got to dash. Tar Ra." Then she abruptly left.

I made two trips to the shops, each time returning with a taxi loaded with bags. I even ordered a colour television set, with its delivery and installation booked for the following Thursday morning. It took me the best part of the day to sort out my flat, moving furniture until I was satisfied. My double mattress was now adorned with soft cotton sheets and blankets, reminding me of Lerina's bed.

The Waitress

Natalie and Keith called at eight o'clock sharp. Natalie and I hugged, giggled and cuddled; while her happy six-foot muscular husband watched two friends meet after five years. I opened a bottle of wine; Natalie had a glass, Keith refused. It seemed he was working nights as a taxi driver, and they both wanted to leave by ten. I quickly showed Natalie my bedroom and the rest of my flat, then we departed.

Keith drove us in his taxi to *Gilbertson's*.

Amanda greeted me with air kisses to both my cheeks and a very enthusiastic, "Hello Milly table for?"

"Three please Amanda," I said and introduced my companions. "I came here last night. It's a lovely place with great food," I mentioned.

We ate a splendid meal, but I felt uncomfortable. I knew I had made a mistake. We couldn't really chat, and neither of us at ease or relaxed. Natalie agreed with me when we gossiped in the women's restroom. We arranged to meet again at my place on Friday night at eight o'clock and then go to the local public house. Today was only Tuesday. I'd only been in Cardiff for forty hours, and I was missing Margie like mad.

I left my red handbag and the half-full bottle of Chardonnay on the table, while I went outside *Gilbertson's* to say a fond farewell to my friend and her husband who had to work.

When I returned, I began to finish the bottle, thinking I was proud of my industrious achievements since my arrival. I pondered what the future held for me. I thought of Mr Noland and the letter I'd reread at least ten times already. I remembered Pat the last day I saw her. My memory of Roly curled up on my lap, her final loving kiss. Except for me, there was only a romantic couple holding hands in the restaurant. I watched when they stood up to leave.

After showing them to the door and locking it, Amanda and Mathew joined me again, we chatted for ages. I told them I had been working in a hotel in Jersey before coming back to Cardiff. Amanda said the restaurant was usually quiet on a Monday and Tuesday, so they always took advantage of this to have a few drinks. A statement they soon proved. Two hours and three bottles later, not only was I good friends with Amanda and Mathew, but I was also an employee. I agreed to work as a waitress for two evenings a week, on Wednesdays and Saturdays from eight until midnight. My first shift was that evening as it was after midnight.

I thoroughly enjoyed working as a waitress. My first night went smoothly enough, except for a table of four boisterous young men. Amanda told me they played cricket for Glamorgan and were good tippers. She winked when she said it, reminding me of Stephen and Margie.

"Do you fancy coming out with me to see a film tomorrow night?" asked a handsome, self-assured blond man. "Milly," he added after glancing at my name tag.

As I was back in Cardiff, I thought I'd go through the old routine, "Sorry. I'm working here."

His three pals guffawed.

Then less confidently asked, "What about the next night then?"

"I'm washing my hair."

The friends roared with laughter.

Later on, one of his friends came up to me when I was writing on my pad and asked,

"Any chance you'd like to come out with me?"

"Sorry I'm engaged," I said the final line of defence, pointing at the ring, a gift from Mr Noland.

During what I now realised was customary after-work bottle of wine, Amanda said, "The tips were great tonight, Milly. Table seven, the four cricketers, left a nice big tip. They said you were a little gem. And by the way, you were utterly brilliant. Now, who's this fiancé of yours? I couldn't help but overhear you mention him."

"I made him up. I'm just not interested," I replied and laughed. And to Amanda's enquiring look, as a brief image and a fond memory of Jasmin came and disappeared,

"In answer to your next question, no, I am most definitely not."

On Thursday morning, I made a point by getting up early to meet my three housemates. Gary, a short, stocky man of forty-five, worked in a garage. Gina, a stout woman of about the same age, had a job in the tax office. Mike, a tall, gangly bloke of about thirty-five, was recently divorced and worked in a shoe shop.

It turned out we all had separate sections in the refrigerator, plus a wall and a floor cupboard, each identifiable by the stencilled apartment numbers on their doors. Though I thought I would have little use of the space as the only drawback with the flat was the shared kitchen. I envisaged that I would be eating out or having takeaways most of the time. I could easily afford it, especially with two jobs, even with paying the rent and living expenses, I'd hardly made a dent in my bankbook with my cash withdrawal.

I went out shopping after my television was installed, bought a radio cassette player and a few things to make the flat more homely. To fill the kitchen spaces, I purchased mostly snack foods, fruit and four different breakfast packets of cereal, knowing I couldn't eat a cooked breakfast every day.

Right was Right

Keith dropped Natalie off at eight, intending to pick her up from the pub at ten. More at ease, we sat in my lounge sipping large vodkas and lime, chatting contentedly about the home, school and the previous five years. She told me more about the tall, muscular Irishman she married when she was eighteen, a man I had only met twice before I left for Jersey. Halfway through her second vodka, she turned to me, looked me in the eye and said in a severe-sounding voice.

"Milly, you frighten me. I know it's you, but it's not you. You've changed, but you haven't changed. You look the same, but somehow, you look different. Your voice sounds like you, only now you sound so clever. Are you?"

I hugged my chum. "Natalie, I'm the same person. And you, my friend, will always be that, my friend for life. I had hard times and brilliant times in Jersey. I met a woman who I eventually thought of as a mother, who loved me as her daughter. I only left her on Monday morning. She taught me, showed me what I had been missing in my life."

"She sounds lovely Milly. I'm so glad for you. I just couldn't work out what it was, sorry."

"Come on, let's go to the boozer," I said laughing.

We were both still laughing as we went through the door, this time at the pavement we turned right.

The Conway public house had two entrances, one on Conway Road and a side entrance on Mortimer Road. The pop music emanating from the general direction of the side entrance made our minds up for us. The lounge was bright, clean, long, and narrow, squashed between the bar and an exterior wall containing four curtained windows and running the entire length of the room was a soft upholstered bench, with ten wooden tables. Each table was accompanied by two padded chairs. Ten bar stools behind them faced the bar, leaving just enough space for someone to walk past.

In the background, the selection of songs was impressive, as chart hits of the seventies were playing.

Natalie and I chose the bench seat nearest the entrance, we sat down in front of two halves of lager bought from a tallish pleasant woman with smiling even teeth. There were a few other customers; a man and woman in the opposite corner, two men on bar stools and four more young men sitting at a table two tables away. We began quietly chatting, happily keeping to the unwritten rule, never to discuss the home in front of outsiders, never to admit ever attending an orphanage. Natalie said she had a job in a supermarket, she talked lovingly of Keith and her home.

We both liked The Conway and appreciated the standard of music.

"I'm starting to get used to you now Milly. You gave me a bit of a shock. By the way, you look absolutely stunning you, bitch."

I knew all was well with us.

"Only a true friend would call you a bitch," I said, and we both chuckled.

Natalie bought us our second drink while I went to the ladies' room. When I returned to sit down in front of my refreshed glass, Natalie nudged me.

"Now there's a good-looking man over there," she whispered, nodding towards the back of a man standing at the bar, murmuring to the barmaid.

I casually looked at him. He was wearing a tweed sports jacket, with his long dark glossy hair just about covering the collar; he was wearing a pair of clean faded Levi's, and on his feet, expensive light tan kickers. Still, with his back to me, he walked away through a door, that said Cellar, on the far side of the bar.

One of the four men approached the bar. "Four of the same please Clare."

"Steve's just changing the barrel now," said Clare.

I had just taken a generous mouthful of refreshing lager and lime when Steve the barrel changer returned. He looked straight at me, we stared at each other, and he smiled a smile I recognised in an instant. I'd seen it a couple of times before and in my dreams a thousand times. Oh my God, it was my Steve, stupid Stephen.

I gulped, gagged, and choked, spitting out lager. Lager streamed out of both my nostrils, spraying over the table, the stinging lime made my bulging eyes water. In a panic, I ran out of the door, coughing and spluttering like a buffoon, to go to the toilet, knocking what remained in the glass over the table in the process spilling lager over the carpeted floor.

In the ladies' room, I splashed water over my face and stuck my mouth under the flowing water. While my plait inadvertently soaked up the water like a sponge. I waited for Natalie to join me, but she didn't.

I walked back in sheepishly. I remembered Margie saying, if you can't laugh at yourself, then how can you laugh at anyone else? I giggled as I went through the door. Steve was sitting opposite Natalie talking. I was acutely self-conscious as I sat down at the now dry table, my plait disrespectfully dripping water down my back. There was a replenished refreshing lager on the table mat. Opposite me sat the boy I'd loved for the last nine years.

I could see he was saying something because the lips I overwhelmingly wanted to kiss were moving. I didn't hear a word, my heart was thumping. I felt dizzy; my nostrils were still smarting and felt swollen. I couldn't believe he was sitting in front of me.

"Are you all right now, Milly?" Natalie asked.

"Yes, Sorry." I put my fingers in my ears in a very unladylike manner, shook my head, spreading the dripping water over my back. "It went down the wrong way," I giggled uncomfortably.

The lad who didn't even recognise me said. "Hi, I'm Steve; Natalie mentioned you've just returned from living in Jersey."

Still, in complete and utter shock, I said nothing.

Steve continued undeterred, "Natalie tells me you went to school together. Are you both from Cardiff?"

"Yes, we went to Mostyn High. We were in the same form until brainy here moved to a different class. We used to live a few doors from each other in Cathays until Milly moved to Jersey." Natalie answered while looking at me, uneasily.

She gave me valuable time to gather some poise. My hammering heart was down to about a hundred and twenty beats a minute, my blood pressure had decreased, and I gradually started to think a bit clearer. I grabbed the opportunity to study the older, more mature Stephen. He was cleanly shaven, smartly dressed, perhaps a tad overconfident. I noted his matrimonial declaration was absent.

Clare asked, "You all right now love?"

I nodded and gave her a thumbs-up.

I could see Stephen looking at the band on my wedding finger, a slightly disillusioned look on his handsome face. I kept my hand where it was, released it from the clinch and showed him clearly.

"It's a present from a friend," I said. "That's the only finger it would fit." I unnecessarily explained.

"My husband is picking me up at ten," Natalie said, showing him her wedding band.

He appeared satisfied with my explanation and surprised by my observation. He looked slightly embarrassed when he grinned like a Cheshire cat.

"Are you glad to be back in Cardiff Milly?"

He asked me in a gentle voice I recognised from long before.

"Yes," I said smiling, immediately thinking I am now.

"I have a little flat on Conway Road. I only moved in on Monday, though I've lived around here for about a year." He answered my unasked next question.

I smiled at him, in a daze, trying to hide my shock.

"Natalie helped me move to my flat on Conway Road on Monday." I lied about Natalie. I only wanted to bring her into the conversation. Though I soon regretted lying and decided I wouldn't lie to him again.

He asked if he could stay and join us, he was an outstanding companion, funny, reasonably articulate and well known by the other customers. As the bar became busier almost, everyone greeted him. I had to wait until Stephen left us to buy a round of drinks before I had the opportunity to tell Natalie who he was.

"The boy I told you about when we were both kids. Stephen, Lerina's brother, the family we met when Pat and I went to Treforest. You remember little Lerina, don't you?"

"I wondered what made you gag. Up to then, you were so relaxed. Are you going to tell Stephen who you are?"

"Can't now, it's too late. Besides, I don't want Steve feeling sorry for me."

All too soon, Keith's muscular frame suddenly filled the lounge doorway.

"Be there in a minute, love," Natalie said. "You may as well stay Milly. Steve will make sure you get home safely." She looked across at the grinning man. "Won't you," she stressed.

The time flew by all too quickly.

"Last orders please," Clare shouted, ringing the bell, slightly spoiling the night by reminding me of my previous life.

We stopped outside my flat at number fifty-four; his apartment was only seven houses away.

"Thanks for a lovely evening. I thoroughly enjoyed myself, especially the trick with the lager." He laughed.

He stooped down and kissed me on my cheek, exactly like he did a lifetime before. My knees started dancing to the beat of my thumping heart. I couldn't say a word. His gaze went deliberately from my eyes to my lips,

"I've been dying to do this all night." He said, he leaned towards me slowly giving me ample time to say no or turn away, he kissed me full on my lips. It wasn't a wet kiss, but a gentle tender kiss that lasted but a few short seconds.

"Can I see you again?" he gushed.

"What do you mean?"

"Will you go out with me? Do you want to have a meal with me?"

“I’ll think about it,” I said and regretted saying it straight away, I wasn’t reasoning rationally. My mind was in turmoil, similar to our first encounter.

“Well, you have a week to think about it, as I’m flying to Majorca tomorrow for six days,” he said a little tersely, then added more lightly, “On my own, by the way. Can I call for you a week today? Seven o’clock?”

I smiled and nodded.

“Great, I’ll book us a table.” Then obeying Natalie, he made sure I was safely through my front door.

Thank god I’d bought that bottle of vodka I thought as I poured a very generous measure. I sat trembling to recall his mother’s words, years before when she talked of the ten longest weeks of her life. Well, this would be a long seven days of my life.

Good Old Karma

My first week in work was a dream as I counted down the hours. I absolutely loved meeting people, and it appeared selling cosmetics was my forte. My induction lasted all of Monday morning. After lunch, Verity Barnes introduced me to my new work colleagues, who seemed a happy bunch. I assumed it would be a week or so before I was welcomed into the fold. The journey to work, by bus or frivolous taxi ride was only ten minutes. Though my preferred option was the half-hour walks, following the flowing river through the tree-lined park, opening a gate and going from the countryside to the city in one step.

I also enjoyed working in the restaurant. I'd worked two more shifts, with the tips; the wage was almost as much as Howells. I couldn't believe my luck, two great jobs and meeting the boy of my dreams within a few days. I wondered when good old Karma would raise its ugly head.

I must have changed my mind and outfits half a dozen times before I sat down nervously to wait, sipping a calming cheeky Pinot. I slipped the red handbag over my wrist on the first of two knocks, he was five minutes early.

I'd hardly closed the front door behind me when the suntanned lad said, "Lovely to see you again. You look nice. Love the hair. Shall we have a quick drink before we go? My car is outside the pub." He kissed me on my lips again, this time for a little longer.

Clare greeted us as we walked through the lounge door.

"I knew you two would get together. You looked like you were made for each other. On the house, welcome back," said the happy barmaid who placed two drinks in front of us.

His car was a white open-top MG midget, so my hair, now free from the restraints of a plait, was a mess when we arrived at the Indian restaurant. I had a nervous, happy evening. We talked about everything and anything. He told me a little of himself, how his marriage split after only three years, his family, his two sons, his two sisters and two brothers, some of what he told me I already knew. I wanted to ask how his family were. I wanted to ask after Diana and Gordon, Lorenzo, Duncan, Lerina and Sandra. At my front door, he tried to kiss me more passionately, I pushed him gently away.

"Not yet?" he asked.

"Much too soon," I smiled.

We arranged to meet at one o'clock on Sunday, at my place. Barry Island was to be our destination. His idea, not mine. I was so much looking forward to it, even more than my first visit.

Saturday night in the restaurant was heaving, with all the tables fully booked. Amanda, calm and collected behind her bar, was in charge, efficiently directing her three waiting staff. The routine was simple. The orders had to be written clearly with any variations underlined. Later two tings of a quiet bell would mean the meal was at the bar, while one ring informed us the food was in the dumb waiter.

I was taking orders smiling sweetly, recommending the chef's special when I noticed Amanda greeting two clients. Even though the man had his back to me and the stunning woman faced me, I recognised them both instantly. The tall, beautiful, blue-eyed blonde girl, Wendy bloody Street accompanied Stephen. Luckily, she didn't remember me or have a clue I was the bullied urchin. Stephen's grin and tan faded when we locked eyes.

I avoided that side of the restaurant all night though I could feel his eyes on me. My years in the home had taught me how not to display my real emotions. It shocked me to discover jealousy was heart-breaking. The four friendly cricketers were there again. This time I flirted back, initiating a lot of friendly happy banter I hoped would verify I didn't give a damn, I even said a very pleasant goodnight to everyone as they left.

Amanda must have noticed something was amiss and asked me if I was all right after the last customer had left.

"Bit of a headache, see you next Wednesday."

"What about your wages?"

"I'll pick them up next week. Goodnight and please say goodnight to Matt."

I telephoned Margie the moment I entered the flat,

"Did he know you worked there?"

"I never got around to telling him."

"All may not be as it appears, Milly. It may be prudent to listen to any explanation."

"What explanation could he possibly have? He walked in with a girl, one who hated the sight of me for years, who goaded Pat and I since our first day in school. Why would he book a table for two?"

"He didn't know you knew her, did he? The proof may be apparent tomorrow, whether he turns up."

"Thanks, Margie. I'll phone you soon. Goodnight, love you."

I wasn't expecting him to show and wasn't surprised when he didn't. I questioned why each period of happiness was always shattered by incidents that created a profound sadness, far more intense than the enjoyment.

I was numb with shock. Even though we only had one date, I was confident Steve liked me. Perhaps my anticipations were too high? Maybe our first date didn't meet his expectations. I tried so hard not to let slip any facts that would give away the inane game I was playing. I thought I should have been honest and told him who I was. There again, maybe I wasn't to his liking. The thoughts that bombarded my mind were unrelenting. I seriously thought of returning to Jersey, a subliminal image of me dressed as a nun, flashed in my mind's eye.

Sunday at three o'clock, I explained how I was feeling to Margie.

"Cheer up, darling. Don't get all cherophobic on me. Come back to Jersey if you think you have nothing in Cardiff."

"I'll give it until my rent runs out. I'll think about it until then. Bye, love you."

I flicked the pages of my Cambridge English dictionary until I reached cherophobia, she knew I would. Sure enough, the word described me to a tee. My mind-set was to go back to Jersey and live with Margie.

My Wednesday stint in the restaurant went by slowly. I kept inadvertently glancing towards the table Wendy and Steve occupied the previous Saturday. Over the traditional end of session glass of wine, Amanda handed me my past week's wage packet, saying there was a note from Stef in it.

"Note from who?" I asked as I recalled a previous conversation.

"Just read it, Milly."

Hi Milly

Please, can I talk to you? I need to explain. I suggest a neutral ground. The Conway on Friday at eight, at the table you enjoy spitting lager on. I've told Amanda, she and Matt are my friends too.

Love Steve.

I thought back to my first night as a waitress, I remembered Amanda saying to Mathew, Stef had cancelled his table, and he and Wendy were no longer an item.

"Stef is Steve?" I said bemused.

They both nodded.

"What about Wendy? Are they no longer together?"

Amanda said, "Wendy assumed it was a trial separation. Meanwhile, Steve told us he'd met the girl of his dreams. He tried to book here on your first date. Unfortunately, we were fully booked; we didn't realise it was you. Especially when he described what happened the first time he set eyes on you. He tried to tell Wendy it was definitely all over between them. In desperation she booked the table for Saturday, virtually forcing him to come, holding her engagement ring as ransom. The ring was his Italian grandmother's ring, and it meant a lot more to him than she realised. In the end, she sold it back to him after she eventually graciously accepted his decision. It's a small world, isn't it?"

"It certainly bloody is," I said, feeling happier than I'd been for what seemed an eternity. What Amanda just announced dissolved all my previous misgivings. I now thought I was floating on air, "I'll tell you how small..."

I told them about Wendy. How she didn't like me during our first nine years in school, before she apologised and how we remained sociable until we both left. Yet she still didn't recognise me. I didn't mention the orphanage, or about me meeting Steve before.

On Friday at eight o'clock, I met Steve in the pub. This time, before he had a chance to say a word, I gave him a hug and kissed him on the lips.

"I thought I'd lost you forever," he said, his expression, changing from glum to gleeful.

Not if I can help it, I thought, recalling Margie's wise words.

That night at my door, we kissed for the first time, it was my first real kiss with a male, a passionate kiss that confirmed and cemented my love for him. I gave Jasmin a mental thank you for his reaction.

After our first little hiccup, we were practically inseparable, we met each other every day and went out almost every night, even when I was working, he'd walk me home each night.

Steve worked as a foreman in the engineering maintenance department of a large bottling plant in Taffs Well, where he toiled eight hours a day, six days a week. The factory's two production lines operated twenty-four hours a day, allowing only the weekend for his maintenance work. His typical day off was a Wednesday. Two weeks after we first met, he changed this to Thursday to match mine.

Finally, we did go to Barry Island, almost surpassing my previous enjoyment. Steve never stayed the night; he respected me and my decision not to become intimate. He was genuinely flabbergasted when I told him I was a virgin. Not because I was a virgin, because a woman of twenty-one was a virgin. I half expected him to run a mile, when I told him when I did it, it would be with the man I loved. I would wait until my wedding night.

He told me he loved my company, was happy with our relationship if falling short of actually saying he loved me. Then one day, he asked if I would like to meet his family. I had been apprehensive about this inevitable reunion for weeks. By the time we arrived in Treforest, we'd been together for ten weeks, the swiftest ten weeks of my life.

Twice Reunited

On my insistence, he walked first through the unlocked door of a small terrace house in Queen Street, Treforest. In the background, beyond the open plan lounge, a young girl and a woman busied themselves in the kitchen. The olive-skinned, dark-haired pretty girl stopped what she was doing, looked up and smiled a warm smile, then turned to the older olive-skinned woman.

"Stephen and his girlfriend are here Mam," she said in a voice I recalled with happiness.

As one, they wiped their hands on their cotton aprons, ready to meet his new girlfriend for the first time. Lerina gawked at me quizzically with her familiar almond eyes for all of three seconds. I smirked back at her, she screamed and jumped at me like Roly did, expecting me to catch her. I didn't, but fortunately, we both fell back onto the settee.

She started sobbing and shouting, flailing her hands excitedly, hitting me playfully.

"It's blinking Milly moo, Mam."

Mum knew who I was one second before her; the charmingly beautiful Mrs Nairs joined us on the settee, giving both her darling daughter and I a cuddle. Meanwhile, Stephen stood still, his mouth agape, looking like Goldie.

"What, what the hell? What's going on?" Stephen faltered, holding out his arms like the statue of Christ back in Nazareth House.

"Doesn't Stephen know who you are?" Lerina asked, her dazzling eyes darting from me to him. His startled brown orbs stared back; looking like a rabbit caught in a car's headlights.

"Not a clue." I giggled nervously.

"Look at her Mam. She's bloody beautiful."

"I told her she was beautiful years ago. I remember telling her, she would be popular with all the boys. But I didn't think then it would be my boy. Although I could tell by the way she looked at him, she liked him."

Three females shrieked in merriment while the solitary male looked on confused and befuddled.

"How come you don't remember the girls who stayed with us? Milly and Pat, the two girls who looked after me in Nazareth House. You pushed us on the swings in the little park after church. Milly had a crush on you. She kept staring at you and didn't think we noticed." She almost shouted at him, beaming a smile I fondly recalled.

Apart from the open mouth and a blank stare, he stood there expressionless, looking from me to his grinning sister, then to his happy mother and back to me.

He finally spoke, "What the thin, sad-looking kid, who changed to happy on the swing?"

"Me," I said, feeling fearful.

"What the shy little girl with the incredible smile? Not the short, skinny kid with the cropped scraggly hair and the striking blue?" He stopped abruptly, clasped my shoulders in his hands and looked at me scrutinising my face, a confused look on his still unsmiling face. "Your eyes. I should have known. I'd only ever seen eyes like yours once before, for the life of me, I couldn't remember where or who it was. And it was you all the time."

I was relieved when his face transmuted from severe to happy, his eyes from blank to unperturbed. All too soon they changed to questionable. With a frown on his face, he asked,

"Why didn't you tell me this before?"

"I didn't want you feeling sorry for me."

"Feel sorry for you? Feel sorry for you?" he spluttered. "I loved you from the first moment I saw you."

Despite his revelation, his declaration of love at first sight, it was with relief I knew the charade was over at last. Even though my stomach was accompanying my jiving heart and knees, I said calmly, "Third time?"

"Third time?" he repeated, with an even more confused expression.

"I'll tell you later," I said.

"Come on, you two. Let's celebrate with a glass of wine," said Mrs Nairs swinging a straw-bottomed bottle of Chianti.

Tragically, Mr Nairs had passed away suffering from the same disease as Mr Noland, and in the same year as him. Steve told me how much his father had suffered. I thought maybe the unexpected bus was a godsend for Clive after all.

Duncan, who reminded me of Duncan from the orphanage, was at the dinner table this time. So was a fit and healthy Sandra. The six of us enjoyed an exquisitely cooked rib of beef and four vegetable dinner. My guess is the Michelin guide, reintroduced to Britain two years prior, the first since nineteen thirty-one would have awarded Mrs Nairs the coveted five stars.

The company and the ambience were absolute perfections. Duncan, a muscular, handsome young man, was an apprentice carpenter, who regaled us with stories of his work experiences and antics. The laughter was both warm and genuine and became riotous when I enlightened Steve about, the 'third time,' when I told the family about waving to Stephen in the Cardiff pub, and him looking around to see if I was waving at someone else. I felt it prudent to omit Nana and the Baba. I thoroughly enjoyed the genial company. When we reluctantly parted company, there were hugs and kisses all around. I felt as though I had never been so happy and relieved in my life.

That night I welcomed a surprised Stephen to my bed. We started off slowly by demolishing the castle walls, by the morning little of the castle itself remained, only the foundations of a steady, unwavering relationship. We suited each other perfectly.

Steve had two children with Nana, Lee and Mark who were five and six years old, they lived in Tonyrefail, a village seventeen miles from Cardiff. I met them for the first time when we went to pick them up to take them to a Radio One roadshow in Bristol. They were and still are lovely children, the youngest son Mark is the spitting image of his father. Lee, the eldest son, is a clever shy boy, who doesn't say a lot but takes in the world around him.

We had been living in our rented two-bedroom flat for about a year when Margie came to Cardiff to attend my equivalent of a hen party.

"Don't worry darling, I'll stay in the Royal for a week. I don't want to put you and handsome out. Besides, you know I love a five-star."

She and Steve liked each other on sight. She also loved the Conway pub and the extrovert regulars, most of whom were our friends by now.

Margie and I were waiting for Diana and Lerina Nairs, Verity Barnes and Natalie in Spiro's, a Greek restaurant just around the corner from Howells department store, when she said, "Still haven't told him about your money, have you?"

"There's plenty of time Margie. He has ambitious ideas. Even though he's just achieved promotion to maintenance manager, he's becoming disillusioned and restless in work and is uninspired by the factory manager. Steve thinks the factory manager and production manager are in cahoots to undermine him and his maintenance department. He says the minutes of management meetings bear little or no resemblance to the actual meeting. Steve has some money of his own, for all I know it could be more than I have, and I wouldn't mind him not telling me. Trust me Margie; I know what I'm doing. I'll do the right thing when the time comes."

"I have no doubt about that my little darling."

I recalled what Mr Noland had told me and written in his last letter when he said I shouldn't tell anyone about my money. My friends should like me for myself and not for the money.

At first, this rule applied to Steve, I was unsure whether to tell him or not when we moved into our flat. As far as I was concerned my money was his anyway, if we needed cash in an emergency it was available. I just didn't want to tell him yet. We had a joint saving account for our house deposit and shared every single expense equally. Margie had instilled into me a work ethic, to work hard for what you want, you appreciate the value even more. I had the idea that our relationship couldn't get any better, besides that, I didn't want him knowing. I thought my life, our life was perfect. I could see no logical reason to upset it by disclosing the existence of the money or its amount.

I wondered if I was overreacting. Or if, in reality, I had an aversion to confessing my wealth due to my upbringing. The reaction of the nuns to us having personal property had ensured we concealed our versions of treasure. For us, this might have been chocolates, a tattered Beano or Dandy comic or perhaps a favourite marble, one that shone with multi-colours in the sunlight, or anything we might call our own before they were confiscated. In my case, it was sweets and money. No one child could own anything, none had any toy or comforting object to cuddle at night, and the only thing we kept was our dreams and aspirations. It was as though they had brainwashed me into being secretive about my property.

Verity, Margie, Diana, Lerina and Natalie's warm personalities ensured they bonded with each other straight away. We had a merry, old fashioned, three-hour lunch. Of the people there, Verity was the only one who knew nothing of my life in the home with Natalie, and for a little time, with Lerina.

Two days after my hen party lunch, I became Mrs Milly Catherine Nairs. Diana was now my mother-in-law and Lerina, my sister-in-law. Margie, my surrogate mother, gave me away. It was a very unobtrusive registry office wedding with twenty wedding guests and twenty more back at the reception. When I invited Amanda, Matt, their mum Lindsey and dad David to the wedding, they tentatively broached the idea of holding the wedding dinner in their restaurant. I said yes, we agreed on a fair fee, they added, the discount was a wedding present from all of them. I didn't think for one second they would close the restaurant for our wedding reception.

Before she returned to Jersey, Margie and I went on a little tour of Cardiff in my little second-hand Fiat five hundred. The car I passed my driving test in six months before. I showed her the dark gothic-style mansion that had been my home for over ten years. We drove to the school on the hill. I pointed out Roly's wall, poignantly recalling the last time I saw her alive. We ended my nostalgic tour sitting on a bench on the promenade of Barry beach, eating fish and chips while watching the crashing waves, comfortable and contented in each other's company.

Margie said, "You probably don't want to know, but baldy has a new victim. I've met her twice. She's quite pretty actually but a bit thick though. It'll take a lifetime to teach her."

We looked at each other and smiled. "She's a pleasant enough blonde with blue eyes. When I think about it, she looks a bit like you. John's probably trying to relive his past, I think she's from Manchester."

As casually as I could, I said, "Her name's not Greta, is it?"

She jumped off the bench in utter shock, spilling her chips on the floor.

"What the Hell. How? What?"

"She's my sister."

"You've got to be kidding me."

While the seagulls vacuumed up her fish and chips, I told her about Greta, and of her fancying John in the Cardiff nightclub.

"Well. Greta has probably had a bit of a shock by now."

I winced when she said it, remembering my disbelief when I saw him on that first fateful morning.

"Please Margie, if it's at all possible, can you do me a favour? Ask her in your own inimitable style if she wants out. And if she does, let me know. I'll get her away from the brute."

"No, no darling. We will."

I tried without success to find Greta and Jasmin hoping to ask them to my wedding. I invited my grandmother, Gretchen and Auntie Doreen, they both declined. It was pointless asking the Mother

Superior, Sister Sandra or Sister Mary to share my joy at an atheist ceremony.

One week after our wedding, we went on a honeymoon. We had two exquisite weeks in paradise. Our hotel on the Greek island of Zakynthos was like something out of a fairy tale. Our bungalow, one of ten overlooking the Ionian Sea, was on a shady, flower-strewn tree-lined mountainside set in a five-star hotel complex. A peculiar, funicular rail car, ferried the joyful guests up and down the tor. The Olympic size pool had a plush bar and fancy restaurant that adorned its perimeter. While we were overwhelmingly grateful to Margie for her wedding present, at the time we both thought it was perhaps a little too ostentatious for us.

Nevertheless, we had a breath-taking relaxing holiday, exceeding our expectation and imagination.

I phoned Margie on our return to thank her for the fabulous wedding present. She told me she was organising Greta's escape. It seems that she was as desperate to leave John as I was, so Margie and I arranged her return to Wales. I picked her up from the airport, and she stayed with Steve and I briefly in our flat, before she and her accent moved back to Blackpool, without her telling me anything. She was totally unaware and still is that it was my money that freed her.

It's a Dog's Life

The years tumbled by in joyous harmony. I was as happy as happy could be. Steve, who was dissatisfied with the short-sighted narcissist management, resigned his position eighteen months before the factory closed, ultimately leaving two hundred people jobless. He had single-handedly redesigned their inferior antique machinery to increase production by a quarter, though to no avail. The rot had set in. The greedy self-centred management had overplayed their hands.

Fortunately, a company he had used to implement his designs recognised his flare and talent. They offered him a share of a thriving business employing twenty people. The correct term is called Headhunting. There he invented, designed, and manufactured pneumatic operated machinery that transformed production in some local companies. His reputation for increasing productivity escalated. One such machine he exported to three European countries. The highlight being when he sold a bespoke model to a company in Jersey, and we both went there and surprised Margie. Steve commissioned his machine, whilst Margie and I were happily reunited. Even though we only stayed one night, the trip was fabulous.

Regrettably, the research and development required for each job fashioned its own pitfalls. For sitting in a public house seeking artistic creativity or playing golf or snooker with potential clients, needed alcoholic lubrication, activities that eventually changed Steve slightly.

We had jointly saved more than enough for a deposit on a decent sized house. I must admit, until then, our life was idealistic. We loved each other passionately, ate out when we liked, went to the pub when we wanted to and holidayed twice a year. We even went back to Jersey this time we stayed with Margie for a week. We had the most fantastic time. She allowed me the pleasure of driving her beloved MGB. Thankfully we didn't see John.

Whilst Steve was having another swift one as he called them, Margie grasped me towards her and gave me a cuddle.

"Sorry love, I have to say it, I noted his copious consumption when you stayed the last time. He's hitting the bottle a little bit hard, isn't he?"

As much as I loved Margie, I resented her words. Though, while I thought back to what she had taught me, had drummed into me many, many times when she instructed me to think before speaking. I gave her words careful consideration and realised, as usual, she was truthful and correct.

"Get yourself a dog, love, you'll be surprised," she advised.

To own a dog had been on my mind for some time. I had given up my job in Howells soon after Verity Barnes left, I was then working mornings in the Pontcanna post office at the end of our road, so I had plenty of spare time to devote to a dog.

We both took a week off work to enjoy some time together. I broached the subject of owning a rescue dog with my boozy darling, immediately driving off in my little red car to Cardiff dog rescue centre when he agreed.

Once there, I was soon staring in disbelief at a little black reincarnation of Roly. She was in a cage with four other bigger dogs who were playing. When she saw me, the humble bundle of matted black hair, turned her tiny head away towards the poo riddled concrete floor as if ashamed.

"Hello, little girl," I said soothingly.

Very slowly and warily, she stared up towards me. Her bright saucer, intelligent-looking eyes widened. A pink tongue shot out from beneath her undershot teeth and licked her polished black nose. With her front paws, she began to climb one square of her wire cage at a time, until she stretched to her full eighteen-inch length, inviting me to join her. I did as she wanted and knelt down, gazing into her intellectual black, brown eyes that seemed to say, you'll do Milly, take me home with you?

I travelled the mile homeward bound with my three-month-old nameless new pal curled up on the passenger seat

"Only you could get a dog as ugly, as beautiful as this Nash," he laughed. He always called me Nash when he was happy. "I love you Nash," was my favourite.

Try as I might. I couldn't shift the restrictive matted mass that covered our newest family member. As uncomfortable as she was, she was patient and tolerant, giving us an insight into her character and confirming her good nature-intelligence. I made an appointment with a dog groomer, who shaved off at least two pounds of thick knotted fur, leaving her looking like a little bald gremlin. While she was being groomed, we strolled around the shop buying anything and everything we could think of buying. By the time we finished the shop counter and floor were stacked with the nameless puppy's belongings. We purchased numerous types of tinned dog food to find out what she preferred. Her new bed was a high sided wicker basket, three times bigger than her, with a small recessed entrance. Her new bedding was a comfortable fleece blanket; on it in bright colours was a picture of Dennis the Menace and Gnasher. There were squeaky toys, two tennis balls, worming tablets, dog treats, grooming combs and brushes. Finally, we bought a collar and lead with a new blank shiny name tag, which reminded me of Roly's whose own was still in my handbag.

The nameless puppy changed our lives. We both enjoyed taking no name for walks, playing, teaching her tricks. After four or five days, we still hadn't agreed on a name. She was somewhat quick at learning, confirming her intelligence, though defiantly stubborn, refusing point-blank to sleep in our most expensive purchase, her basket. Each morning, for the first few days, we'd find her snoozing on my side of the bed. Each day she progressed further, the first day she had her little chin on my feet, by day five it was on my waist.

Before we knew it, Steve and I were both due back in work. I suddenly realised we had hardly touched a drop of alcohol all week. The love of my life told me he was packing in his job and said he was fed up with the boozing. He realised he was drinking too much and wanted a stress free life. He decided to set up his own business, working on electrical, plumbing and handyman services. I agreed wholeheartedly, grateful and pleased I hadn't needed to broach the subject.

Steve was trying to coax nameless into the basket, waving her blanket at her, while attempting to entice her. When I noticed the blanket fold showed the word Gnasher, like a street name and number, in the entrance to her basket.

"Stop," I said in an urgent tone and smiled at his startled expression, "Come here. Sit down, tell me what you see?" I patted the space next to me and pointed at the basket.

He looked to where I pointed for a few seconds, then his face transformed into a beaming smile on realisation. “Gnasher. Nash. Her name was staring us in the face all the time,” he said and laughed.

Seconds later, we both agreed that Gnasher was an appropriate name for her. Little Gnasher watched us hugging and laughing maniacally, her minuscule tongue lolling, her big bright eyes happy. She started to sneeze along with our laughter, an idiosyncrasy she developed and used all her life to demonstrate how contented she was.

During the first two months, as Gnasher began to trust us, we realised our little furry pal never barked. Her first croaky yappy, a sneeze of a bark occurred when the three of us went to Barry beach. We were teasing her by throwing a tennis ball to each other and Gnasher was jumping up trying to catch it. It was a telling off sounding little bark, not too dissimilar, though not as intense, as little Roly’s bark when she chastised me. Gnasher looked like she was smiling; it was a moment I’ll never forget.

Steve and I changed our professions during the next five years of harmony. We were still saving for a house, and rightly or wrongly, I kept the secret of my wealth to myself. We wanted for nothing; our lives were both rewarding and gratifying.

“In a year we should have enough money for a deposit to buy a decent property, but not around here though,” he told me one day.

Gnasher’s patience, God bless her, was the reason behind my career change, not that licking stamps twenty hours a week was a career. I hated the radical transformation to her appearance each time she was groomed; it reminded me of my haircuts in the home. I had the idea a groom should be that, a groom, not a Sister Tom’s hack. So I decided to buy professional scissors, clippers, a large drier on wheels and specialist dog shampoos. Gnasher with her fast-growing curly hair was the perfect model, over time, I gradually progressed and improved.

The Pontcanna and Llandaff fields' area was bustling with dog walkers. Because of Gnasher's unique appearance and amicable manner, we both made many friends. Her weekly spruce was not unnoticed; her coiffure was fluffy and had a hale and hearty gloss. My fellow dog walkers soon began asking me to groom their dogs. Before long my reputation grew, I made an agreement with a fellow dog walker, who owned a large house, to rent a room for dog grooming. The rental fee was one dog groom a week, for one of his three dogs.

During this period Steve was doing well, he had a few decent, hard-working fellow tradesmen working for him. With no more maintenance payments to the ex-Mrs Nairs, as she had remarried, he was financially much better off than ever. From our first day together, we shared expenses and saved equal amounts. We enjoyed living in our large comfortable flat, neither of us saw any need to move. Not yet, anyway. I knew with the money from Mr Noland, we could afford a four or five-bed property in or around our area. I didn't see the point. I didn't want to spoil what we had. I had the thought my life couldn't get any better anyway.

My faraway friend, Margie, worried that if Steve found out how much money I had may end up resenting it after all this time.

I responded by saying. "We have never needed it. I'm not sure our relationship would be as rock-solid as it is now if we had a big house with a couple of flashy cars on the drive, a cleaner coming around three days a week. You told me it was healthy to work hard for what you have in life. I thought I was doing the right thing. Besides, we both realised the potential for growth in the dog grooming business and have agreed that I should pursue my own ambition."

I enrolled on a one-year dog grooming course, training at the London Academy of Dog Grooming. Oddly enough, the academy was located in Cheltenham, Gloucestershire, a gentle hour's drive away in my slow economical little car.

While I was training full-time and still grooming dogs, I spotted a small lock-up shop for auction just around the corner from our flat. It was in a perfect location to attract potential customers.

A week later, the auction house was almost full with around a hundred people. Steve watched me proudly through his torpid eyes, beaming as I danced uneasily from foot to foot and tried to wait patiently for lot number twenty-two. When the bidding began, there appeared to be quite a few people interested in the shop. A turban-wearing, bearded man with suspicious eyes, opened the bidding. The bid was ridiculously low, almost half the guide price. I apprehensively waved my numbered auction paddle at the auctioneer after each counter bid until only three of us remained. Number three dropped out soon after, leaving the bearded man, whose wary eyes examined me, jogging my memory, reminding me of the other Saturday auctions. The auctioneer pointed his wooden hammer from turban man to me. Each time he directed his gavel towards me. I raised my paddle, confidently staring back at Mr Turban shifty eyes. Steve glanced at me, nervously as I went over our agreed maximum.

"Going once, going twice," The silver-haired auctioneer scanned the room, hoping for more bids and no doubt more commission, before slowly repeating, "Going once and going twice. Going three times." He glanced at his sheet of paper. "Sold to Mrs M C Nairs." Then he whacked the gavel on the sound block of his rostrum with a loud bang.

I was kissing and hugging Steve squealing in delight.

"Good job, you didn't go over our fixed figure," he said sarcastically.

I nudged him playfully in the ribs.

We queued up to pay. Steve had our joint savings account chequebook at the ready.

I touched his hand. "You won't need that."

He watched me shaking his head, a look of pride on his face, curiosity in his eyes. I paid the equally surprised woman in cash, with neat bank-stamped thousand-pound bundles that the bank manager, Steve Holmes, handed me the day before. I'd only seen him twice since he came to our wedding with his charming wife, Sue, the Cambridge graduate. He told me that even with this cash withdrawal, my account would be back to the original figure within a year or two.

"It's an inheritance I was going to surprise you with it one day,"

"You did that all right," he said. "I did wonder, though. You never ask the price of anything, and you don't care about money."

My quandary, of having to tell him about my independent capital, was over. I knew him well enough to know his reaction would not be disappointing. He didn't dishearten me, he demonstrated a complete indifference by not even asking me a figure.

A couple of weeks before my renovated shop opened its doors to the paying public. I passed my exams, gaining my City and Guilds diploma in dog grooming.

We had a double celebration for my thirtieth birthday, with the grand opening of the aptly titled, *Dog -Groomer,* located on Severn Road, Cardiff.

The dog grooming parlour I had conscientiously designed had finally come to fruition, thanks to the blood sweat, tears, not to mention the dislocated shoulder of my little soldier. Steve was standing on one of the three grooming tables, installing an extra light I'd insisted on when he missed his footing.

Steve invited the local newspaper, even organising the sandwiches, buffet, wine and lager for my thirty invited guests. Grandmother didn't attend. However, Auntie Doreen made a brief appearance.

Margie arrived the day before, "I wouldn't miss it for the world, darling."

Within two years, I had almost seven hundred dogs on my books and two women working for me full-time. Little Gnasher, who I loved as much as I did Roly, never left my side. She had her own sleeping space on some fluffy drying towels and never ever slept in a basket. She was a contented smart dog, who on our regular walks never failed to receive admiring looks.

With the grooming parlour fully booked every day, and Steve's business thriving, we decided to put a very sizable deposit on a four-bed terraced house in Pontcanna. Steve employed another tradesman, I hired a lady dog washer. We ran our personal businesses in-between renovating and decorating our new home. The big airy front bedroom now had an en-suite shower room. Consequently, the bedroom next to it was a little smaller; due to the invasion of its space, it now had a short recess. I made a seemingly innocuous comment to Steve while we were discussing the decor.

"That recess is the perfect size for a cot."

He nodded.

I tried it again, "I'm not sure whether to have trains and cowboys. Or Dolls and Teddy bear wallpaper."

Slowly he raised his head from the notepad, with a knowing little smirk on his handsome face, threw the notebook and pencil in the air and cuddled our baby and me ever so gently.

"How long?" he whispered in my ear.

"Three months. Our baby might just be born on my thirty-third birthday."

"I wondered why you were off the wine," he chortled.

Margie couldn't have been more delighted if she had been my own mother. She started making plans to stay with us for a month, especially when I told her, her guest room was better than the royal.

"You have a queen-sized bed and a chaise lounge, it even has an en-suite bedroom with a shower and a bath. And I've bought you Blue Mountain coffee beans darling." I informed her during our hour-long chat. I confided to her that my maternal instincts had kicked in and I now was even more curious than ever to find my own parents and if possible Pat, Heidi and Janice.

My grandmother, with whom I had lunch with about once a month, continued to refuse to answer any enquiries regarding my parentage, despite my probing questions. I told her the fantastic news about my baby.

"I hope you're a better mother than your mother was," she said with callous indifference.

Almost daily, Gnasher reminded me of Roly. Both of them were little black furry bundles of energy; with the same undershot teeth and large pink tongues, they splashed on their black noses.

Gnasher had a gap in her bottom teeth, from a missing tooth knocked out by a stone. I was splashing her, tossing pebbles towards her as she paddled in the River Taff. She lurched forward to catch one in her mouth. The look on her face, when she heard the crack was amusing, though the loss of her tooth, less so. I was mortified, her brown saucer eyes appeared to look down to where her tooth had been, and her pink tongue probed the void. I'm not sure, but with her face scrunched up, and her undershot teeth, it was probable she could see the gap.

Gnasher didn't enjoy sitting on the floor and made it blatantly obvious. She was at her happiest sitting next to me, like when we were in the Cameo Club; she would welcome the customers with a wriggling tongued bright-eyed smile. Almost everyone knew her and would greet her first. As with most people who met the friendly little dog, the Club's owners loved her and always had a treat for her. Though, she'd have to perform one of her tricks first.

Steve was pleasantly taken aback one day after he went on a walk with Gnasher, "I didn't take her for a walk, she took me, and I just followed," he said on his arrival back home.

She took him to a different part of the extensive greenbelt of Cardiff, he hadn't been to before. When he returned, he was amused to mention that almost every encounter with another person was a "hi or hello Gnasher."

Due to my pregnancy, my body started to change in preparation for the birth of our child. My mother's decision to abandon two children confused me even more because the love I felt for my unborn child intensified daily. My other little eggs were also growing at a steady rate, though not quite the size of requiring a bra, the small bump on my eight and a half stone body was just about visible. Steve told me I looked more beautiful than ever.

Body-blow

The parting gift from my father was more than likely responsible for my baby's death. The severity of the pain in my tummy intensified during the night, the accident and emergency doctors and nurses could do nothing to save our baby or the bits of my body needed to make any more. The walls of my womb had a weakness because of a trauma inflicted when I was a baby. As my baby grew, uterine abnormalities developed; as a consequence, a significant haemorrhage occurred, causing it to die. I say it because we didn't know the sex of our child. I still don't want to know now. It also threatened my own existence. I was close to death myself; a priest was even summoned to administer the Last Rites. I was unaware of these facts until my weeping, grey-faced, and lifeless eyed, Steve told me a week later.

Margie was sitting on the sofa with Gnasher on her lap when we returned from the hospital. I gave Margie a hug, while little Gnash had her front legs on my knee silently pleading attention. When I picked her up, she licked my face and sat next to me on the sofa, her brown watery saucer eyes darting from my own to my middle. Dogs, and particularly Gnasher, never cease to amaze me. I'm practically sure they are telepathic. She knew what was wrong. I sobbed when she put her little head gently on my belly like she was listening for little heartbeats. My womb and the baby growing in it for a hundred and ten days were both gone forever. And I wished I had died as well.

Though he was reluctant to leave me, Steve went back to work. He checked the three grooming parlour girls were all right, reordered supplies for them, completed banking and paid the wages. Margie stayed with us, comforting and sweet-talking me, persuading, almost forcing me to eat, without quite getting to the Horlicks and raw egg stage.

Once I was up to it, Margie drove Gnasher and me to Barry beach in my Noddy car, as she called it. The wet sandy beachscape was entirely different from the summer. We strolled across the barren sands, throwing a ball for Gnasher to fetch, which she did with alacrity; every time returning to drop the ball at my feet, inviting me to throw it again, her twinkling eyes pleading with me to have fun.

"Hey, you little bugger. I threw that, bring it back to me," Margie complained succinctly.

While we ambled aimlessly, she told me how her plans for her future had been thwarted by John. As agreed with Colin, a codicil in his will stated, that in the event of her death or her decision to quit, the legacy of the hotel would pass to his sons. She told me that at almost fifty-seven, she'd had enough of working hard. She wanted to hand over the reins to the eager, enthusiastic offspring of Colin. But John refused to leave her house, vowing to fight her in court; he actually went to a solicitor to seek solutions to safeguard his tenancy, when she threatened to evict him quicker than Jack Robinson.

"So I've decided to give up the hotel. And with their agreement, stay in the living quarters for a maximum of six months, while I fight John in court. Or until I get that ungrateful little bugger evicted. They say the Bahamas is wonderful in January. Why don't you come with me? Do you a world of good. Come to think of it, me too," she ended with a giggle.

"Sorry Marge, I couldn't possibly go on holiday. I've neglected my husband, Gnasher and my business enough as it is."

Undeterred, she continued a little more cautiously. "Steve and I have had a little chat. He agrees with me, the climate will be beneficial for us both. Besides, we've booked it. We booked it together yesterday. He said you wouldn't go otherwise. You have yourself a fantastic husband there, you know?" she finished triumphantly.

She didn't need to tell me, I was well aware of his attributes. When Margie went back to Jersey, Gnasher never left my side. She relentlessly licked my hands and face and at night, slept on the bed again. I could feel her comforting little body touching mine through the blankets. It was akin to her first few weeks with us when she continuously did the same when she was most probably craving attention after staying in a cage. Though as she gained more confidence and assurance that the life she was now living was permanent, such was her contentment, she slept anywhere and everywhere she wanted.

After a quiet, subdued Christmas, during which I began to feel slightly better, I was looking forward to going to the Bahamas. I busied myself with the necessary preparations. I was grateful for having the women in the shop; they had run my business efficiently enough during my absence, so I knew it was in good hands. I wasn't worried about Gnasher either. She loved being with Steve, enjoyed sitting on the passenger seat of his car, her head out of the window, the wind blowing her tongue all over her face. He would look after her well enough.

On the third day of our holiday, we lay on our sunbeds with our eyes closed against the sun's rays, talking to each other over the sound of the Caribbean Sea lapping a few feet away.

"My god Milly, you looked absolutely stunning last night. Red suits you."

The words reminded both of us of the night that changed our lives.

"And I love that little black bikini you're almost wearing now. You'd better not mention to Steve how many men have asked you out."

Margie, whose only concern was my wellbeing, neglected to say how many silver-haired men showed an interest in her, as she was without question still a beautiful, stylish lady. I know she said it to bolster my spirits, but she needn't have. I was feeling much more at ease, in-between the unpleasant memories, I was enjoying myself. Though, I still felt guilty each time I laughed.

My scar was only occasionally visible under the hem of my bikini bottoms, my bikini top was filled out nicely, with a pair the size I've always wanted, though they were decreasing in size weekly. But both were a reminder of the baby I'd lost.

As a youngster in the orphanage, when I first realised and became aware that girls could have babies one day, I dreamt about having my own little boys and girls, children like Duncan, Lerina, Janice and Heidi. Even after Margie told me in graphic detail how conception happens, I still wanted too. Well, after I recovered from the shock, I did.

My way of life changed to exhilarating when I first met Margie. I thought my life couldn't get any better, though I knew I had to live first and attempt to expunge the sad memories of the first sixteen years. Then Stephen returned to my life, we married, I waited and planned our first baby. We bought a spacious house to fill it with beautiful children, our own children. The day I found out I was pregnant surpassed all prior elations a hundredfold.

The holiday did me a power of good physically, I felt stronger and invigorated, though the hollowness and misery refused to budge. I am never sure whether I should be grateful for not being able to conjure up a mental image of my baby.

Both of us agreed the holiday was unparalleled, and we both enjoyed ourselves immensely. It was settled we should have another one next year and possibly make it an annual event, with Margie unwillingly agreeing that it was my turn to pay. She stayed in Cardiff for a few days before returning to Jersey. I drove her to the airport in Noddy where Steve, Gnasher and I said a happy bon voyage to her outside the terminal building. We made arrangements for her return to Cardiff on the weekend of my birthday, ten weeks later.

"We'll dine in *Gilbertson's* darling, my treat," she said as we hugged our goodbyes.

We spoke with each other as usual over the following weeks. Margie said she could hear it in my voice I was getting better. And I was, but I hadn't reached stage three. We arranged I should pick her up at seven-thirty from the airport.

Gnasher and I sat on the steps outside the arrivals terminal until eight-thirty on the prearranged Friday morning. I locked Gnasher in Noddy, went inside to ask at the inquiry desk.

"Yes, madam. It arrived on time and has already departed on schedule," the attractive uniformed lady said.

I wished people would stop calling me madam. I wasn't especially worried, as Margie was always a little laid-back, still leaving things until the last minute, I assumed she had probably missed her flight. Though, I was concerned when her own private phone wasn't answered. I called the Galaxy's business number, cheering up when I heard a woman's voice sing out.

"Galaxy hotel may I help you?"

It wasn't her voice though, Margie's words, but not her voice.

"May I speak with Margie, please? Can you please tell her it's Milly?"

There was an uneasy, eerie silence, broken a few seconds later with, "Who did you say you were?"

"Nash mm. Sorry, Nairs, Milly Nairs." I thought of Martinis.

"Just a moment, please."

Whoever I was speaking too had me worried for a moment. Then a man's voice was speaking.

"Hello, Milly. I'm Gary, Colin's son. I'm very sorry, but I'm afraid I have some bad news for you. Margie was unwell last night last, we sent for the doctor who immediately called for an ambulance, I'm afraid Margie died before she reached the hospital."

I didn't hear anymore because I was out cold on the floor. The accumulation of all my recent experiences, my lack of strength, the sudden feeling of intense sadness and shock, I fainted. I woke up to find my ashen-faced husband cradling me in his arms. An ambulance arrived, containing two concerned professionals who checked my blood pressure and pulse, while I told Steve of our friend's fate between sobs. They decided a visit to the hospital was unnecessary and left without me. Directly after I had sufficiently recovered, I phoned Gary back, the first of a couple more during the following days, as we made arrangements for my overnight stay in Jersey.

My birthday came and went without me even thinking about it, ten days afterwards I climbed into Colin's son's car. Gary drove me to the Galaxy a few miles away. Margie's funeral was four hours later, in the mid-afternoon. I gazed at Margie's mahogany coffin as it was being lowered into the ground, feeling deeply ashamed. All I could think of was, what am I going to do now? I was so full of self-pity and pent-up rage, questioning God and the world, asking why this was happening to me.

I wasn't really there. My mind was numb. I felt fatigued, fragile and lightheaded, as if always on the verge of fainting. Nothing short of my own demise would have kept me away. I felt compelled to pay my last respects to the woman who changed my life. The woman I thought of, as my true mother. Without her, I'd probably still be a little urchin. I loved her, and I missed her. I knew I would reminisce forever. When she stayed with us after our baby died, she talked about buying a property in Cardiff. She said she'd spend winters in Jersey, and the summers in Cardiff, as there were too many bloody tourists in Jersey during summer. I considered this the perfect scenario and thought it highly likely she would have.

I saw an old man huddled inside an overcoat, on his head, a black fedora. He smiled at me serenely. I returned the same smile a second before I realised it was John looking like a cowboy from one of his books. He came towards me after the internment, as in the past probably considering the returned smile an invitation, and placed his hand on my shoulder.

Before he had a chance to speak, I said to him, "Get your hands off me, you nasty little bugger."

Gary walked towards us, John immediately scampered away. Gary noticed the confrontation. I noted that the slightly raised corners of his mouth exhibited his satisfaction with the outcome.

"This is Brian La-Forge, Margie's solicitor," he indicated towards a short chubby man wearing a smart pin-striped suit, he had a thin pencil moustache and was wearing half-round spectacles perched precariously on the end of his nose.

"He's going to read Margie's last Will and Testament back at the hotel. As you are a beneficiary, you are required to attend."

Back at the hotel. Brian La-forge said sombrely, his treble chin varying from double to single and back to treble as he huffed and puffed out his cheeks. "I Brian La-Forge solicitor to the executor of. This the Last Will… Testatrix of Margie…"

The room was spinning; I didn't hear anymore, I was feeling too faint. Thankfully I was sitting on a chair when I slumped over and Doris the waitress, another beneficiary, prevented me from tumbling to the floor.

I regained full consciousness and came to my senses in my room. A tall man in a black suit and tie was holding my wrist, checking my pulse. Gary and Doris were hovering in the background, looking concerned. The man was a doctor who attended Margie's funeral; he ushered out the two worried onlookers.

Doctor Sutherland was an exceptionally agreeable fellow and was Margie's own practitioner and a good friend of hers, he comforted me by telling me he was in the ambulance with her when she passed away without suffering.

I told him briefly about my medical history and of the last few months. His prognosis was I was suffering from a lack of sleep and sustenance, though he did give me other advice. I had been awake since dawn, stupidly I'd only had a cup of Blue Mountain all day.

A short time later, Doris, now in her uniform and her princess tiara, brought me a plateful of hors d'oeuvres. I thought back to Margie and her laughter when I once jokingly called them horse's hooves.

Before we left for the airport, Gary gave me a heavy decorated jewellery box.

"Margie left this for you in her will. Margie never stopped talking about you. My brother and I would smile at the obvious pride she displayed when she spoke of you. Margie unquestionably adored you. She told us of your loss, and the holiday you both had together, I'm not sure, but I think she might have known she didn't have long, because she changed her will about six months ago. I hope you don't mind, but I gave Brian La-Forge your telephone number. He said to tell you he'd call you in a week or so."

During my short flight from Jersey, I decided to heed the advice of Doctor Sutherland. When I arrived at Cardiff airport, I was pleasantly surprised to see Diana and Lerina with Steve and Gnasher, they greeted me with cautious hugs and kisses. Steve finally let the tugging Gnasher off her lead, and she came bounding excitedly towards me. For the first time she performed a trick I'd been trying to teach her for quite a while, she leapt up into my arms. During the journey home little Gnasher tried to lick at the tears trickling down my cheeks, I had to reassure my fellow travellers, they were happy tears. Gnasher leaping into my arms like Roly first did twenty years earlier, brought to mind many poignant memories.

My Doctor prescribed me antidepressants that literally kicked in after about ten days. Brian La- Forge rang the same day, my tranquil friends changed my life's perspective. He asked after my health, I told him I was much better. Not telling him it was thanks to my little yellow oval pills. I asked him to thank Doctor Sutherland for his advice. He queried whether I had taken out insurance on the jewellery Margie left for me. I told him I hadn't even opened the lid.

"If I were you. I'd get those insured as soon as possible," sounding shocked, ultimately giving me an insight as to the value. When I thought back, I always admired the chunky gold and sparkling rings, bracelets and necklaces Margie always wore, never once wondered how much they were worth.

He told me there wasn't any problem concerning me not being present for the reading of the Will. He explained that Will readings were infrequent these days and were only used when custom dictated as such. Illiteracy was more common among the populous long ago, and so a Will reading was a requirement. The cynic in me wondered what he was trying to say.

"Did you get my letters, Mrs Nairs?" he asked.

Right on cue, Mr Postman shoved a chunky A4 envelope and two smaller ones through the letterbox.

"Hold on, please. Something's just arrived," I said going to retrieve the letters that bore the same handwriting and were franked, Jersey. "Yes, they've just been delivered."

"Don't worry about the large one for now. But get it to your bank as soon as possible as it contains the deeds."

"The what?"

"The deeds to Margie's beach house. Well, your beach house now, seeing as she bequeathed it to you in her will. Didn't Gary tell you?"

"No," I spluttered. I was in a complete state of shock and disbelief even before he continued.

"Inside the letter, you'll find a cheque made payable to Mrs Milly Nairs. I'd get that in your bank account as soon as possible as well. Ring me back when you get over the shock," he chuckled as the receiver clicked and fell silent.

I sat still for quite a while holding the receiver steady with my chin, solemnly thinking about Margie, the beach house and the money. I stared blankly at the total amount and all the numbers on the cheque. I let out an involuntary sad, nervous giggle as I imagined Margie looking down from heaven, knowing she'd given me a shock more significant than when she explained where babies came from, where they can't come from anymore, I thought sadly.

I phoned Brian La-Forge about a week later when I knew Steve was busy working. I decided not to tell Steve about my new inheritance money or the beach house. I didn't want to experience any joy in benefiting from Margie's death.

Mr Le-forge told me the sitting tenant was still paying rent, under the false illusion his tenancy was adamantine. He said that he and Margie were, "on the brink of getting him evicted just before her." He didn't complete the sentence. He informed me we had less than a week to register my name as the new owner with the courts. The tenant and his solicitor wouldn't know who now owned the house; they'll only know the new owner wanted the current illegal trespasser ejected, and the law and the police in Jersey must uphold this ruling.

"What would you like me to do? I was close to granting Margie's wishes before her," he stopped short again.

He sounded particularly pleased when I told him to keep working on Margie's behalf.

"Send me the bill," I said.

"Don't worry, I'll deduct it from his rent cheque," he replied.

Two weeks later, during which I formulated a probable plan for the settling of old scores. Mr La-Forge rang to say the Jersey courts had issued a subpoena, stating the squatter had a week to prove his right to remain. If there were any noncompliance, the bailiff's enforcement team's instructions would be immediate.

"Mr La-Forge," I said "do you think we could arrange for the bailiffs to arrive on a Friday? At say about lunchtime. And there are a few more things I'd like you to do."

He listened intently, chuckled, and then said he'd immediately make the arrangements.

Brian La-Forge, who rang me on Monday morning could scarcely contain his excitement, breathlessly said, "Hi Milly, Brian here."

I smirked into the mouthpiece, thinking all must have gone well, for he considered his actions warranted first-name terms. "Morning Brian, how did it go?"

"As you instructed, I hired a private security firm to watch the house twenty-four hours a day. We successfully prevented the loss of furniture and valuables. A van arrived at three in the morning. The security took photographs and threatened the tenant with attempted burglary and the driver with accessory to the crime. Come Friday lunchtime, you should have seen the look on his face when I told him what you said I ought to say to him. He went completely berserk. He turned red, purple and blue, then he started running around in a frenzy, throwing stones at the windows, unsuccessfully attempting to rip the door off its hinges. He only succeeded in dislodging his wig. I felt no pity for him whatsoever, especially after the disgraceful way he treated our friend. As you rightly advised Milly, I had already telephoned the police beforehand saying there was likely to be a disturbance. They were waiting around the corner; even so, he still managed to break half a dozen windows before they grappled him to the ground and cuffed him. That's when his wig finally fell off completely. He spent the entire weekend in custody. That's the reason you wanted it on a Friday, wasn't it? He was only released an hour ago when the courts resumed, and payment for replacing the broken glass and damages were received. Oh, and by the way, I added lock replacements and the security team to his bill. I can't believe it; he seemed completely placid, almost resigned to be leaving. But when he handed me the keys to the beach house. I said, By the way, the new owner asked me to convey this message. Dear John, Goodbye, Milly, you knew what would happen, didn't you? I must confess Milly, it was by far the most fun and satisfaction I've had for years. I'm proud of you… I know Margie would be thrilled."

I laughed with him and said. "There's nothing more rewarding than an eye for an eye, and a tooth for a tooth is there, Brian?"

"Indeed not. Indeed not," Brian La-Forge said and laughed louder than ever.

Dog Eat Dog

Except for my walks with Gnasher I rarely ventured out, I only went into the parlour once a week to pick up invoices and receipts. The girls had done a marvellous job running my business during the previous months, proving they were highly efficient and more than capable of running a busy grooming parlour. So much so, that they both handed in their notice to quit on the same day. They established a competitive grooming business three miles from mine. I didn't blame them, why should I? My interest in life and living had disappeared, lost in a haze of prescription pills and alcohol. My two to four hour daily walks with Gnasher and my once a week wine delivery were my only real comforts.

Ultimately, the new business partners did me a favour, for their actions forced me to return to work. The fact they took half my clientele and dog washer with them was, in reality, a blessing. I hired a new dog washer, a very nice retired gentleman and together we groomed a couple of little dogs a few days a week which suited us both. Owners who wanted earlier appointments or who had large, boisterous or unruly dogs, I recommended to my former employees.

When I first designed my spacious kitchen, it was to make it the family focal living room. The pine farmhouse table and six matching chairs I bought hadn't been sat on for months. The two tea chests I'd painted the word toys on in different colours, stood empty in a corner. I had made so many plans.

We had a builder break through a wall and fit a stable door to have access to the garden, which opened directly onto a newly laid lawn that caught the morning sun. I imagined my blonde-haired brown-eyed baby girl sitting on the grass, gurgling and clapping her little hands together in delight. I would teach her the way Margie taught me, with love and patience. Our little girl would have been the happiest, most beautiful baby in the world. If our first baby had been a boy or girl, I would have been delighted. Though I knew in my heart of hearts, I wanted a little girl someday, even if it took a football team of boys before it happened.

My patient husband was now resigned to our way of life, an existence I know he was dissatisfied with. He tried the best he could to drag me from the abyss of depression. I hated the kitchen and cooking. I even refused to socialise. Some mornings I could barely get out of bed. I probably wouldn't have ventured out of the door, if it wasn't for Gnasher and my work.

The garden and the play lawn I had proudly prepared was now neglected and overgrown. To camouflage my painful reminders, I came up with an idea to sell the shop and convert our kitchen into a new grooming parlour. So Steve ripped out all the kitchen furniture, the sink and the cooker, then he sold the table, chairs and the Welsh dresser, leaving the room bare and unrecognisable. We put the tea chests in the loft as I couldn't get rid of them, they remained like my memories.

Steve built a wet room where the play lawn had been. He tiled the kitchen from wall to ceiling with white and beige tiles, following my meticulous design drawing. It looked as though the beige tiles were scattered haphazardly among the white tiles. It wasn't until he had installed the large mirror over the ten-foot-long stainless steel grooming table that the design manifested. He smiled wryly when I pointed at the mirror and showed him the effect. The rectangular beige wall tiles in-between the white tiles spelt out the words *DOG-EAT- DOG* in mirror image. Summing up my feelings unerringly.

We transported the rest of the contents from the shop over the weekend; the transfer turned out to be seamless. We had converted the kitchen into a parlour which was much bigger and better than the old one. One downside was the size of the new conservatory kitchen.

"It's not much bigger than a wardrobe," Steve said dismissively after he installed all the units.

We sold the old lock-up grooming parlour for almost four times more than its original auction price.

Steve Holmes greeted me in his usual manner; the only difference I noticed was that his goatee beard was now whiter. I hadn't seen him since I deposited the deeds and the cheque.

Both Steve and I had various accounts with the black horse bank. I paid the parlour cheque into my investment account and transferred half the total to Steve's current account. I left the bank and the smiling bank manager, who always talked fondly of our mutual friend Clive, with the deeds to my beach house, well my ex-beach house. Brian La-Forge had just completed the last stage of conveyance.

Without the kitchen reminders and with the help of my yellow associates, life was becoming more bearable.

Gnasher and I were walking home from a delightful late afternoon walk, when my little Roly lookalike, dragged me to the open doors of the Cameo Club as we passed. What she did next, made entering unavoidable. Gnasher danced at the entrance on her hind legs, performing a trick that was always rewarded with a treat from Barbara and Jeff the owners. An hour later, Gnasher and I were joined by Steve, who could barely contain his delight as we hadn't been out together for months.

I still hadn't told him of the beach house or the fact it was now sold, though I would soon, as a cheque from Brian La-Forge had arrived that morning. As soon as I received it, I telephoned Colin's son, Gary, as he was now the new owner of his father's old house. He had made me a very generous offer for the beach house, not resenting the fact it could have been his anyway. I couldn't have lived there, not with the memories, the miserable ones with John, the nostalgic ones about Margie. I spoke with Gary soon after Margie's funeral when I tentatively brought up the subject of the jewellery, the money and the beach house. I was concerned he would feel cheated out of his inheritance. I need not have worried, it appeared Margie, because of improvements, building extensions and a complete refit, had increased the value and profits of the Galaxy substantially, the business account balance was very healthy. She had discussed the contents of her will with Gary and his brother six months before her death. They both knew of my inclusion and agreed wholeheartedly with her decision. Without telling me the actual figures, he explained he and his brothers bequeath from Margie was more than adequate, was enough to buy half a dozen beach houses.

My considered parting words to both Gary and Brian La-Forge were the same. "Thanks a million." One point three million to be precise.

We stayed in the Cameo most of the night. Having a lovely evening, just like old times, with Steve and Gnasher displaying an animated happy demeanour, one I realised I sorely missed. I decided there, and then I would neglect Steve and her no longer.

The next morning my, happier than I'd seen him for a long time husband, brought me my favourite breakfast in bed. I felt guilty, so very guilty; to grieve so intently, when all the time he had been grieving himself. I realised my understanding husband had given me all the time in the world. We had been sleeping apart in separate bedrooms for a few months. I tucked into my soft-boiled eggs and crisply toasted soldiers and asked him to say my name.

He had a puzzled expression on his face, but said,

"Milly Nairs."

"What does it sound like when you repeat it very fast?" I could see he was thinking and recapping the words over and over in his mind.

"Millionaires?" he said, sounding confused.

"That's what we are," I said.

Money can't buy you love or happiness, but in some cases, it can make life more pleasant. Just the thought of me not having to work if I didn't want too, was enough to make me start living life again.

While I understand that antidepressants are sometimes necessary, I didn't want them as a crutch forever. I began to stop my reliance on them by decapitating a third of the pill and swallowing the remainder. I gradually reduced my intake to a fifth of a tablet until I was off them entirely. I'm not suggesting it was easy. Far from it, I almost relapsed a few times, when suffering prolonged night sweats and insomnia. I finally flushed my, 'crazy pills,' as Steve jokingly named them, down the toilet. Though, I kept two seven day foiled packs and popped them out of sight in the medicine cabinet.

A Scottish Lament

To avoid the sad memories of the anniversary of the loss of our child, we hired a car and went to see two friends of ours, Rita and Tom, who moved to Scotland. Tom was a peculiarity, a Welsh-speaking Scotsman of ample proportions, who usually had a long-lasting smile on his purplish-red face, his passion for whiskey was on a par with my love of wine.

I rented a small pet-friendly cottage on the Mull of Kintyre that I initially thought was near to their home.

To break up our journey, we stayed in Lytham St Annes where Greta now lived. At long last, she had found somewhere to live that suited her accent, for all the locals talked like her. Steve was and still is a happy-go-lucky amiable character, who socialised with practically everybody, though Greta however, was not in that category, he disliked her intensely. The feeling was entirely mutual as our frosty reception proved.

"You all right me love?" she said, greeting me in a northern accent, and ignoring Steve.

Steve disliking her rebuff, mocking her choice of clothing and mimicking her accent said,

"You all in white, me love?"

After all these years she still wore all-white clothing. I had my theories concerning this but said nothing. Such was the ill-feeling between the two; we decided to complete the return journey without a rest break. Greta and I spent the night at her home, whilst Steve and her boyfriend Wayne went to his business men's private club.

We left for Scotland early the next morning. Sloppily, I hadn't done my homework correctly for we only managed to visit Tom and Rita twice. They lived forty miles away from our rented cottage. In my defence, their one-bedroom cabin was twenty miles away from the nearest town Oban and was only accessible by a single track road, making it a three-hour round trip. On their advice, we rented a large static caravan nearer to them, on the scenic banks of Loch Gilp, in Lochgilphead, an area famous for its kippers. We arrived in darkness, so we missed seeing the incredible vista.

The next morning Steve and Gnasher went for an early walk, leaving me to shower and cook breakfast from the provisions we had purchased the previous day. Returning, he breathlessly described the scenery they observed as they strolled along the east bank of the small loch. He finally told me Gnasher, who typically had the constitution of a horse, had severe diarrhoea.

While Steve showered, Gnasher and I went for a walk. My sense of direction was totally disoriented as we passed through the sea of static caravans, though Gnasher impatiently tugged on her lead and took me on a trek. We passed by, and I witnessed all the places Steve described. I knew they had both walked the same route, the trodden grass and disturbed dew showed where they had previously hiked. Even though my knowledgeable guide was keen to show off, I could see my usually bouncy friend was not well. Her nose was warm, and she was unusually thirsty; during our walk, she steadily lapped at the loch's water. When I returned I insisted we cut short our holiday and return home.

Two days later back in Cardiff, Gnasher was diagnosed with type two diabetes mellitus and admitted to the intensive care unit of a veterinarian hospital. As her leg was shaved in preparation for the intravenous drip, my thoughts went back to little Roly. Though the chronic disease was the primary cause of her symptoms, her severe dehydration was because she drank the seawater from the shores of Loch Gilp. Both Steve and I thought it was a freshwater Loch, as are the majority of lochs in Scotland.

Martin, the condescending veterinarian in charge, was a self-centred person with his focus fixed solidly on money, to such an extent he insisted I pay him daily. He told us in plain words, without any emotion or apparent concern for his patient; the prognosis was not good, leaving me back in the pits of deep despair. He informed us that ninety percent of dogs diagnosed with diabetes are dead within six months and that nine out of the ten survivors die within the next twelve months.

It soon became palpable why the mortality rates were as high as they were, for there are a lot of factors to take into consideration. Most dogs are scavengers and will eat at any given opportunity. For a diabetic dog, this would result in imbalances that would make them unwell, causing a loss of appetite as well as higher readings of ketones. Any refusal to eat after the injection was also a grave concern for most owners. More often than not, a visit to the vet for intravenous liquids would be necessary to prevent the coma and death that would inevitably follow. Establishing a routine was essential to sustain the correct balance of blood sugar levels.

Gnasher left intensive care after three days and was allowed home, though we had to return with her and her urine sample each day.

During this period, the vet demonstrated the test procedure. He placed a measured amount of urine in a test tube before adding a tablet which produced a chemical reaction that literally boiled the liquid changing the colour of the urine depending on the concentrations of ketones present. By checking the colour in the test tube against a colour chart, it was then possible to determine the quantity of insulin that needed inoculating.

We both practised by injecting oranges before we were competent and confident enough to start inoculating Gnasher in the scruff of her neck. Immediately after each injection, she needed to ingest a set quantity of carbohydrates to maintain her blood glucose levels. I'm sure my confused dog thought she had done something wrong and we were punishing her.

Additionally, we couldn't reward her for suffering the daily injections or give her treats anymore, as they could ultimately cause the blood insulin levels to fluctuate. She'd perform her tricks for us and look downcast when she wasn't rewarded.

As well as being gravely ill, Gnasher was depressed, as if going through the five stages of grief, and didn't want to sleep upstairs anymore. So I slept downstairs to comfort her. I became especially worried when she started to sleep in the basket I know she hated, curled up in a ball and only getting up to relieve herself.

The difficulties of having a diabetic dog soon became apparent; though having an exceptionally intellectual dog was decidedly useful. For instance, just obtaining a urine sample from a squatting girl dog was a hard task to perform; following her around the garden, waiting to pounce at the first signal was sometimes unsuccessful. If this occurred, the previous day's insulin dosage was used. I eventually taught Gnasher to pee in a small Pyrex dish lid, even without the help of training treats, allowing us an accurate analysis each day.

I was determined to make my little friend as happy as I possibly could. I sent away for books on canine diabetes and researched books from the library, through this, I recognised the value of a high protein diet and what foods to give her if she refused to eat. We could force-feed her if we had to, her praiseworthy docile nature made the task more straightforward than it sounds. I would ask her to sit, kneel down with her back to me. Then I would grip her with my knees, lift up her head and open her mouth. Keeping her head up and mouth open with one hand, I'd plop in a dollop of Weetabix, which in the correct quantity contained the perfect balance of carbohydrates and protein required, to the back of her throat with my other hand. Stroking her windpipe then ensured she swallowed the life-saving food. Within half an hour, the transformation in her and her energy levels were astonishing and well worth the unpleasantness of the force-feeding. We adjusted the amount of Weetabix to enable us to give her four or five well-appreciated treats a day.

During the following weeks, we established a strict routine that ultimately helped me cope with my depression as much as it helped Gnasher manage her diabetes. Well before we passed the deadly six months marker, six weeks to be precise, she was back to her happy, bouncy self again, and thankfully, so was I.

I decided that however long we had left together in this world, I would endeavour to make it both memorable and pleasurable for us all. At long last, I had attained the fifth stage of grief, strangely though it required another tragedy to fulfil this.

Another delighted person was the ‘parasitic vet’ as Steve called him, for he had the notion he fed off the emotions of animal lovers. He might have been right, for we would have gladly parted with all our money to have Gnasher well again. Steve used the example of the lovely, sad old woman we met in the vet’s waiting room. Her ancient and thin black cat was in the throes of dying, was in intensive care the same time as Gnasher. A week later, the cat seemingly made a Lazarus-like recovery and was allowed to go home, only to return again after four days. For three days the cat was pumped full of life-preserving drugs, in the profitable Lazarus section of the animal hospital, recovering enough to go home with the happy old woman, only for the cat to return a final time for its costly fatal injection. Steve reckoned the money she paid him would have paid for a lovely holiday or a personalised car number plate.

Who am I?

I was now even more resolved to find out more about my parents. I was determined to find out more than, how my father punched my mother in the stomach and hurt me while I was in her womb. With this in mind, we followed every avenue of research we could think of to answer my conundrums. Steve and I separately visited the archive section of our local library on alternate days, to read every edition of Cardiff's daily newspaper from nineteen fifty-five until nineteen seventy-one. We had the thought, a high profile place such as Nazareth House was sure to be included in some editions of the newspaper, that there might be a slight possibility of Horace or Jane Nash being mentioned. Fortunately, during the nineteen fifties, entire libraries were stored on microfiche in an attempt to preserve information for future generations.

Steve and I spent countless hours hunched over a microfiche machine; between us, we must have scrutinised over four thousand copies. Then we took turns to read and pore over the pictures of the thirty-six volumes of the *'Cardiff Yesterday'* series, trying to glean any information to fill the void.

Finally, I could barely contain my excitement when I came across the photograph and the news article à propos my First Communion. Just that one photocopied faded picture made all the hard work worthwhile. Not to be outdone, Steve found the Barry Island article and grainy photograph.

During the following six months, we accumulated around fifty articles and photographs as we diligently cross-referenced and photocopied each item. Not long after, we went by appointment to the South Wales Echo's press archives on a Sunday morning. The man who showed us the archive files knew Steve, so he left us alone to look through the contents of hundreds of filing cabinets. There, we found half a dozen Hasselblad negatives of the Nazareth House and Barry Island newspaper photographs. The man told us to keep them.

Peter Hopkins, a tall, good-looking man of about forty, was sitting on our tan leather armchair with one leg crossed over the other, his suit jacket draped over an arm. He was reading enthusiastically from a bundle of handwritten notes, as he spoke his brown winkle picker boot twitched nervously at his ankle as though conducting his performance. I had contacted Mr Hopkins soon after the librarian from the archive section recommended the amateur genealogist as a likely candidate to help us with my quest to discover my parents. As with me, the only information he had to start with was from my birth certificate. He was now delivering the results of about a month's research from his notes, reading with fluidity and proud confidence; pausing for a few seconds after each paragraph to examine our faces questionably with his keen, bright brown eyes.

He rubbed his hand over his short jet black hair and said his favoured first contact was at first reluctant to help until he knew the whole story. However, the help from Rev David Kellan of St Mellons, a Church of England vicar, was beneficial but yielded no results.

By the look on Mr Hopkins face and his previous sentence, I knew he was leaving the best bits until last.

"Fred Booker, a retired publican who lives in St Mellons, has no recollection of your mother or father, but he will make some enquiries. I have tried four times, without success, to contact Len Hales, who is ninety-four years old, and did weddings and funerals using horse-drawn carriages. Surprisingly Pastor Williams, who was at the Baptist Church of St Mellons for thirty-three years, did not know of the family. But nevertheless, he was accommodating and provided me with names and addresses of locals he thought might be able to help."

He grimaced as he took his first sip of my favourite coffee. I could see from his posturing that the next page would bring some positive information.

"Frank Maggs, of Old St Mellons, remembers your father and his father very well… Though, he didn't have much to do with them. They were friendly rather than friends. He described them both as well-dressed and well-spoken. Your father, it seems, was a bit wild for the ladies and the beer. He also had something of a reputation for dodgy dealings and was often involved in brawls. Frank Maggs has no knowledge of you or your sister. He wasn't even aware Horace was married. However, he knows Horace had a long term relationship with a barmaid called Beryl, who worked in the Fox and Hounds public house in St Mellons, other than that he provided no further information."

He glanced down at page three, holding his most extended pause before continuing, "Fred Bird was extraordinarily helpful, he is well known as an amateur historian and remembers your father well. It appears," he said jubilantly while stroking his clean-shaven square jaw. "That your father was either very well known or not known at all. No in-between."

Steve went to St Mellons to follow up on Peter Hopkins findings. He first knocked on Fred Bird's door, and receiving no answer, went to the farmhouse and adjacent cottages to make his own enquiries about Horace Nash and his whereabouts. Blank stares and shaking heads answered his queries. He then visited the Fox and Hounds and asked a few of the regulars the same questions, and getting no luck, he tried the Bluebell Inn public house, striking the jackpot when he found Fred Bird sitting supping a pint.

"Yes, I knew him. He had all the shire horses off Five Mile Lane. Ladies' man he was, a handsome bugger, and as strong as an ox. Most women fancied him, he and his father were always dressed well."

Over a couple of pints of Brains Brewery ales, the brewery that employed my father, Fred was very chatty and informed Steve he hadn't seen hide nor hair of Horace Nash for years.

"The last time I saw him was in nineteen eighty-five or six, before that only a few weeks before the crash that almost killed him. He was in hospital for months. I haven't heard a word about him since. Charlie Wallace bought his old property and lives there now."

Fred said to Steve in a blunt, honest fashion, only an old man with total disregard could demonstrate. "I didn't like the smarmy flash bugger, anyway. Mind you, he was always immaculately dressed. He always wore his tie in a Windsor knot."

With his tongue well lubricated by his fourth or fifth pint, the frank and open blood-shot-eyed Mr Bird delivered his most fruitful fact. "I tell you who will know where he is, Jimmy Davies. He worked for him driving the lorry. Thick as thieves those two were. I'll have to ask him first though; I don't want to give you his telephone number without his permission. I'll let you know by next week."

Fred Bird was waiting for us in The Bluebell Inn, St Mellons, close to my father's old farmhouse. He stood up as we approached his table. I smiled warmly and shook his hard knurled hand. His yellow-toothed smile reminded me a bit of Clive Noland.

"My God, you're the spit of your old man, same eyes and the same smile," he growled gruffly before telling me about my father from his early days.

Although he didn't say so, it soon became recognisable, he disliked my father. Steve thought it likely he was jealous of him. That he had only seen my father once in fifty years quickly became apparent as he struggled to update or corroborate details. He did, however, provide us with the phone number of Jimmy Davies, which, it transpired, was the biggest prize on the goldfish stall.

I phoned Jimmy at lunchtime the next day. He spoke with affection of my father and unquestionably adored him. It was unfortunate, he hadn't seen him for many years. I thanked him for his time and was about to say my goodbyes when he said he had a negative of a long-lost, almost forgotten photograph taken before I was born. One I could have. We agreed to meet the next day.

Jimmy pointed at the grainy negative I held towards the light. "That's me there, and there's your father. The other bloke is Don, the stableman, we worked for your father and his father for years."

Steve met me in the Cameo Club with the framed A3 photograph of my father wrapped in Christmas paper under his arm. He had taken the negative to be developed in a specialist photographic studio.

"Are you ready to see your father for the first time in your life?"

I held my breath as I ripped the paper off the silver-framed black-and-white photograph.

Standing near the buckboard of an open-backed battered lorry carrying bales of straw stood a fulfilled looking clean-shaven, handsome man, his light hair swept back revealing a proud forehead. He wore a smart raincoat buckled at the waist and had his leather-gloved hands crossed below the belts buckle. Just visible around his neckline, his suits collar and a starched collared shirt and tie. His smile is reminiscent of *Leonardo's, Mona Lisa*.

Two men wearing what appeared to be old army caps stood beside him. One was Jimmy Davies, standing on the ground wearing a light boiler suit belted at the waist. Don, the other man, eighteen inches higher, was standing on the buckboard wearing an equally shabby jacket, the outfits confirming their status.

I felt my knees give a long, forgotten jig as I stared at my father, urgently trying to adjust all the images I had of him from my imagination over the years. I had never thought or envisaged that he looked like me. Or rather, I looked like him. I know my grandmother, my mother and Fred had said something along those lines, but the resemblance in front of me, seeing my own eyes, face and mouth smirking back at me, was disconcerting.

Gnasher was sitting between us, greeting the customers as the bar gradually became busier. I left the picture face up on the table, picking it up now and then to study my father's face until I had the photograph etched in my mind's eye.

Ken Jones, a BBC rigger, a good friend of ours, entered the club. Gnasher gave him her warm, happy open-mouthed sloppy tongued welcome. He greeted Gnasher with a polite, "hello Gnasher," nodded to us and gave a disinterested glance at the photograph. He abruptly stopped and twisted his head to have a better look at the picture.

He had a quizzical expression on his bearded face. "How come you have a photograph of Horace?"

Both Steve and I had Goldie expressions on our faces as Ken continued, "Horace was a good friend of mine. I used to meet him over the Albany pub for a drink. We met nearly every Friday for years and years. That was until he died about six months ago."

"He's my father. Or he was. In light of the information you've just given me Ken," I said sadly.

Ken was mortified and apologetic. After a short while, he said, "Come to think about it, you look uncannily like him."

I blamed myself. If I wasn't so secretive about my life in Nazareth House and was more open about my parentage, or lack of parents, it was highly likely I would have met my father. After all, I felt Ken was undoubtedly a good enough trusted friend to have confided in, he quite possibly would have put two and two together especially if he knew my maiden name was Nash, and he no doubt would have told me about Horace then.

Throughout the evening, Ken told us stories about my father, Horace lived with a black woman called Gwyneth in Albany Road, in the Roath district of Cardiff not two miles from us. He said, "Horace never mentioned he had been married or the fact he had two daughters." Ken described my father as five foot five, and impish faced. He was an immaculately dressed handsome man, who always greeted him by saying, "Hello, dear boy, how are you?" He used to shuffle rather than walk to open the door to him, dressed in his pure silk dressing gown with matching sheepskin slippers. It appeared he was a bit of a lad and still had an eye for the ladies, a man who could drink whisky without any effect until the cows came home.

A little later he told Steve privately that he was a scoundrel and a likeable reprobate.

Goodbye My Friend

Gnasher survived six years of diabetes, which surprised and pleased the vet. Steve estimated he had ten cracking holidays out of us.

Gnasher, Steve and I had become adept at coming to terms with her condition. She lived a full and happy life as did Steve and I.

Ralph, the dog washer, was so proficient I trained him to pre-groom dogs. Ultimately becoming a good friend of ours. Both of us taught him how to test and inoculate Gnasher, trusting and confident of Gnasher's wellbeing; we even went on holiday, only for a week though, we attempted to stay at the same hotel we honeymooned at in Zakynthos, but it was now all-inclusive.

We were particularly fortunate to book a room at the superb Cronulla Hotel in Kalamaki, the family-run establishment was perfect on all accounts, lounging around the vast pool by day and dining in the tranquil atmosphere during the evening, with the sound of relaxing music playing in the background was a welcome relief. The other bonus was Zackynthian wine, which is the finest I have ever sampled.

Towards the end, our best friend was virtually blind and partially deaf; she couldn't climb the stairs anymore, so she slept downstairs. Steve and I took it in turns to sleep downstairs with her. We covered the carpet with newspaper pages in case of her little accidents. I hated seeing how fragile she was, but I didn't want to lose her, as long as she wagged her tail and ate her food, I was contented to keep her alive.

Finally, I realised we were going through the same motions as the little old lady and her cat. I ignored the similarities until she was home with us after spending three days in intensive care. Gnasher's condition had deteriorated almost as soon as we arrived back from the vet's. We replaced the newspaper and cleared up any accidental mess, while she looked away as if embarrassed when she had the misfortune. It reminded me of our first encounter in the dog pound. I glanced at my vulnerable little friend, seeing the poorly disorientated little girl bump her head on the furniture as she attempted to re-familiarise herself with the surroundings.

I glimpsed Steve's aggrieved expression. I knew then it was time to say goodbye and said painfully. "She has a few days of her life left. Hasn't she?"

"Yes. I think so," Steve said in a croaky wounded voice.

Steve cuddled Gnasher as he said his last goodbyes to the little dog he loved. She licked his face as he handed her to me.

He stroked her head and said, barely audible and tearfully. "So long Gnash, you've been the greatest dog in the entire world."

Gnasher looked in his direction, her tail did a few happy sweeps as if to indicate the feelings were mutual, her eyes were half-closed like she was ready to go to sleep, to sleep forever.

Steve just couldn't face coming to the vets to witness the 'execution' as he called it.

Keith drove Natalie, Gnasher and I to the veterinarian hospital. I sat in the back with Gnasher curled up in my lap unerringly like Roly was all those years before.

After kissing and cuddling Gnasher I suddenly and immediately concluded that dogs and perhaps all creatures know when they are going to die because I'm positive Gnasher knew what was about to happen, like little Roly, Gnasher was unusually serene on the examination table. Usually, she would be slightly apprehensive and fidgety. I knew she couldn't see the tears streaming down my face as I held onto her shoulders, propping her up, I stared into her half-closed misty eyes as the vet gave her the lethal injection. It shocked me her death was so quick, no sooner had the needle pierced her little body, Gnasher made a quiet little squeak like sound, slumped to the table and was gone. I scanned her dead body and the room to see if I could see her soul rising and climbing to doggie heaven. Even though I knew she had passed on, the tranquil atmosphere when the vet left me alone with my best friend, made me feel like I was in heaven with her; even though I was inconsolable. I was contented, but with a difference, as though I finally accepted death as part of life. I thought my faith might be returning, I was starting to believe in God again.

Catalogue of Coffins

The last time I set foot in a Catholic Church was 1971 when I attended Mr Noland's funeral.

This time it was December the 16th 1995, my brother-in-law Duncan's birthday and his mother's funeral.

Nine days before, my mother-in-law and a great friend Diana Nairs had died, she had a severe brain bleed, a stroke. Surviving for barely a week before succumbing.

Before she died, Steve and I visited her at East Glamorgan Hospital. It was the same hospital her five children were born, and where Steve went when he had scalded his arm. There we saw the severity of the stroke confirmed in her posture, in her drooping and sagging jaw. The vibrant, funny, caring Diana I knew, would not have wanted to live as the prognosis was bleak. Incredible grief and sadness surrounded her hospital bed as she drifted in and out of unconsciousness. Even though she was heavily sedated she thrashed about with her right arm; the only one she could use, trying to pull out the tubes in her nose and throat until a nurse strapped her arm to the bed.

She died surrounded by her children and their husbands and wives.

Steve had a worried look on his face for days afterwards, for as well as coping with his own sorrow, he had to suffer the anguish of trying to organise the funeral.

"They give you a bloody catalogue of coffins and the prices. It's like you're buying a shirt or something," Steve said, sounding exasperated.

While this was a concern on the practical side, the family also faced another predicament.

Her five children held a problematic discussion regarding her last requests. It appeared Diana hadn't obeyed her husband Gordon's final wishes. He had not been cremated as he wanted but had been interred instead. Diana vetoed his request as on her death she wished to be buried with him in the same grave. However, during the ensuing twenty-four years between their two bereavements, Diana changed her mind deciding she wanted to be cremated.

The dilemma for the family reached an impasse. Steve was unsure and said he would go along with a majority vote. The two girls were for the cremation, the two boys wanted a burial.

"Why don't you suggest to the others you'll stand by the wishes of your mother and go ahead with the cremation? Then have her remains interred in the same grave as your father." I suggested.

He almost shouted, "You're a bloody genius, Nash."

The rest of the family agreed. On the day of the funeral, we filled the first two pews of St Dyfrigs church. I sat next to Steve, on the same bench I occupied twenty-eight years earlier, though, instead of Diana sitting next to me, she was dead and lay in a wooden box a few paces away.

Diana Nairs was laid to rest one week after her cremation while the parish priest conducted the observance around the open grave. When the formality ended, he handed a little square oak case containing Diana's ashes to the gravedigger who straddled Gordon's coffin, his feet respectfully just above it in two dugout footfalls, and gently placed the box on what would have been her husband's chest. The priest picked up a handful of soil and sprinkled it over the two wooden caskets. Steve repeated the ritual, followed by all of Gordon and Diana's children, their husbands, wives and ten grandchildren.

None of her Italian family attended either of the services. Steve's telegram to her brothers and sisters in Piazza Vecchia consisted of just three words, '*Diana Cabianca. Morto*'.

The Mummy Returns

I was sweeping up the hairs of my previous customer when Auntie Doreen phoned me. Her message stunned me, seemed so out of place, it was like her telling me she saw the Mother Superior cycling with her habit blowing up in the breeze to reveal a skull and crossbow tattoo on her ankle.

"Your mother has been in touch and would like to speak to you," she said to me so casually, she made it sound like my mother had just returned from buying a loaf of bread at the local shop, instead of returning fifty years later.

When I phoned Greta with the news of our mothers' re-embodiment, she sounded enthusiastic. I, on the other hand, was suspicious and sceptical. All my emotions were contradicting each other, I wasn't sure if I was angry or ecstatic.

Jane Nash walked through the front door, into the spacious hall of our terraced house, sniffing the air with a look of bored arrogance on her attractive face. She was tall, a good four inches taller than me, wearing stylish clothes that had undoubtedly been tailored to fit her slim body. Her short blonde hair had the appearance of a new trim, but beneath her fringe, her blue eyes expressed counterfeit warmth.

Her one-week visit was the culmination of about an hour's worth of conversations between us. In the six phone calls we had, I learned absolutely nothing about her, except the youthful sound of her voice.

I couldn't help but imagine her as a teenager during our initial phone conversations.

I was acutely aware of first impressions being vital, we studied each other for a few seconds. However, my first impressions were not impressionable. Jane's apparent arrogance and aloofness surprised me, I dismissed this as a case of the nerves. I suppose my expectations and trepidation showed on my own face.

I still maintain the same looks and stature I had in my twenties, though like her, I had made a special effort for this occasion. The previous day, Howells department store had provided me with two hours of beauty treatments. I hoped she liked the look of the woman now smiling at her, the baby she gave away.

Up to this point, I had let my emotions run wild as my sentiments changed daily. I wondered why, after all these years, Jane wanted to meet me, why was she keen to see me? There again, I straightaway wanted her to be proud of me and wondered if she would appreciate any of my life achievements. At one point, I thought she might have found out I was a millionaire. Though I dismissed the notion, no one but me, Steve and the bank manager knew about the money. I found it almost impossible to sleep with all these questions bombarding my mind.

I was unsure whether to hug or kiss her or neither. She snatched the decision from me. I felt numb when the woman who bore me a half-century before touched and hugged me, though it was more two hands on my shoulders, for all of two seconds. I had hoped, prayed and dreamed for this day almost every wakening and sleeping hour up to the point of meeting Margie. I wanted to experience the love and attachment I had felt for my mother during my life in the children's home. Most of all, I needed my passion reciprocated. I yearned for her to tell me she loved me. I wanted her to cry and hug me. Tell me she was sorry. Ask me for forgiveness, say it was all a big mistake, she had been institutionalised, had amnesia and only now had her memory returned. I tried to evaluate my emotions, I questioned myself and the motives of the woman who was going to sleep in Margie's room. Steve had the notion she had a terminal illness and was trying to recompense her past mistakes.

Jane sipped her cup of Blue Mountain appreciably, in a polite, dignified manner, as she glanced around our stylish living room. A room-based partially on Margie's modish sagacity. She suddenly appeared shocked and upset with a look of extreme irritation on her face. I could see she was looking at the silver-framed picture of my father, her husband. A photograph positioned in the pride of place in the middle of the chimney breast above the oak fireplace.

"I'll take it down if you want me to," I said, thinking perhaps I might have made a mistake, had quite possibly been inconsiderate.

"If you would be so kind," Jane replied, sounding insincerely pompous and oddly in a voice that could have been one of a fourteen-year-old shy, timid little girl.

She watched me looking smugly satisfied as I replaced the photograph of Horace and his two employees with an Andy Warhol print of Campbell's soup cans. I tucked Horace and his pals safely out of sight in a dark drawer. Now would have been the perfect time for her to elucidate, I thought excitedly. But she didn't say a word. To say she shocked me would be an understatement. My mother was in my home, yet she appeared to have no love, emotion or excitement in her eyes. Her cold stare reminded me of Sister Terry.

During her stay with us, my mother and I had endless conversations, from which I gleaned nothing about her. Even though she was almost seventy years old, she talked and sounded like an adolescent. I felt the obligation of any explanation was entirely her responsibility. Each day I waited on tenterhooks for her to give me details, anything, any clue as to my identity, her past, or of my father and what happened to make her put us in an orphanage.

I hugged her each morning and said a cheerful, "Good morning, mother," like I jokingly did with Margie, though without feeling the love I felt for Margie and the overwhelming knowledge she loved me.

As the days progressed and the end of her stay was fast approaching, I felt I had learned nothing from the woman who carried the title of my mother. I had rarely been false in my entire life, but I was a little during her stay. Like Margie, I considered myself a plain-speaking, honest, straightforward woman, but I was so desperate for her love. Even though she was pleasant enough, her blue eyes thoroughly lacked any emotion. I irrationally thought perhaps she didn't like me, was maybe disappointed in me. The only thing she did say, in what I perceived an unguarded moment, "you have your father's eyes". That and the incidence with the photograph were the only enlightening experiences during her visit.

I heeded the perceptive advice of my true mother Margie and gave my birth mother the benefit of the doubt. All she needed to do was to demonstrate her love, her regret, her reasons, anything.

Steve told me to ask her outright. "Ask her why she placed the two of you in the orphanage. And more significantly, why she never came back, and why has she come back now?"

I was in the kitchen conservatory preparing a meal. Jane was leaving the next morning, when I heard Steve say in a voice louder than he would customarily use, one unusually coupled with anger,

"You think you've had a hard life, take a look over there at your daughter. If you think you've had a hard life, what do you think she's had, a bloody picnic? She was in a bloody orphanage for fifteen bloody years. And now you appear fifty years later. Big deal lady."

My husband rarely lost his temper and never his composure. He entered the kitchen and pointed at my nonplussed mother through the open door, saying irately,

"Do you want to know what she just said to me? She said you don't know how hard it's been for me."

Out of Jane's vision, he winked at me and belaying his gleeful looking eyes said, sounding angry, "I'm going to the Conway, see you later."

I knew exactly what his motives were; he had taken advantage of my mother's careless words and had seized upon the opportunity to coerce her to give me answers.

My mother and I ate our meal while Steve was at the pub. We drank wine and talked throughout the evening. I broached and hinted, but she said nothing. She never even asked about Greta. My mother gave a near-flawless impersonation of the proverbial ostrich with its head in a bucket of sand, though with her high-pitched twitter she was more like an annoying sparrow. I wondered why she even bothered to get in contact with us at all.

I used the trick Margie used years before when she plied John with whisky. I poured out measures of gin and tonic for both of us, only my glass held more tonic than gin, and she had more gin than tonic. It was during our third glass of gin I realised she was a lightweight when it came to drinking. Soon her lifeless eyes glazed over and her tongue lolled exactly like Gnasher and Roly's. She began to slur her words, then quite suddenly, her slurring speech revealed the truth. My intuition and supposition were correct.

"It was your grandmother's fault. She was the one who made me put you and Greta in Nazareth house,"

"Why, what did she do mother?" I shuddered when I said mother.

"She wouldn't give me any money," she whimpered in her infantile voice.

"It must have been awful for you. How did you manage to survive?" She failed to notice the cynicism in my voice or the words.

"I thought of you and Greta every day of my life," said the inebriated old woman with the young voice. She was too drunk to make much sense after that, though it was more than enough for me to realise what type of woman my mother was.

I helped her up to Margie's room and left her sprawled on top of the bedclothes. I went back to my gin and mulled over the evening's events. I loved my grandmother, yet the woman upstairs blamed her. I felt the excuse was pathetic and lame; after all, my grandmother came to visit us, took us out and brought us gifts on a fairly regular basis. We still met about once a month for lunch. I considered the responsibility of care for us was down to our mother and father, not my grandmother.

Steve, though, had other ideas, saying it wouldn't happen in the Valleys, meaning that an echelon of relatives or friends would adopt the responsibility to care for children in need. I remembered Paul from Nazareth House and his mother's best friend when he said she wanted to look after him.

I concluded I had no pleasant feelings towards the person without any maternal instincts sleeping upstairs. However, I bore no ill will towards her. If anything I pitied her. I wondered if she would ever tell me the specifics one day. I thought about my baby and the love I still feel. I didn't tell her about the loss of our baby, I didn't want her sympathy.

Even after her revelations of the previous evening, I said an emotional goodbye to her the next morning. Steve watched with his arms folded as I kissed my mother on both cheeks and hugged her. Her own arms were dangling at her sides.

She looked questionably at Steve and said, "No, hugs?"

Steve shook his head.

"You did when I arrived," Jane said pouting, in her most pathetic baby-like voice.

"That was then, and this is now," Steve said with a polite-looking smile on his face.

I hugged Steve after waving goodbye to my mother feeling relieved she was gone. I had my head on his shoulder. I said sarcastically, "Well, she said she'd come back. And fair play to her, she did." I paused for a second and said chuckling, "It might have been fifty bloody years, but she came back."

Steve and I roared with laughter until we had tears streaming down our faces, my own tears though were bittersweet.

Not for Adoption

Jane Nash telephoned me about a week after she stayed with Greta, her boyfriend Wayne and son Malcolm. It appeared she had had a wonderful time in Lytham St Annes. She and Wayne had played golf, and she defeated him by two shots, she gloatingly added in her juvenile manner.

I already knew her visit went well as Greta had phoned me the moment our mother had left her house. Like me, at first, she was sceptical about her motives, though unlike me, she warmed to her. I was absolutely mortified. I was speechless as she praised the woman who had left us at the mercy of nuns and Nazareth House for nigh on sixteen years, a woman who then decided after half a century to return to the fold. It appeared, for reasons I couldn't possibly imagine, Greta had fallen under the charmless woman's spell.

What my mother and Greta didn't know was that a few months before I had attained information concerning Jane, and gathered explanations regarding our incarceration, evidence that possibly influenced my negative thoughts, though I'm confident I gave Jane the benefit of the doubt. I decided not to disclose or share the acquired proof with Greta as I thought she wouldn't rationally cope with the information.

During my research, I contacted the archive section of Nazareth House in Hammersmith, about a month before the announcement of my mother's return from shopping. They had replied by post after nearly a week and provided me with all the information they had regarding my incarceration. Inside an A5 envelope were five sheets of paper. One of them was an original document, the rest photocopies, all of them dated back to the nineteen fifties. My mother handwrote two of the pages.

The accompanying letter starts.

Dear Ms Nash,

Re; Your records

Milly Catherine Nash; d. o. b 18/04/1955

Thank you for your enquiry regarding records for the period you spent in the care of the Sisters of Nazareth. We have searched all the registers and records for Swansea and Cardiff Nazareth House and have found the following information. You may see some details about your background upsetting to read, but I hope that in the end, it will prove helpful to know a little more about your early childhood.

Firstly, we found an entry for you at number 126 in the Swansea Children's Adoption Book. (Very young children were often entered into this register before it was known whether or not adoption would be an option for them.) According to this Register entry, you were born on 18th April 1955 and baptised at Our Lady Star of Sea, Mumbles.

I wasn't sure about my baptism and here was the confirmation in my shaking hand, written in ink. I was number 126 and Greta 127. Next to my name was the word, 'admittance' and the date 7th May 1955. The title stated; *Nazareth House Swansea, tinies observation book.,* and below this was a short account indicating that the parents were separated, the father was Protestant, the mother Roman Catholic, who had to work and had no home for the child, and that the father did not make regular payments.

I looked at the small piece of paper not much bigger than a business card with a sense of relief, akin to solving the last question of a crossword. Now I know I spent nineteen days with my mother but was evidently baptised by the nuns.

The letter continues. *You were recommended (with your sister Greta) to the Sisters of Nazareth by the Catholic Rescue Society and were admitted to Swansea Nazareth House on 7th May 1955. You were transferred to Cardiff Nazareth House on 30th July 1960.*

There was also an entry for you in the Cardiff Nazareth House Register of Sacraments that you made your first confession on 9th June 1962, your First Holy Communion on 10th June 1962 and were confirmed on 6th June 1965.

The last entry we found for you was in the Cardiff Nazareth children's disposal book (an after-care report book). I am enclosing a copy for you, and you will see that in 1971 the Sisters recorded that you were doing well at the Heath hospital.

This is all the information we have found about you in the general archive, and I do hope it proves helpful. We have very few photographs of children in our collection and none from Cardiff and Swansea while you were there.

Yours sincerely

The second slip of paper twice the size of the first one and was stamped COPY, inked on the left-hand border was the number 1401, three words on the article stated. *Milly Nash*, the third word on the bottom right handwritten in ink was the word *Left*.

The third paper was hardly more revealing. The number on the register was 1401. Name, *Milly Nash.* Date of admission *30/7/ 1960.*

Date of discharge *6/10/1970.* Age on discharge *15years. 1971 Milly is doing catering at the dental hospital at the Heath. She comes in often and is doing well.*

That this remarkably brief account of my life may appear to be concise, to me, it was a revelation. This information thrilled me, for at last, I was provided with indisputable evidence. I was and still am tremendously grateful to the lady who was, and perhaps still is the general archivist of the congregation of the Sisters of Nazareth, at Nazareth House in Hammersmith.

The fourth A4 sheet of paper is, without doubt, the original double-sided questionnaire form that was completed in ink by my mother in May 1955. How they included it with the other documents was indeterminable, at least I thought so at the time.

I had a professional frame made for the form which Steve later fitted and hung in the toilet after Jane had left.

The questionnaire form was old and on a parchment-like paper. It was typed in red ink, leaving spaces for the answers, which were filled in by my mother's hand in blue ink.

In bold red letters at the top of the page were the title words,

CARDIFF ARCHDIOCESAN CHILD RESCUE AND MORAL WELFARE SOCIETY. PRIVATE APPLICATION FOR A CHILD NOT FOR ADOPTION TO A RESIDENTIAL HOME.

ALL QUESTIONS TO BE ANSWERED IN BLOCK CAPITALS PLEASE.

Questions one to six demanded answers for general inquiries like; *the name of the child? Date of birth. Was the child born in wedlock? YES. Has the child been in a residential home, institution, or in the care of a local authority? NO.* An answer that ultimately confirmed I did stay with my mother. I wondered if I was breast or bottle-fed, her visit failed to provide any solutions aside from her real personality.

Does anybody suffer from T. B, insanity or another disease likely to influence the child's health? My mother had answered *NO.* I had some doubts, pretending to be a child was one, selective amnesia maybe another.

Is FAMILY ALLOWANCE being drawn for this child? To which she wrote; *IT WILL BE.* There was a small section that required the father's name. *What is his occupation? What are his wages? What sort of character is he? Is he dead? If so, how long ago did he die?* To which she puzzlingly answered them all with a question mark.

The last section was titled; CASE HISTORY and my mother's claim for assistance.

Here state the reasons for the application, and any further information likely to be useful for consideration by the case committee of the rescue society.

My mother ignored the request for block letters and wrote in a right, angled tidy scrawl that is reasonably easy to read.

I, Mrs J Nash, am separated legally from my husband on the grounds of persistent cruelty. I have no home of my own to which I can take the children. I am taking a position in about a week to enable me to support my two babies and to save money so that one day I can take them with me in my own home. I have a court order by which my husband is supposed to pay me £3.00 per week. Since the court order, he has only paid it three times, and then he stopped paying it, after which I had to obtain National Assistance. From now on, I shall have to try to support them myself, and I am certain that I can once they are happily settled.

My mother signed her name in the space provided. *Jane Nash (Mrs)*. I suppose the emphasis on Mrs was to provide proof we were not born out of wedlock.

I have reread the form's contents many times to fathom the reasons behind the answers given, to try to and read between the lines. I was especially curious about; *I have no home of my own to which I can take the children to,* and her answering questions with a question mark.

The other statement, the one I suspect the Mother superior was reading when she said, "I see your mother has declared. She will come back to take the two of you home as soon as she can arrange it. Were actually. *So that one day I can take them with me in my own home.*

The image of the Mother Superior reading, speaking the words I repeated and thought about daily while I waited for my mother to return, came to mind.

Tiny hairs on the back of my neck bristled when I realised I was most likely reading the same documents.

The final photocopy is of three notepad sized pages my mother had written, which was dated November 4th, 1955, the address was Coldstream Terrace, Cardiff. This street only has houses on one side facing the River Taff. The three-story properties overlook the city centre and Cardiff Arms Park rugby ground. I have been unable to find out what type of property it was in 1955, but any feature that near to the city centre was in a prime position

Dear Rev Mother,

I am writing to explain why I was unable to come down and see Greta and Milly last week as I promised sister I would. I already had a very bad cold coming on the previous week but due to the fact that

last week it developed into influenza. I thought it unwise for me to come and take Greta out and give it to her.

I also explained to sister that my husband had not recently been paying me my allowance for the children so I was finding it difficult to manage on the money I was earning. Nevertheless, I had saved five pounds, which I was going to take with me last week. Instead, I am sending it with this letter, Next week I shall try and send more again as I am taking my husband to court for not paying the maintenance order.

I shall never be able to thank you, the sisters and the nurses for what you are doing for me and my two dear little girls. I think God was very kind to find someone to care for them during this very difficult time.

As soon as my cold has gone, I shall be down again to see the children. In the meantime, I think my mother will be going down to see them as she has some little presents to take to them.

I hope I shall be seeing you in the very near future.

I remain,

Yours Sincerely.

(Mrs) Jane Nash.

Though I knew the content of both the form and the letter before my mother visited me, I wanted the person responsible for my incarceration to explain her reasons. She provided no legitimate excuse and much worse, any proof of love. My mother's letter to the Reverend Mother mentioned the words Greta and I, and my two babies. But when she said she thought it unwise for her to come and take Greta out because of her cold, she made no mention of me. Was that a Freudian slip of the pen? Or was it me getting paranoid?

As far as I know, that was the last correspondence between Nazareth House and my mother. Otherwise, I would have the evidence. I still try to consider my mother and father's motives and wondered many times whether they really wanted us in their lives. If only she had explained to me and enlightened me with a woman to woman conversation about what happened to her during her absence. I wish she had provided some answers.

Did she actually get employment to corroborate her letter? She wrote I am taking a position in about a week. Did she genuinely intend to? Well, to have money, one must work, but to work means one can't properly care for two babies. Did she really want to save money to support and provide a home for her two babies and was she genuinely grateful to the sisters and the nurses? I questioned her belief that God was very kind to find someone to care for us during a challenging time. Helpful to who? Her? It indeed was not for us. All I ever craved for was a loving father and mother. We could have lived in a shoebox for all I cared, or even in the room in which my mother slept.

Surely there must have been some point in time when there was an opportunity for her to visit us? A birthday or a Christmas visit, perhaps. So, on a final note, I believe the duration of Jane's cold should be entered in the *Guinness Book of Records*.

I must have read the information provided by the Nazareth House archivist at least twenty times before it hit me like a thunderbolt. I felt a burning rage surging through my body; it was a fury almost greater in intensity than my first encounter with the big black-clad nun. I had been desperate to find a reasonable excuse for my mother's actions. I had wanted to forgive her and felt obliged to feel some attachment towards her. That all evaporated in a second.

I had concentrated too much on reading between the lines and scrutinising her every word. I had been so engrossed in the documents I failed to heed the advice of Margie and use lateral thinking when solving a problem or attempting to comprehend a conundrum. To use one of Margie's favourite quotes, 'I failed to see the wood for the trees.' The answer I'd been searching for lay not in the answers or the questions, but in the title.

CARDIFF ARCHDIOCESAN CHILD RESCUE AND MORAL WELFARE SOCIETY. PRIVATE APPLICATION FOR A CHILD NOT FOR ADOPTION TO A RESIDENTIAL HOME.

The explanation of why Greta and I were in the orphanage all our young lives was because we were in care and not up for adoption. The form ensured we could never be adopted while living in the home. Our darling mother had signed a document that would keep us in the orphanage. She said she'd come back. But she never came back or gave us a chance to live a decent life with another family.

So why did I have the odd weekend away with a family? For if the couple said they wanted to adopt me, they would have told it was impossible, as my mother was in the process of sorting out a home for me. I presume my brief warm sojourns into the illusion of family life were for purely cold financial concerns. At the very least, it was a few days in which they didn't have to provide me with food and lodgings while I had a taste of a life with more freedom.

All she needed to do was sign a consent form, which might have freed us. Though, if that occurred, I might never have met Steve, Pat, Clive Noland, Little Roly, Margie, Heidi, and all my other loved ones. Was God responsible? I questioned my faith in God when my baby died and stopped believing completely when Margie died. Strangely, my faith in God rejuvenated albeit slightly when Gnasher died, so I don't know why I was asking a deity I was unsure about. I judged I had given him enough time to prove himself to be a caring God up to that point.

I took long enough, but my thoughts regarding the actions of the archivist at the Sisters of Nazareth in Hammersmith only became clear to me about five years later. I am now totally and utterly convinced the woman who sent me the original document containing my mother's signature, gave me the unique form to say, it wasn't our fault you were in Nazareth house for five thousand six hundred and thirty days, it was your mother's. Here is the proof and here is her signature, signing you away.

It's entirely feasible my mother's intention was to gain employment and to save money to enable her to come back for and support her two babies so that one day she could take us with her in her own home. She was convinced that she could once we were happily settled. She didn't though.

The Family Grows

I was engrossed in my morning crossword when Steve tapped me on the shoulder and said,

"This one looks interesting."

He passed me a letter, written in handwriting similar to Clive's. I opened the envelope with trembling fingers, my own senses alerted by his usually astute observations, to find the letter was headed Fiona Crimings from an address in Cornwall. The letter was dated the 9th of August 2006.

Dear Milly,

I hope you will not be offended by my writing to you directly, but it seemed the easiest way to make contact. I am writing to you not only for myself but also on behalf of Rachel Baddeley. We believe we are your half-sisters.

The writing on the paper blurred, I'm unsure whether it was my shaky hands or quivering body. I handed the letter to Steve. "I can't believe this, Steve. Please read it to me, I'm shaking too much."

He started reading the letter, and when he came to, *we believe we are your half-sisters,* he had to pause before continuing, shaking his head every so often.

Rachel and I both have the same birth mother, Jane Nash, formerly Thomas. I was born on the 15/02/1964 and Rachel on 29/08/1958. We have different fathers. Rachel was adopted almost immediately, and I was adopted at about nine months old. Rachel and I didn't know of each other's existence until I came across her name on a missing persons website while I was trying to find out about my birth family. We have met once and kept in contact by phone since. I became aware of your existence from my adoption records, and both Rachel and I would like to make contact.

This is a little bit of a complicated story. I don't want to cause any disruption to your life and will respect any decision you make, but I would be very happy if you would like to make contact. Please feel free to write or phone me directly if you would like. I know that Rachel would also be very happy to hear from you.

The letter ended. *Yours hopefully* and was signed almost calligraphically, *Fiona.*

The flowing text was comparable to Mr Noland's hand. I detected Fiona had chosen her words thoughtfully and carefully. The wording was similar to the way Margie had taught me to write so as not to offend or upset the recipient.

Whilst Steve was reading the letter, my emotions fluctuated from elation to disbelief. It was though, deep in my heart, I envisaged a divine intervention was destined to give me answers to all the conundrums. To say I was excited would be an underestimation, but my anger and resentment towards my mother intensified. By the sound of things, it transpires my dear mother was a bloody bunny rabbit on constant heat that left her offspring like discarded raisin-like droppings in her wake. I speculated how many more half brothers and sisters I might have. I'm almost glad my mother didn't nurture me and ultimately influence my life with her unnatural unsociable behaviour. I am tremendously grateful for having both Clive and Margie in my earlier life.

"That's it, I'm going to phone her now," I said thinking, please; please let it be true I do have half-sisters.

Steve persuaded me not to be hasty, to think about my words and sentiment and at least sleep on it. I reluctantly and impatiently heeded his advice until the next day when he was out working.

I dialled the number, my heart was racing, I felt more nervous and apprehensive than I'd experienced in a long time. I said out loud, "Here we go."

The phone rang a few times, then a woman's voice said, "Hello" and repeated the number I'd just dialled. I was shocked and horrified the voice sounded like my mothers, even though I was temporally stunned, I asked with some self-control, "Who am I speaking to?"

The impatient voice repeated my own words, "Who am I speaking to?"

I felt a massive surge of relief when I understood the speech. That initially sounded similar to my mothers, wasn't hers, now I'd heard a few more words.

"I'm Milly Nairs. I believe I may be your half-sister." I said and could feel the release of all the pent-up tensions drain out of me instantly.

"Oh my God, Milly… I'm so sorry it's me, Fiona."

I liked her gentle voice, she sounded so lovely, and I imagined her as a Margie lookalike even though she expressed herself a little like my mother. I recognised her letter had been written with a great deal of thought and intelligence, as we talked, she confirmed my assumptions.

I had been dubious and disbelieving, thought irrationally that perhaps this was a hoax, but now I was sure she and Rachel were my sisters. By the end of the conversation, I was convinced this was the start of a different chapter in my life.

Four Sisters Three Fathers

Three half-empty cups of Blue Mountain coffee sat on the glass coffee table next to three empty crystal glasses. I immediately liked the two women when we greeted each other with double cheek kisses. Both were extremely attractive and confident. The edgy cautious preliminary encounter evaporated during the first few sips of coffee.

Rachel had short dark brown hair, reminding me of the home cut, and a skin colour that was lighter than olive covering a slightly sallow face that exhibited how fit and healthy she was. Her sparkling brown eyes were not too dissimilar to Steve's. Her happy demeanour and no-nonsense approach to life were typical of a girl from the Valleys. She was a little slimmer and perhaps an inch taller than Fiona who was about two inches taller than me.

Fiona had a heart-shaped face with smiling sea-green eyes topped by wheat blonde hair. She too had high cheekbones, she glowed with fitness and good health. The way she spoke reminded me very much of Margie.

My assumption they would probably meet beforehand proved correct.

"We've just had a cup of coffee in the cafe down the road, but I did bring this," Rachel said in a gruff, broad Welsh accent. I recognised it was from Merthyr Tydfil, a town twenty-four miles North of Cardiff that was once a thriving mining community. Out of her overnight bag, the high-cheekboned, casually dressed forty-eight-year-old produced a bottle of my favourite brand of Chardonnay.

It emerged we had a shared passion for fine wine. Fiona laughed and clicked open the two clasps on her small suitcase, after a short rummage, in her hand was a bottle of wine with identical labels.

My two half-sisters clasped their little finger around the other's little pinkie and in synchrony said, "I wish for."

They both paused as they made the silent wishes that are supposed to bring good luck for an accidental happenstance.

They stopped laughing when they noticed I was shaking my head. To enlighten them, I immediately went to my refrigerator and opened the door and from it produced two identical bottles of wine. I held the bottles by the neck and twisted them around to show them the labels. "Now if you think that's a coincidence. What about this?" I said.

The joy, laughter and squealing that followed ultimately sealed the beginning of a fantastic and unforgettable weekend. Steve's curiosity got the better of him when he heard the commotion, opening the lounge door, only to see three virtual strangers laughing excitedly with their little fingers entwined. He closed the door with a satisfied smile on his face. Steve and I had arranged this weekend's meeting; we were both in total agreement I should meet with the two girls on my own. So after the preliminary greeting, he had discretely made a quiet, dignified retreat.

I showed the two happy, relaxed women, the bedrooms and told them to make their own choice. Although the bedrooms are both en-suite, Margie's room, as I still called it, was without question far grandeur. They both playfully argued who should have the bedroom, Fiona won the game of rock, paper and scissors. She had travelled on a three-hour journey in rush hour traffic from her cottage in Cornwall and wanted to shower and change before dinner.

I didn't want to cook, I needed to converse; I was excited and eager to listen to the two women's stories. With probably fifty or more take away restaurants within a mile of our location, we eventually settled for an Indian curry with all the trimmings.

While Fiona changed, Rachel told me a little about herself, though we stayed astutely clear of the weekend's focal point. Rachel had a full-time job as a sales representative and moonlighted three nights a week as a singer. She demonstrated her prowess by singing a few bars of *Hero* by Bonnie Tyler, sounding exactly like her.

She said to me enthusiastically, "I do a gig in Cardiff once a month… You and Steve must come and see me play."

"When are you here next?" I swiftly asked.

"Not until next month now. I cancelled this weekend's show so I could meet you and Fiona. She's so pretty, isn't she? You are both so much alike. Me, I take after my Italian father."

Throughout the leisurely meal, in which we ended up sharing each other's meals, we quickly established a camaraderie and growing affection towards each other. By the time we were on the next bottle of wine any qualms, I may have felt about this union vanished. I was reasonably sure my two good-natured dinner companions felt the same. Even though the small talk was interesting, the conversation relaxed and uninhibited, each of us was still carefully avoiding the main reason and topic for this meeting.

I felt an adrenaline rush surge through my body as we walked the few paces from the dining room to the lounge, knowing that the time had come to approach the subject we had been avoiding. Earlier in the day, I had rearranged the layout of the room to be more appropriate for an intimate conversation. I had repositioned the settees into a u-shape around the coffee table with wine glasses positioned on the table, offering a subtle invitation. As planned, Rachel and Fiona sat down facing each other; whilst I was in the middle of the three-seat settee with them on either side. I wanted to see, and I wanted them to see the eyes and expressions of each of us as we related our personal chronicles. As one and without thinking, we stretched out a hand to our respective glasses, immediately laughing at the symmetry created, before we clinked our glasses together with a happy hearty, "Cheers." We glanced from one to another, each giggling nervously when we realised what we were doing.

Fiona took a gulp of wine and said, "As it was me that instigated the events that led to this meeting, I'll go first."

She started talking in a quiet, pleasant, confident voice. There were no stuttering stops or overlong pauses informing me she was used to oratory. Fiona virtually told us the same story as was in her letter, only adding that she never found out who her father was. Apparently, the space on her birth certificate that asked for the father's name had a line struck through it.

On the personal side, she said she never married, had a few boyfriends but never anything serious, her dogs were the loves of her life. She had graduated from Exeter University with first-class-honours in ancient history. She said she had a few health issues but quickly moved on, as though telling us she didn't want to divulge any further information. The more she spoke, the more she reminded me of Margie. She said she had loved her mother and father who had spoilt her when she was little and had provided her with home life, excellent schooling and plenty of holidays. I wondered why such an attractive woman hadn't married, I assumed she felt a moral responsibility towards caring for her elderly adoptive mother and father.

When Fiona stopped speaking, Rachel and I asked her a few questions, both of us sidestepping the health issue subject.

Rachel opened her account by saying she was adopted a few days after she was born, she told us the arrangements were already underway when our communal mother was six months into her pregnancy. She mentioned that her birth father was an Italian man she hasn't been able to trace. Her adoptive mother and father coincidently were both Italian who owned a cafe in Merthyr Tydfil. It was a town she had lived in all her life. She attended a local school where everyone in the close-knit community knew each other. Like Fiona, she had never married. She still lived with her parents, who were now retired.

Her mother and father played the piano and accordion, instruments Rachel learned to play. She also played a nineteen forty-seven Gibson guitar they gave her for her twenty-first birthday. Rachel sang in local groups for years and was now the lead singer of an aspiring band who played venues all across Wales. She ended her account by saying the one thing she wanted out of life was to find her birth mother and didn't care what she was like, Rachel just wanted closure.

I wondered why they hadn't asked me about our mother and presumed they thought I didn't know of her whereabouts either. So I thrust my back into the seat and took a deep draught of wine before opening my version of events. In contrast, I started from the end of my story and not the beginning.

"Our mother was sitting in this very chair, not so long ago."

Their incredulous facial expressions that formed answered my queries.

“What?” Rachel said in a loud, shocked voice.

“But. But.” Fiona stuttered. “I saw you on a missing person’s website, where you were looking for information about Jane and Horace Nash and Pat O’Toole. You were also seeking Heidi, Lucy, Jasmin and Janice? I don’t understand. I didn’t see any replies.”

Her retentive memory impressed me. “She only came back into my life about eighteen months ago,” I explained.

They had both shifted to the edge of their seats, eagerly waiting for more information about our shared mother. There was no way I would disappoint them with the truth or my real opinion of our parent. What I said, in essence, was a summary of my own emotions.

“Our mother showed up after almost fifty years away. I yearned and dreamt of her and my father every day when I was in Nazareth House. Nonetheless, I loved her. When she sat here in this room, it seemed surreal. She was kind enough, though she appeared to be distant. I had the idea that maybe she didn’t like me. She speaks eloquently, is attractive and well-dressed. She didn’t really give me any answers. Having said that, I asked no questions. Instead, I waited for her to tell me what happened. To explain, to communicate what was so bad for her to never come back?” I didn’t want them to have any false illusions about our hard-hearted mother. So I said.

“Also, she made no mention of you two, even though we are still in touch and I phone her about twice a month. We haven’t developed a bond, but who knows what the future holds? I know you two are desperate to contact her, and whatever happens, I will give you her phone number. But not now, I’m sorry. I haven’t told her or Greta about the two of you yet. I promise I’ll give you the information by next week, I must speak to her first. I hope you both understand that

I need time to think of what I'm going to say to her. I know Greta will want to speak to you. I'll have to talk to her first."

I'd been studying their faces for signs of disappointment or annoyance, I noticed neither, both of them nodded, smiling amiably.

"This has been one of the best times of my life, finding out about you and meeting you… It's been an absolute delight," I said and smiled back.

Rachel asked after my known family. I told them about my grandmother and the auntie who had phoned me with the news about our mother's return to the land of the living.

I shifted track and started from the beginning, using all the facts and the results of my research, while omitting elements I thought unnecessary. They both made sympathetic noises throughout the fifteen-minute-long account of my life. When I finished, their eyes showed signs of tears.

I mildly chastised them, "Don't pity me, I've had a great life, even though it didn't start until I was almost seventeen,"

Fiona said in a tender, compassionate voice, "Milly, I didn't realise you were in an orphanage. What happened when you were seventeen? You look great; you sound so confident and knowledgeable."

To enlighten them, I gave them a brief synopsis about Margie and the hotel, of meeting Steve when I was twelve and then again when I was twenty-one.

Throughout the night and into the early hours of the morning, we regaled each other with tales of joy and woe. Our shared passion, apart from wine, was our love of all animals, especially dogs.

Whether it was irrational, or not. I experienced a deep sense of anger and antipathy toward my mother for not telling me the truth. There again, what did I expect after all those years?

The next day the girls went home after lunch. Their visit had exceeded all my expectations. I was thrilled and excited to have three sisters in my life.

There was the quandary of introducing and announcing their manifestation.

When I considered my reactions and emotion rationally, I realised jealousy had reared its ugly head. I was jealous that my half-sisters had loving, caring families to nurture them and steer them into adulthood. My sentiment varied between perplexed and enlightenment. The explanation for the resentment towards my unaffected mother and my two lovely half-sisters was quite simple; my mother had given Rachel and Fiona their freedom by signing them away for adoption. Rachel first in nineteen fifty-eight, three years and four months after she gave birth to me. Then again five and a half years later, she gave Fiona away, while Greta and I were left to rot and experience the harsh reality of life in an institution.

When my mother stayed with me, I had thought perhaps she was ashamed of herself for not coming back for us. She must have known the repercussions of her actions.

The following Sunday, I phoned my mother late in the afternoon at my usual time. We chatted idly about her dog, the weather, what she had to eat.

"How's Steve?" she asked.

"Oh he's fine; by the way mother, I had two visitors who stayed with me last week."

I had pondered what I would say to her, I even rehearsed my speech. I was more angry than nervous; my knees that hadn't knocked for a while came back to life.

"Yes, they are two lovely women, mother. Both of them were adopted when they were babies. Rachel was born in nineteen fifty-eight and Fiona was born in nineteen sixty-four. They've both matured into happy, successful, contented adults. The one thing that's missing in their life is their own mother. Yes, mother, they want to contact you."

My phone went silent; she was still connected because I could hear her walking.

I didn't raise my voice, I kept my tone neutral. "Mother... Are you still there? Are you going to answer me? When I finish this phone call, I will phone them to give them both your contact details. I promised them I would. Hello. Hello, what have you got to say, mother?"

"I've got to go. I have a funeral to go to," the young-sounding voice said, then our call disconnected.

Later that week, Fiona phoned me and told me she had spoken with our mother.

"I only managed to say to her, hello, it's me, your daughter Fiona. And do you know what she said Milly?"

I detected a slight sob as her voice faltered.

"She said. She said, not today, thank you. I'm rather busy. She actually said, not today, thank you. When I told Rachel about my call, she told me our mother said exactly the same thing to her. Not today, thank you, I'm rather busy. Rachel shouted at her, but she thinks our mother had disconnected by then."

"I'm so sorry, Fiona."

"You knew what her reaction would be, didn't you Milly?"

"I had a good idea. Jane wasn't that much different to me, still isn't, in fact."

I continued to phone my mother and tried to negotiate and reconcile her with her daughters, my sisters. Though every time I broached a particular subject, like Rachel, Fiona, anything regarding my past or anything she didn't want to talk about, she'd say, I have to go now and hang up.

For some reason, Jane Nash, Thomas or whatever she called herself now stubbornly refused to communicate with Fiona or Rachel.

I grudgingly realised it was pointless talking with her. It was the same as meeting a casual acquaintance in the park, one you didn't particularly like. My conversations with her became more strained and difficult to maintain. Our phone calls became shorter and shorter until I stopped phoning her. She still had the option of telephoning me, but didn't. We had reached a stalemate, we no longer communicate, and I thought I don't give a damn. But I do, of course, I do.

The divide between me and all three of my sisters intensified during the period after my initial encounter with Rachel and Fiona. I was dissatisfied with the outcome of what should have been a happy conclusion. I felt sorry for Fiona and Rachel and a certain amount of chagrin towards Greta, who was in constant contact with our mother. At some stage in my constant meandering thoughts about my mother's motives and her salacious decisions regarding her children, I briefly considered that perhaps she may have been institutionalised to a lunatic asylum. I would have understood and supported her without question had she told me that.

I kept in touch by text messages and telephone with both Rachel and Fiona, but that petered out after almost two years. We had nothing in common apart from the same mother. It seemed to me we had been reunited too late in our lives to make any radical changes to our lifestyles. I only met Rachel twice and Fiona once. The second time I had met Rachel was when she performed her act. Steve and I had been drinking lager out of plastic cups while we watched her strut her stuff like a female Mick Jagger on a floodlit raised stage. The show's venue was in a club in Cardiff's Womanby Street, a fifteen-minute walk from our house.

She and the band's performance was slick, impressive and totally professional. In-between one of her songs, Rachel slightly embarrassed me by introducing me to the two hundred appreciative spectators, by pointing a finger in my direction from the stage, while her voice blasted through the microphone.

"That's my sister there."

I was proud when she introduced me to her audience. Though the short sentence was a poignant reminder, I had two more sisters, I had a feeling she'd never spoken those words before.

I liked them both immensely and have little hesitation in saying that if we had gotten together much earlier, we could have been bosom buddies. I imagined the four of us living in the same house as children. In a place like the public house where Steve and Lerina lived; the four of us playfully fighting over makeup and clothes and possibly even boyfriends.

I'm saddened I lost contact with the girls, the reasons are not all one-sided. The health issue with Fiona turned out to be breast cancer. I phoned her about a year after our last phone conversation to wish her a happy birthday. The person on the end of the phone told me she had died of cancer a few months before, I was lucky to get a reply as she'd only popped in to switch the heating on. It was heart-rending to hear of her demise, alas without the fitting feelings of a real sister.

As the years passed by, my relationships with my other four relatives oscillated, and at times they seemed to be out of my control. Throughout all of those years, my mother, who has a lot to answer for, remained tight-lipped. I have a single picture of her that my grandmother gave me. Jane is looking beautiful and glamorous in a polka dot dress standing next to Cecil Parker, a famous actor of the time. The photograph was taken at a garden party before she met my father; my grandmother surprised me by giving me the picture along with a gorgeous gold chain and cross, one that was similar to the stone statue of Christ on the parapet of Saint Dyfrigs church. She gave them both to me shortly after I lost my baby. I thought I knew the motive for the gift, why my grandmother waited all those years to produce an image of the woman I cherished. I didn't, though. The picture is now in the drawer that Horace occupied for a week.

By tradition Greta, Doreen, grandmother and I, would exchange Christmas presents. Greta would always hint of dwindling finances as Christmas neared, she didn't know about my money. Even so, I would still send her and Malcolm a generous cash gift inside their individual presents. Greta was no pauper herself. She particularly liked men with money. Her boyfriend Wayne owned half a dozen gift shops on Blackpool's golden mile. Her desire for the expensive designer label, all-white clothing, filled a walk-in wardrobe that was once a bedroom in her garishly furnished, four-bed seafront property. She was a bit of a hoarder and exceptionally frugal. She once sent me a chocolate Easter egg as a Christmas present. Doreen visited me on the same

Christmas morning, we exchanged gifts, she noticed the unwrapped egg under the Christmas tree, picked it up, and examined the box. She stood looking wryly at the egg; with her mouth wide open, before shaking her head and saying incredulously. "I gave this to Greta last year to give to Malcolm as an Easter gift."

Happy Families

My grandmother demanded I give her back the cross and chain, two years after Jane's reappearance. Her abrupt hostile manner towards me took me by surprise when I visited the seriously ill woman in the hospital.

She pointed at me as I neared her bed and asked, "What are you doing here? I see you're still wearing the chain. Give it back. I don't want you to have it anymore."

I was naturally distraught and thought the ninety-four-year-old was delirious, so I ignored her demand. She then started shouting at me.

"Get out. It's all your fault. I never want to see you again."

Aunty Doreen came to see me about a week later, reiterating my grandmother's request. I wanted answers regarding her unpredictable behaviour and received none. She was as puzzled as I was, for my grandmother was neither delirious nor seriously ill anymore. She had made a rapid recovery and was now resting at home, but she remained adamant. I should return the gift she gave me. I handed Auntie Doreen the chain and cross that had adorned my neck for years, with a heavy heart.

From that day, my grandmother refused to take my calls, my grandmother exorcised me from her life, and I never saw her again. She lived to be a hundred and one years old. Auntie Doreen invited me to be present at her funeral. I didn't see the point; she didn't want me in her life, so I didn't go to mourn her death.

Greta attended the funeral and phoned me from what was now Doreen's house. She was very distressed, though foolishly made a point of chastising me. I didn't think Greta was in a position to chastise anyone so I told her to mind her own bloody business. I was flummoxed, and a tad upset myself. Though not overly. I didn't understand why I'd been ostracised by what little family I had.

Doreen and Greta had become close confidantes over the years, Greta would stay with her and my grandmother for a week a couple of times a year. I only found out about their clandestine meetings when Doreen mentioned Greta, whom she called her little princess, stayed with her one August. She said, giggling like a schoolgirl, "Greta would sunbathe at the bottom of their large garden topless, wearing only a thong, she and her boyfriend Peter, ten years younger than her, used to laugh at her frolics." I found it bizarre that Greta would display her semi-naked body even if she thought it was far enough away.

Greta would come to Cardiff and stay with my grandmother and auntie, not even bothering to visit me. Why did they keep the visits secret? I concluded it was probably her dislike of my husband; though I also started to question my personality and whether it was me who was at fault.

These days Doreen and Greta no longer speak to each other. It appears that, while Greta was staying with her and Peter, she did something that was so disgusting, so hurtful to Doreen, she was immediately exiled and banished from her home. From that day Doreen vowed never to speak to her again. One can only speculate what the act was, for they both refuse to discuss the subject with me

Though auntie, who rarely talked about family matters or much else concerning personal themes, did enlighten me somewhat about why my grandmother suddenly came to despise me. Doreen didn't know what was said, but my grandmother changed her attitude towards me immediately after a long conversation between her and Greta.

"She's always been jealous of you, you know," she said as if this explained everything.

The End

On a brighter note and on the plus side, though no conclusion, I eventually found out what happened to Pat, my best friend. She went to Australia almost as soon as she left Nazareth House. She still lives there now.

I used the same website for missing persons as Fiona and found a message from a woman called Lisa Griffiths, who was looking for information about the parents of her mother, Pat O'Tolle. The post continued and ultimately confirmed it was my Pat by stating she was in Nazareth House from nineteen fifty-five until nineteen sixty-eight, and that soon after she went to live in Australia.

I couldn't believe my luck or my ignorance. All the years I'd been searching for Pat I had been spelling her surname wrong, though I'm reasonably sure she spelt her name the way I spelt it when we were kids. I replied to the post that was a few years old, but unfortunately, the email bounced back to my Inbox with a server error, signifying the email address initially used by Lisa was no longer in use. I left my own posts on the site hoping Pat or her daughter would see them. I still haven't given up hope, though I'm so pleased for her to have had a daughter to love: a daughter who adores her mother, a loving daughter searching for her mother's mother. I often wonder if she was successful and if the outcome was as Pat expected.

My own child would have been thirty years old this year. I would probably have been a grandmother myself by now if it wasn't for my father. Or perhaps it could have been Sister Terry who caused the damage to my reproductive organs. A picture of the father I never met still hangs above the oak fireplace, his enigmatic smile the only image I have. I regret never meeting him. I've studied his eyes, contrary to the stories about him, they appear kind. I would have asked him so many questions, especially why did all this happen? I have so many unanswered questions in my life.

I have no clear answers to all the queries I wanted clarifying. The nuns never gave us any information. If pushed, they would erect an invisible barrier as if crossing their arms across their chests to keep the devil away. Looking back on my early life, I existed in a world that was both good and bad. It was the time of the nice nun versus the evil nun. For years I was confined within an invisible straight jacket supplied and tied by the Catholic Church. One in which I had to be a good religious girl or face the consequences. It was a prison that didn't need barbed wire on the walls to confine us, for it was guarded by dominating nuns armed with the nuns' pinch, a technique that could numb an arm if deftly applied for they had plenty of practice on unwilling participants.

Throughout my institutional life, I looked after kids, the majority of whom just disappeared without warning, never to be seen or heard from again.

When I reached school age, going to school was like crossing a border into a foreign country, one that spoke the same language but was far more culturally advanced. We time travelled into the near future every day as the dark shadow of the institution locked us in the past and ensured they separated us from the wider community.

When they granted me my autonomy, they didn't help or prepare me for a life outside of Nazareth House.

The final time I walked from the home to my freedom was the day my life began; to have no one ordering me about or admonishing me was sweet relief. Though, it took a trip to Jersey and five years bonding with Margie before I became part of modern-day life. Then meeting Steve again and being married to him for forty-two beautiful years.

I sometimes wonder what I would have become if I was nurtured in a more enlightening environment. My sister Fiona became a scholar of note because she was brought up by people who provided an excellent education. My sister Rachel became a superb musician when reared by a musical family.

I have only recently been back in touch with Rachel on Facebook to bring this book to its conclusion. I wanted to wish her a happy sixtieth birthday and tell her about the contents of this book and her inclusion, more to the point ask for her permission. While she accepted my friend's request and sent a message back, saying she would get in touch, she hasn't. I don't blame her, for she barely knows anything of my life.

Greta remains locked in her own world contented and happy, and I'm pleased for her. Taken together, the four of us might have made an interesting psychological case study on the effect of environment and upbringing.

Why did my grandmother hate me for the rest of her life? Why did she say it was all my fault? What was, all my fault? Why didn't our grandmother try to bring us up? She had a large house and was wealthy. Ultimately, I know it was my mother's responsibility, for her own selfish reasons, my mother just didn't care to nurture the little girls she brought into this world.

Deep in my heart of hearts one thing I know for sure, if I were fortunate enough to have been blessed with children and grandchildren, I would have fought with Satan to keep them away from, and out of an institution. Throughout my life, I never contemplated adopting or fostering. I wanted my own children, babies I could keep without losing them.

For over sixty years now, I have been innocently following a preordained, surreal path as if I was being punished for my mother's mistakes, while she trekked along undisturbed through the back-alleyway of her own life.

I followed my natural survival instincts, as I travelled through my life's ups and downs, on a rollercoaster ride stuck on a rail track with no deviations. I have experienced many regrets and suffered long periods of sadness, though I realise without one incidence there wouldn't be another. My life has been a succession of choices, like turning left or right.

Margie's untimely demise, her heart attack after her joy at the prospect of becoming a surrogate grandmother, the heartbeat of my baby snuffed out after a hundred and ten days, ripped my own apart.

It was as if I was the subject of a film or a book, whose editor changed the script for better entertainment.

"Milly is too happy, let's kill her baby then. Shall we exterminate Clive, Roly and Margie, or what about getting rid of Pat?"

At times it felt as if my life was being unfairly rearranged by a higher entity. As if I was being tested by divinity in preparation for spiritual immortality, after the inevitable conclusion, death, the definitively unequivocal end of each life-cycle.

However, I have maintained my faith in God, despite the suffering in this world, and my own world, losing Pat, Roly, Clive Noland, Margie and my baby, Steve's baby. The baby I cherished, the baby who would never have been frightened, alone or punished. A baby that would have grown up with brothers and sisters who would never leave her. The baby girl that would become the woman that Margie helped me become because, in my imagination, our baby was a girl. I don't look back in anger, but I often reflect on what my life might have been if the woman who gave birth to me had left one specific piece of paper unsigned.

Acknowledgements

Susan Thompson, whose pseudonym is Milly Nash for relating her life story.

For Steve Holmes, who without his input, this book would never have been accomplished.

Paul Smith, for his dedication and editing expertise.

Jasmin Phillips, for lending me her forename, her editing prowess and our ultimate rapport.

The Cronulla Hotel Zante, for the tranquil book writing setting, good meals and wine.

Suzanne Bennett, beta reader extraordinaire.

The Romilly pub Cardiff, for my penning table, alcohol, food, warm radiator and electricity.

in

.